Management
Operations
Research

MODERN MANAGEMENT SERIES

Management

Operations

Research

▶ ▶ ▶ ▶ ▶ ▶ ▶ ▶ ▶ ▶ ▶ ▶ ▶ ▶ ▶ ▶ ▶ ▶ ▶ ▶

Norbert Lloyd Enrick

PROFESSOR OF MANAGEMENT
KENT STATE UNIVERSITY
AND
MANAGEMENT CONSULTANT

HOLT, RINEHART AND WINSTON

NEW YORK • CHICAGO • SAN FRANCISCO • TORONTO • LONDON

Foreword

This book offers the principles and methods of operations research (OR) as a management science in a simplified nonmathematical form for the practical manager and interested student.

Since OR utilizes quantitative methods to solve complex and interlocking business problems, it is only natural that it was originated in a rather mathematical atmosphere. Yet, in order to be of greatest value, OR must be used by managers, supervisors, and staff people, and be understood by students who may have had little mathematical training. It is this need which has motivated this text. While it can not make the reader an expert, it should equip him to make many applications of OR himself and caution him when he will need to call for assistance from experts. In any event, in a business world that is increasingly oriented towards OR applications in all phases of production, sales, and administration, a person who has read and studied this book should be better able to serve and function effectively.

Inevitably, a simplified text involves some compromise with the subject matter. Some topics, such as waiting-line management, which are treated in one chapter, would really require an entire large book for proper coverage. Moreover, the derivation of many working formulas can not be given without advanced mathematics. Therefore, this book must rely on an inadequate substitute: explanations, given within the context of practical examples and designed to give an intuitive understanding of the validity of the formulas given.

I am indebted to many. Business organizations provided the opportunity of consulting work, thus aiding me in developing the practical aspects of OR in this book. My students in college and industrial training courses pointed out deficiencies in earlier versions of some of the material used. Various contributors provided additional materials, as acknowledged specifically in the proper places throughout the book. Finally, Professor Thomas R. Hoffmann reviewed the manuscript, making numerous suggestions, all of which were gratefully accepted.

If *Management Operations Research* serves to broaden the base of understanding and application of OR in the fields of management practice and management training, then its aim will have been accomplished.

N. L. E.

Charlottesville, Virginia
November 1964

▶ ▶ ▶ ▶

Contents

**Management
Operations
Research**

►►►► PART ONE

The General Nature of Operations Research as a Management Science

▶ ▶ ▶ ▶ **1**

Introduction:
Operations Research
in Modern Management

In recent years, the demonstrated power of modern techniques of management science or operations research, as an aid to business, has made this approach of great interest to everyone in executive and managerial positions. If a still disconcertingly large minority of management people tend to avoid these methods, it is probably because of the forbidding reliance on quantitative mathematical methods that is often demonstrated by the expert in this field.

One need not be a mathematician, however, to be able to understand the basic concepts and principal tools of modern management science or "OR." Moreover, once a good understanding of the basic ideas and methods has been gained, the manager is well-equipped to promote the installation of OR in his business with enthusiasm, and so to avail himself of the better management that will result from his use of the information gained from OR studies. The advantages of the OR approach will be presented in this chapter from the viewpoint of the basic aspects of over-all management problems, with special regard to the decision-making phases.

Over-all Management Problems

Faced with the increasing complexities of engineering, production, sales, and marketing operations in a highly developed and often strongly competitive economy, management must deal with a multitude of interlocking and often far-reaching tasks involving many decision-making and control problems. These activities generally include several major phases noted here:

1. Policy Formulation The policies established by management serve as guideposts to all concerned in the daily activities of the firm's opera-

3

tions. In addition, policies become historical markers, providing reference points for evaluating the success of past policies and considering changes in future policy.

For example, a policy may be made to diversify the company's product lines regarding the number of styles or models to be produced or types of customers to be sought. This policy, with its detailed implementations, serves to direct the efforts of all personnel concerned with the attainment of management's goals and objectives. At the same time, if it should become necessary to review and revise the policy, perhaps because of new market trends or new competitive developments, this can readily be accomplished by management. By being able to refer to old policies and observing how they worked out, management is in a position to profit from past experience in deciding how policies must be altered.

2. Careful Planning   Any policy requires a great deal of thoroughgoing implementation, generally affecting not only production and sales, but also purchasing, development research, engineering, and administration. Careful planning is needed therefore.

For example, a decision to diversify production will necessitate further market evaluations. One must first decide just what new styles, patterns, models, and colors are to be offered. Then the firm must plan for suitable raw stocks, efficient production standards, requisite quality requirements, new equipment where needed, proper scheduling, consumer testing, trial runs, and many other related activities.

3. Effective Control   Assurance must be had that standards are being met in actual production regarding both general progress as well as costs, quality, efficiency, distribution, and customer satisfaction.

For example, when planning for a new model or style, estimates of expected production rates, costs, sales, and related factors are prepared as part of the planning phase. Unless some degree of checking and control exists, the factors of quality, cost, and efficiency may tend to drift. On the other hand, with good control it is often possible to achieve better results than those envisioned in the planning stage.

4. Evaluation and Review   Management's program deserves careful periodic analyses and reviews, in which both qualitative and quantitative information should be considered regarding such vital questions as:

How has the program been working out?
Do results measure up to expectations?
Are returns adequate?
Do revisions seem desirable from a short-term or from a long-term viewpoint?

For example, quarterly meetings may be arranged for the purpose of reviewing progress and results of various programs. The accumulated data from the daily checking and control activities would be among the items of information used in the periodic evaluation-and-review meetings.

5. Renewed Decision Making   Using the information resulting from the evaluations and reviews of managements policies, plans, and programs, new decisions are evolved. Decision making will now involve:

a. A review of past results.
b. A consideration of alternatives available.
c. Weighing of any limitations on action and anticipated follow-up.
d. Consideration of risks and uncertainties involved as against potential gains.

For example, the policy of diversification may have worked out exceedingly well, resulting in a greatly expanded sales volume and a considerably improved over-all return. Should management continue with further diversification? Such action is one of the alternatives available. Other alternatives to be considered are whether to initiate such further diversification within the firm itself, or to obtain contract production and distribution, or to use still other methods. Plant and productive capacity, available managerial manpower within the company, financial resources, and a host of other factors must be weighed because they have a bearing on the limitations of management's scope of activities. Again, uncertainties of economic and market developments, and the risks involved in further financial outlays to support additional product diversification must be considered in relation to the gain in increased returns to be derived.

This managerial process is a continuing cycle which, beginning with an initial set of decisions, gives rise to policies, plans, and controls that, after evaluation and review, result in new and revised decisions. This is illustrated in Figure 1-1. The process is also adaptive,

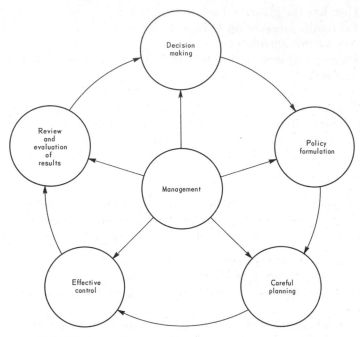

FIGURE 1-1.   Concept of modern management processes.

in the sense that new decisions are derived in part from past experience and in part from forecasts of future expectations. The new or revised decisions serve to adapt business operations in a changing environment toward optimal goals. The manner in which these optimum-seeking decisions are developed is illustrated in Figure 1-2. Those aspects of this process that are capable of quantitative expression will usually also exhibit many interlocking relationships. It is the function of the mathematical techniques of OR to evaluate the interrelated and combined impact of these quantitative factors, as an aid to management in the decision-making process.

Managerial Decision Problems

Typical examples illustrative of the wide range of problem areas in which management must make decisions appear in Table 1-1. Several groups of decision problems may be noted.

Long-term Decisions   Many decisions are of long-term consequence, such as a decision to increase capital outlay for plant and equipment.

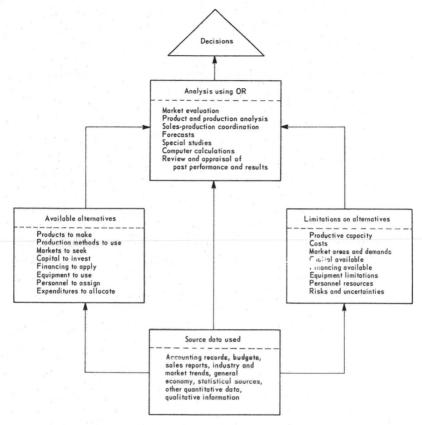

FIGURE 1-2.   Decision process using OR.

Efficiency, productivity, distributive capacity, and general competitive position of the company will be affected for many years to come. Much time and thought must be given to the selection of the most suitable plant and the best equipment consistent with costs.

The author recalls an incident a few years ago where a new piece of finishing equipment was bought on impulse by top management. The plant was then held responsible for producing volume and quality with it. It soon became apparent, however, that the machinery was poorly designed and unable to perform as advertised. Nevertheless, the plant's management was held responsible for "making the equipment work" and operate at expected returns. When, after some years, the machine was finally removed from the plant, it represented not only a loss of capital, but even greater losses in quality, production, rework expense, and customer allowances, not to mention the effect on employee morale. Even if the organization had no formal OR program, yet the principles of evaluating new equipment through trial runs and economic investigations might have been useful in avoiding a wrong decision.

Modern OR techniques, using methods of evaluating the expenditure on capital equipment and establishing optimal equipment replacement cycles, will generally enhance the quality of all capital budgeting decisions. This is accomplished by incorporating in the analysis such factors as rate of cash flow-back, discounted interest on financing, and alternative investment opportunities.

Short-term Decisions   Certain decisions, such as what range of colors to offer this season, are relatively short-term in nature. Yet, even in such short-range areas, various OR techniques of market evaluation will enhance the validity of decisions. Moreover, some firms are using helpful operating controls to avoid faulty emphasis in short-term decision making.

Levels of Decision   Decisions may also be classified according to levels of management involved in them. While capital budgeting and financial decisions usually fall within the province of top management, questions of production, personnel, raw stock, and administration will be of primary concern to middle and lower management. There are also interlocking aspects to all decisions. A decision to enter a new market may involve concomitant decisions on capital budgeting, methods of financing the outlay involved, engineering of requisite manufacturing changes, switches in sources of raw stock to be used on the new equipment, and changes in policy or emphasis of sales efforts.

Figures 1-1 and 1-2 are thus oversimplified visualizations of the exceedingly complex management processes that occur in a modern business organization. Moreover, as the levels of progress in basic and applied research, production and transportation technology, administrative techniques, data processing, and general information handling continue at a rapid pace of acceleration, management processes may be expected to grow in complexity. To the extent to which the unaided human mind becomes unable to deal with these growing complexities of interacting factors and variables, OR techniques must be called in to solve those aspects of decision problems that are amenable to quantitative formulation, integration, and solution.

Managerial Yardsticks

As the purpose of managerial decisions varies, so will the yardstick of success that is most appropriate. For example, in deciding on a capital investment, the past record of capital growth and net profit and the corresponding future expectations would be the critical yardsticks. On the other hand, a decision to offer a price concession in order to obtain volume sales on a certain item, though it will ultimately affect net profit, is more appropriately evaluated in terms of what accountants call the "variable margin" or "operating profit." This criterion measures the amount of money that each increasing unit sold contributes to profit. The "variable margin" excludes all fixed costs and overhead, since these costs exist regardless of the volume produced, and thus can not be affected by the pricing decision.

Managerial yardsticks are most appropriate if they are directly related to the effects of the decisions that can be made under the alternatives available. Table 1-2 presents typical examples of such yardsticks.

Optimization

Management's efforts are concerned with the utilization of the productive, financial, sales, personnel, and related resources of the company towards optimization regarding final profit. In seeking this aim, the requirements of the productive and sales factors must be considered in relation to the limitations imposed by productive capacity, available financing and personnel, the nature of the market, and the potential counteractions of competing firms and industries.

With the complexity of problems facing management, the varieties of alternatives of action to be considered, the multiplicity and types of decisions to be made, the uncertainties and risks attendant to business operation, and the problem of the right performance yardstick, it is doubtful whether the goals of maximum profit can be defined precisely for any firm. Nevertheless, it is the aim to be sought, which justifies the very existence of management. In this search toward the optimum, various OR techniques have been found extremely useful. They help management weigh the varieties of aspects involved in a decision and in integrating the quantitative components of cost and returns by various mathematical means. Management has always made such evaluations by means of simple data, comparisons, and intuitive approaches. The contribution of OR is that it lends further precision to the evaluation process, and that it provides a mechanism of supplying these evaluations concisely before major decisions are made. Moreover, by turning the chores of data collection, analysis, and evaluation over to specialists, who in turn use computer calculations where indicated, top management saves valuable time. The cost of the extra personnel needed for evaluations as well as the computer expenditures are usually minimal compared to the gains made in terms of more effective management.

Operations Research Techniques

A few of the principal tools of OR deserve brief presentation. The most well-known OR technique is mathematical programing, which has found its primary use in production-sales coordination. It provides a tool for management to relate the variable margin of each product model or style against productive requirements and capacity limitations, so as to arrive at an optimal marketing goal. In practice this goal will not be fully attainable, but it will show the direction toward which sales efforts are best directed.

Inventories can be optimized by considering cost factors. In ordering supplies, for example, the larger the quantity, the lower will be the costs of ordering on a per-unit basis, and there will be the additional gains from quantity discounts. On the other hand, large orders mean large inventories of supplies, which will tie up valuable capital. An optimal balance in these opposing cost factors exists for practically all kinds of inventory — raw stock, supplies, goods-in-process, and finished product. OR techniques have been developed which show what inventory policies and corresponding quantity decisions will minimize inventory costs.

With increasing automation, the number of operators per output has decreased. Yet special operations, such as occasional changes in the feed hopper or output flow, or machinery-setting adjustments, or corrections of temporary malfunctions (chokes, spills, and such) require some human activity. The proper number of machines to have per operator in any group of machines depends upon two costs: (1) the costs of having a machine produce bad work while the operator is busy attending another machine that broke down only a short while ago, and (2) the cost of having too many operators stand "in waiting" for just such a double breakdown. Operations research weighs these two cost factors, arriving at the optimal machines-per-operator ratio, which will minimize total cost.

Further useful OR applications are being made in scheduling transportation economically, in ordering sequences of production effectively, in forecasting for market planning, in "network analysis" of large projects that depend upon the proper integration of hundreds of subsidiary schedules, and in many other fields.

When analytical methods become inadequate, it is often possible to "simulate." This involves the replication on a computer of basic data and relationships and then examining how certain management policies and decisions would work themselves out under these relationships. The optimal choice among the alternatives examined may then be adopted for actual decisions.

New and useful OR techniques are being developed constantly, but the principles are generally unvarying: to analyze, correlate, and interrelate as simply as possible, but nevertheless adequately, all those factors of a business problem that can be expressed quantitatively. Thus OR becomes an aid but never a substitute for good management.

TABLE 1-1

Examples of Managerial Decision Problems

Problem area	Selection among alternatives	Planning and finalizing of commitments
Capital budgeting	What new equipment and plant expenditures to authorize.	Allocating and timing disbursements within budgeted rates.
Financing	Various types of loans, or equity issue.	Detailed financial arrangements for quantity, terms, and timing.
Inventory policy	Production to orders only, or to orders and inventory.	At what times in the season and to what extent shall production to inventory occur?
Production	What styles, patterns, and colors to emphasize.	Scheduling start-up and volume build-up of each item.

TABLE 1-1 (*Continued*)

EXAMPLES OF MANAGERIAL DECISION PROBLEMS

Problem area	Selection among alternatives	Planning and finalizing of commitments
Raw stock	What source and quality of raw stock to use.	When, where, and how much to buy of each stock.
Administration	What data-processing would be most feasible?	If computer is to be used, providing for installation and phasing-in of all administrative operations.
Over-all	How will the individual decisions mesh to lead to an effective accomplishment of over-all objectives?	Detailed analysis of the interlocking effects of all planned commitments to yield an efficiently coordinated attainment of over-all objectives.

TABLE 1-2

MANAGEMENT YARDSTICKS OF PERFORMANCE

Yardstick	Information provided
Capital growth	Patterns of increase (and decline) of over-all value of company.
Net profit	Earnings before and after taxes. Since there is variation in the method used to set up various reserves, such as for depreciation, and in making valuations, such as for inventory, "net profit" is greatly affected by accounting practices used.
Flow-back of cash	Actual or expected excess of cash receipts over cash expenditures, as a measure of the rate of replenishment of money invested.
Return on sales	Percent of net earnings on the total amount sold.

TABLE 1-2 (*Continued*)

MANAGEMENT YARDSTICKS OF PERFORMANCE

Yardstick	Information provided
Market share	Portion of the total market gained by the company as a measure of relative success vis-à-vis competition.
Return on investment	Proportion of net earnings for each dollar invested.
Contribution to profit (and overhead)	Also known as "variable margin" or "operating profit," this measure is usually applied to individual products and styles in evaluating which products are most desirable and thus should be pushed heavily as building up profit.
Profit per machine hour	A frequently-used yardstick, but applicable only where certain machines represent a bottleneck process.
Over-all appraisal	A review of the firm's entire operation, applying all pertinent yardsticks to both short-range and long-range performance, as a basis for further management decisions, planning, and action.

▶ ▶ ▶ ▶ ## 2
Operations Research
and Accounting Methods

When introducing modern techniques of operations research, it seems appropriate to compare it with an older, more established quantitative method of attacking many business problems: accounting. As Richard V. Mattessich points out: "In actual practice, the accounting department was the major source of quantitative financial information until the emergence of the operations research team challenged this position. Such a challenge is a serious one. For not only do operations analysts pretend to have solutions for problems which accountants refuse to attack, the operations research men even claim the ability to solve less forbidding tasks better and more accurately than accountants do."[1]

In evaluating the contribution of the two quantitative methods, and the sources of possible conflict and reconciliation of the two disciplines, Mattessich has prepared an analysis which is presented in the following chapter which is based on his writings.[2]

The Case of Accounting

Trade, manufacturing, and governmental activities require internal and external control systems that traditionally have been provided by accounting. There have been two decisive criteria: (1) custodianship, control primarily directed toward checking the honest

---

[1] Mattessich, Richard, "Operations Research and Accounting: Competitors or Partners?" *Quarterly Review of Economics and Business*, vol. 2, no. 2, August 1962, p. 7.

[2] *Ibid.* pp. 7–14. See also his book *Accounting and Analytical Methods*, chapter 10. Homewood, Ill.: Richard D. Irwin, Inc., 1964.

stewardship of the person subject to it, and (2) objective evidence, control based on documentation of a highly "objective" nature.

Control regarding the efficiency or ability of an enterprise or person was long restricted to crude evaluative criteria such as sales or profit figures. Even then the accounting system could not and did not need to indicate what better sales volume or amount of profit could have been attained under a more efficient operation. In many cases the manager was the entrepreneur and, above all, the industrial structure was simple enough to let experience and intuition control the aspect of efficiency. With the increasing complexity of industry, the problem of efficiency control became more urgent. Obviously it was the accountant's task to remedy the situation by extending and articulating the bookkeeping system. Thus control and cost figures for individual departments, products, and so on were generated on a large scale and have proved useful — even if not always "correct." Because of the lack of precision, allocation assumptions have had to be made more on grounds of thrift than of accuracy, a fact that limits the usefulness and validity of cost accounting data. Thus accounting has been confronted with a problem (which it shares with OR and any other "practical," quantitative discipline) that has not yet found a systematic solution: the question of the optimal relationship between the amount to be spent on measurement and the degree of accuracy to be desired. The difficulty in determining this point of equilibrium between these two "conflicting" variables lies not so much in the lack of analytical thought as in finding a measure for the degree of accuracy of an accounting system, and above all in relating various accuracies to the benefits attained from them by the enterprise. In other words, the setting up of a reliable function between "degree of accuracy" and "yield" is the major hurdle.

As a result of this difficulty and the traditional methodology, accountants (even cost accountants) have restricted themselves to tasks of a quantitative descriptive nature. Thus the activities of classification and allocation, as well as the definitional and evaluative problems connected with them, have constituted the main concern of the accountant. This is comprehensible in the face of the bearing that accounting has upon many legal aspects, the taxation system, and the credit rating, as well as the security trading procedures. Even cost accounting occasionally affects these areas more than the realm of managerial decision making. The choice between the "fifo" and "lifo" inventory evaluation methods and the controversies connected with it amply illustrate this assertion. Traditional cost accounting, however, does perform functions of direct use to the various echelons of management, and the emergence of "managerial accounting" (about ten years ago) was no surprise. This term is still not clearly defined; some identify it with cost accounting, some with accounting in general, and others with something in between these two concepts. It has, however, succeeded in deceiving many laymen and even some accountants about the capability and range of this discipline.

Thus accounting grew out of the immediate need of actual practice and was chiefly developed by practitioners who adjusted the accounting model (1) to the availability of documentary and documentable material, (2) to their relatively unsophisticated mathematical abilities, and occasionally (3) to the need of a particular purpose or department without regard to general or over-all managerial considerations. Therefore, accounting and its effectiveness can be understood much better from a psychological than from a logical point of view.

It may be farfetched to compare the main function of accounting to the role Tolstoy assigned to General Kutuzov in his *War and Peace*, but a certain analogy undoubtedly exists. In the novel, an institution (the commanding general of the Russian Army) was painted as one whose importance lay in the representation of a stable (but perhaps purely fictitious) authority in the midst of chaos. It would be too dangerous to carry this analogy further, but it is notable that this commander, whose actions were not backed by any systematic strategy and whose actions usually defied logical analysis, ultimately carried the victory over the precisely logical and highly strategical war machinery of Napoleon. Certainly, it was not Kutuzov but the Russian winter that won the war. The lesson of Tolstoy, however, consists in the implication that in spite of the winter Napoleon might have won had it not been for the belief of the Russian people in an undefeated, though constantly retreating, army. Likewise, the effectiveness of traditional accounting lies not in the preciseness of information to management for maximizing profit or any other entrepreneurial goal, but in its authoritative character. The institution of control checks upon people and enables the depiction of the firm's financial structure in a simple and crude but over-all model which constitutes a mighty bulwark against chaos. This comparison is by no means intended as a defense of irrationalism or unscientific methods; it has been presented merely in the hope of facilitating understanding of accounting by OR men and other people for whom accounting seems to constitute a stumbling block. There can be no doubt that more scientific methods are better, absolutely speaking. There is merely the question about the threshold where they become more profitable for a certain firm.

The Case of Operations Research

Operations research emerged from the wartime need for solving decision-making problems of a military nature by way of mathematical-scientific methods. In many complex situations the intuition of the strategist was inferior to the solution that the mathematicians provided by means of their models. Thus it is understandable that OR methods came into vogue, not only with regard to military problems, but especially within the realm of business where the problem structure is similar or at least amenable to the same methodology. The main feature of this approach is the construction of analytical models that permit the determination of maximum or minimum solutions. The trend to substitute, in highly complex situations, purely analytical devices by iterative, heuristic, or even simulation approaches (which usually are restricted to satisfactory instead of optimal solutions) is another characteristic of OR research and was strongly furthered by the advent of electronic data processing.

Out of all this grows an additional feature which may be covered by the term "systems approach." This is the conceptualization of the problem under a viewpoint that considers the interdependence of all variable incorporated in the model. We may call such models *mutatis mutandis*, in contrast to the *ceteris paribus* models. The latter assume all but one variable constant, whereas the former take many possible feedback reactions to other variables into consideration. This contrast in methodology is familiar to us from traditional economics.

With respect to these mathematical tools Herbert Simon offers a "general recipe for using it in management decision-making."[3]

1. Construct a mathematical model that satisfies the conditions of the tool to be used and that, at the same time, mirrors the important factors in the management situation to be analyzed.
2. Define the criterion function, the measure that is to be used for

---

[3]Herbert A. Simon, *The New Science of Management Decisions*. New York: Harper and Row, Publishers, 1960, pp. 16–17.

comparing the relative merits of various possible courses of action.

3. Obtain empirical estimates of the numerical parameters in the model that specify the particular, concrete situation to which it is to be applied.

4. Carry through the mathematical process of finding the course of action that, for the specific parameter values, maximizes the criterion function.

Operations research may, then, be regarded as a field of applied mathematics and statistics whose concern is the developing of sets of standard models, as well as their modification for practical application, in the micro economy (that is, inventory, queuing, and such) that control the efficiency of particular, limited areas within an organization. The last part of this description will be stressed because it hints at one of the major shortcomings of OR: the inability, at least so far, to provide models for over-all optimization. This is partly conditioned by the technical limitations that a huge number of variables impose even on a computer, and partly by the unfortunate fact that the sum total of a series of suboptima does not necessarily yield the over-all optimum. A thorough analysis even reveals something more embarrassing, namely, that in order to optimize a part correctly, the whole ought to be optimized first. The ambition toward a global model of the firm is thus restricted to the area of simulation instead of optimizing. Attempts are under way to construct comprehensive control models of the firm, such as the construction of Mark I, a management control model of the System Development Corporation, Santa Monica California. Persons interested in this area expect great theoretical insight from the final results. With regard to the practical application of such complex models, however, skepticism is justified, for the huge number of unwieldy variables and the exceedingly high costs of such a project exclude any hope for establishing in the near future a control model of this sort for most of the industry. It seems instead that a combination of operations research models with the accountant's budgeting model as an over-all frame is, from the point of view of practicality of realization, a more promising solution.

This is also stressed by a management scientist in the following sentences: "But primarily, management science has failed to assist top management because the philosophy and objectives of management science have often been irrelevant to the manager. Mathematical economics and management science have often been more closely allied to formal mathematics than to economics and management. . . . In many professional journal articles the attitude is that of an exercise in formal logic rather than that of a search for useful solutions to real problems."[4]

The Source of Conflict

From the description of OR and accounting it would not appear that their interests clash to an extent that makes conflict unavoidable. Therefore the existing differences of opinion have to be demonstrated separately. The literature dealing with this borderline problem of accounting and OR is relatively scarce, and a listing of the arguments will have to rely primarily on Churchman's *Prediction and Optimal Decision*[5] and personal experience in conversation with operations analysts and accountants.

The main objections made against accounting may be summed up in four items:

1. The cost accounting models, in spite of standard cost systems, are still too closely tied to the approach of historical costing, while considerations of alternatives in the form of a variety of opportunity costs are not sufficiently taken care of. Above all, accounting does not reveal the profit which would have occurred had alternative decisions been made.
2. The accounting models are chiefly of a quantitative descriptive nature instead of a quantitative analytical nature and are not designed to search systematically for optimal solutions.
3. On one side the accounting models apply concepts and collect many data which are irrelevant to decisions of the higher echelons of management, but on the other side they do not generate many data urgently needed for decision processes. In this way, accounting ignores goals other than profit and related aims and identifies the profit goal with the goal of the organization.

---

[4]J. W. Forrester, *Industrial Dynamics*. New York: John Wiley & Sons, and Cambridge Mass., Massachusetts Institute of Technology, 1961, p. 3.

[5]Englewood Cliffs, N. J.: Prentice-Hall, Inc., 1961 (primarily Chapters 3 and 13); see also C. W. Churchman and R. L. Ackoff, "Operational Accounting and Operations Research," *Journal of Accountancy*, vol. 99, no. 2 (February 1955), pp. 33–39.

4. Accounting uses allocation procedures that are not based on a knowledge of the optimal organization structure; this distorts the measures that serve managerial decision making.

Thus accounting does not supply an objective scale of values that can be used for selecting optimal decisions or for an evaluation of managerial performance. Further arguments and sub-arguments are that the time over which profits are being calculated is not sufficiently defined, that psychological factors which would seem significant because of the stimulus that costs exercise upon human actions are rarely considered, that the balance sheet is not comprehensive enough and its inclusive criterion of "measurable" is too superficial, that the good will of the enterprise, if taken into consideration at all, is incorrectly measured, that the additivity assumption with regard to many assets is unrealistic, and that accounting measures are not accompanied by error estimates.

After a penetrating analysis of many of these points Churchman concludes:

> It isn't that accounting systems are "slightly" defective here and there, and that the wise manager will ignore some figures and add or subtract from others. In view of the fact that asset utilization and non-utilization, and organizational policy are both highly critical in managerial decisions, and because the values of these policies are not measured by accounting information, it is safe to say that cost and profit information is seriously defective relative to a scientific understanding of policy information.[6]

To parry some of these attacks, accountants have asserted that their major concern is not prediction but measurement of past performance. This rejoinder, however, will hardly do, for even the correct measurement of past performance needs asset valuation through opportunity costs and value allocations based on an optimal organization structure.

Another argument, that the center of the universe is not necessarily management but alternatively, the consumer, the investor, or the government, seems somewhat stronger but abandons cost accounting and provokes the answer that even the investor wants to get reports of past performances which are based on opportunity rather than on historical costs; only then can he continue to make the "correct" investment decisions. The argument, however, points in

---

[6]*Prediction and Optimal Decision, op. cit.*, p. 66.

the right direction by indicating the existence of diverse and occasionally conflicting goals which accountants have tried to satisfy by a compromise that might not do in the future.

But the strongest counterargument to the above criticisms may lie in the fact that, surprisingly enough, they ignore the previously mentioned relationship between the costs of operating an accounting system and the yield from it. All these arguments seem to assume that the way of creating more accurate information by operations analysts costs no more, in relation to its marginal yield, than the way of creating less accurate information by accountants. This implies, of course, that both accounting and operations research can attain only approximations to reality, approximations of lesser or greater accuracy, under lesser or greater costs, of a relative benefit that is not necessarily in proportion to these costs. It can well be argued that accounting is what it is, not because accountants reject analytical thinking, but because in the past more sophisticated approaches would have been financially unbearable to the enterprise.

In close connection with this problem is a dilemma of OR which cannot remain unmentioned: the difficulty of creating the raw material of OR analysis in the form of input data. Many of these data are not regularly supplied by the accounting department. A fairly accurate measurement of most of these data is still, and will be in the future, forbiddingly expensive. Some cannot be measured at all, and accountants mock the OR men with the question of whether the crystal ball that might supply them with the required information has already been found. The only way out of this dilemma is obviously to make a crude, and often very arbitrary, estimate of the magnitude of these variables; this, however, defeats the operations analyst's claim to supply more accurate information than the accountant does. Therefore, even if cost accounting and OR were direct competitors, the problem would be more complex than it appears to the operations analyst who sees only the mathematical superiority of his own approach. The question must be posed in a different fashion: we have to ask instead, where in a particular enterprise does the golden middle lie between "the pitfalls of oversimplification and the morass of overcomplication."[7] Since this middle road is differently situated in every firm, no fixed answer is available. It will take considerable time to

---

[7]Richard Bellman, *Dynamic Programming*. Princeton, N. J.: Princeton University Press, 1957, p. x.

find the critical size of enterprise for which the mathematical over-complication and "technical" oversimplification of operations research models are less disadvantageous than the mathematical oversimplification and "technical" overcomplication of the accounting model. This in itself is an optimization problem and one we hope will be solved eventually by some of OR's own methods, such as learning theory. Until then the superiority of modern OR methodology will have to find its proof by trial and error, which means through the evidence of practical results on a large scale. Thus the hope for abandoning accounting or an immediate general acceptance of a "universal" information system of the firm, in accord with the suggestions of some operations analysts, is not great.

Possibilities of Reconciliation

Once accountants and OR men learn to recognize their own deficiencies and discover that their strong points are not of a competitive but of a complementary nature, however, the "optimal solution" might be found in a cooperative effort of both groups. Close collaboration between scholars from many disciplines is required to develop tools that master the ever increasing complexity of our economic environment. Coordination between applied mathematics, behavioral economics, and accounting seems to provide the ingredients required to make the envisaged vehicle run properly. The more moderate advocates of management science recognize that cost accounting provides an effective control mechanism and supplies important raw material to the operations researcher. They are well aware that implements as well entrenched as those of cost accounting cannot be displaced overnight without serious damage.

The camp of the accountants, too, has various reactions to the new movement of management science. One group wants to disregard or deny the impact that this new development makes upon accounting; they refuse to acquire even the basic mathematical knowledge necessary to understand OR methods and behave in a manner which is erroneously attributed to the African ostrich. The second group recognizes the importance of the achievements of OR for the field of accounting, is willing to sacrifice enough time and energy to learn and understand the working methods of management's new science, and admits that major revisions are due in managerial accounting, but firmly believes that the main structure of accounting will survive in this process of reformation. Most of the members of this group do not favor sudden and radical adjustments, and some believe that a first step toward cooperation with operations research is the translation of accounting models and submodels into mathematical terms. On one hand they are aware that the future accounting system of the firm cannot do without many technical and often apparently trivial details, but on the other hand they are skeptical of the idea that a central information system of the firm, in which are also stored and elaborated the innumerable, purely technological, personnel, psychological, and market data, can fulfill all the functions of traditional accounting. Such an information system may perform useful services to many departments, but can neither be identified with what is commonly understood as accounting nor replace it overnight.

The call for a novel approach to accounting comes from several directions and the need for a broadening of this discipline has many facets. Thus accountants are confronted with choosing one of the following alternatives:

1. To acquire a profound knowledge of many aspects of jurisprudence (civil law, commercial law, corporation and partnership law, and tax law) and develop their discipline into a purely legalistic-dogmatic field of knowledge
2. To acquire proficiency in modern quantitative analytical methods and try to maintain the old status of their discipline, namely that of the most important quantitative tool of economic practice

Probably, these will become alternatives for the profession as such rather than for the individual accountant. The past has revealed clearly the importance of accounting as an instrument for the fulfillment of legalistic requirements. Our present system of financial accounting, however, constitutes a compromise that neglects some legal aspects almost as much as some managerial aspects. This anticipated diversification of accounting need not create a chasm within accounting, but may well lead to a close cooperation between specialists.

Conclusion

The material presented in this chapter has served to clarify further the position of modern operations research as a quantitative management tool. The opinions expressed are, of course, those of Richard V. Mattessich. It is of interest to note that both the accounting and the OR functions of an organization are increasingly utilizing computer technologies for the complex data-processing and analytical procedures involved in both fields.

Small businesses have ready access to electronic computers on a rented-time basis. Larger organizations who have such equipment "on location," are indeed wasteful if they use computers merely as high-speed adding machines for routine clerical functions, instead of developing applications of value to accounting and OR analyses and procedures. The waste resulting from failure to make maximum use of both accounting and operations research skills in an organization is usually in the form of inadequate management information, which in turn handicaps management in its planning, decision-making and control activities.

▶ ▶ ▶ ▶ **3**

Decision Making
under Uncertainty:
A Case Study

"We have decided that we must diversify product lines,"
declared the chairman of the board at the annual meeting. It sounded
logical. Having experienced a rapid growth during the first half of
the 1950s, based almost entirely on the manufacture and sales of
military and commercial aircraft engines, the company expected increasingly fluctuating market conditions during the second half of the
decade. Product diversification would cushion or offset such effects,
management reasoned. Yet, near the end of the decade the company
was in difficulty and near liquidation. What had happened? A review
of the actual case history will show why the logical-sounding decision
was actually a poor decision, and will also indicate how the use of
modern quantitative techniques might have aided in arriving at a
better decision.[1]

Background

During the 1940s, the company was almost entirely concerned
with producing a reciprocating engine of high efficiency and reliability which, because of mass production, was also economical.
After buying a license from a foreign firm, the company also began
production of military jet power plants in the early 1950s. The
rapidly increasing market for commercial reciprocating aircraft and

---

[1]Case data adapted from a paper by S. B. Alpert of Hydrocarbon Research,
Inc., and H. Weitz of System Development Corporation, "Decision Making,
Growth and Failure" presented at the Seventh Annual International Meeting, The
Institute of Management Sciences, New York, October 20, 1960, and reprinted
in Transactions of the Professional Group of Engineering Management, Institute
of Radio Engineers, vol. EM-8, no. 3, September 1961.

the military change-over to jet power plants, during the first half of the 1950s, resulted in a fourfold increase of company sales during the period of 1951 to 1956.

Measures of Performance

The excellent progress of growth made by the company is represented in the form of comparative index numbers for the years 1951 and 1956 in Table 3-1. The fourfold increase in sales dollars was, in more exact terms, an increase of 337 percent, from an index of 100 for 1951 to 437 for 1956. While the number of employees increased 54 percent during that period, the sales per employee rose by 184 percent. The doubling of the market share, as represented by an increase from 100 to 200 of the market share index, was accompanied by an astounding acceleration in profit margin, which now stood at 536 percent of 1951 profit.

Moreover, the price indexes in Table 3-2 show that the increased profits were accomplished despite increasing labor and materials costs of some 30 percent and a reduction in selling price of a similar 30 percent. Improvements in product design, processing methods, and productivity, as well as other cost reductions, were making these achievements possible.

Erroneous Decision

It was at this stage of success that the erroneous decision to diversify was made. Yet, a sound analysis of factors, supported by OR evaluations, could have shown the error of the decision, and helped management in formulating a better approach. The following factors could have been brought out:

1. By 1956 the commercial jet age was imminent. Such engines required entirely different designs than some of the military jets.
2. For military requirements, rockets were beginning to replace jet aircraft.
3. Foreign firms had not developed any commercial jet engines or rockets that could be licensed.
4. Because of high research costs, domestic firms could not be expected to be willing to sell licenses on their new jet engine or rocket engine developments.
5. In view of the specialized sales, marketing and production

requirements of new product lines in a variety of fields, a management reared and nurtured in one industry, could not hope to adapt itself quickly to the problems of a variety of other industries.

The decision to diversify was thus a decision not to allocate resources for research and development in the company's existing field — engines. The risks involved in research and development were foregone in favor of the even greater risks of adaptation to new industries. Table 3-1 shows that within two years of that fateful decision, the company had suffered a major loss of market share and was in a general state of decline.

The Decision Problem

The case history presented provides a good illustration of the complex and interlocking problems that go into decision making. Several aspects are involved:

1. Evaluation of alternatives. Management must evaluate the alternative courses of action that are open. In the present situation, some of these alternatives were (a) to diversify, (b) to initiate research in commercial jet and rocket engines, (c) provide for both (a) and (b) but to a lesser degree for each, (d) or else do nothing about (a) and (b).
2. Allow for uncertainty. In evaluating alternatives, expected trends, and developments in markets, technologies and political, economic, and social environments of business activity must be taken into consideration. All such activity, reaching towards the near or farther distance in time, is subject to some uncertainty. For the engine company, certain questions come up as to the real extent of the future commercial jet and rocket market, expected government purchasing policies, likely actions of competitors or competing defense systems, availability and cost of research personnel, chance of success, and anticipated productivity of such research, and many similar factors. From engineering, statistical, and economic analyses, forecasts can be made. But around these forecasts there is always some error, some degree of doubt, uncertainty — and therefore risk.
3. Make the decision after evaluating the alternatives. This includes weighing the risks under the uncertainties pre-

vailing, and considering the over-all goal of long-term corporate profitability, consistent with the responsibilities to investors and employees.

Could Management Science Have Helped?

This question should undoubtedly be answered in the affirmative. Here is what management scientists could have done for top management, thereby aiding in coming to an optimal decision:

1. Working with engineers and scientists of the company, and using industry data and available statistical information, definite estimates as to the future market for commercial jets and military rockets could have been developed.
2. Similar data, showing the decline of military jets and commercial reciprocating engines, would have been a ready by-product of this study.
3. Expected outlays necessary and anticipated risks in research and development for commercial jets and military rockets could have been prepared.
4. The anticipated greater risks of embarking on a whole series of new products — plastics for consumer products, ultrasonic devices, earth-moving equipment, electronic transducers, and other new items — could have been demonstrated, by showing relatively slim success ratios in those industries and allowing for the additional problems faced by a new management in these areas.
5. Combining these factors and relationships, considering the technological, economic, statistical data, and relative risks developed, and presenting a summary of these evaluations.

The data so gathered would have clearly pointed away from intensive product diversification. It would have shown that, far from avoiding risk, the route of diversification involved greater risk and less profit expectation than management action to promote current research in the development of better and more modern engines.

Prerequisites

The prerequisites for the management-science approach to work are many. The chief needs are two:

1. Qualified management scientists who are able to work with the engineers, physicists, chemists of the company and with other sources from outside the firm in collecting, analyzing and presenting pertinent technological, economic and statistical data.
2. A top management that is aware of the value of management-science applications, has developed the management-science approach throughout its organization, and is ready to make use of the services of its management-science staff whenever and wherever they can be of help.

Among both the management scientists and top management there will, at all times, be the knowledge that not all factors can be evaluated in quantitative terms and therefore not all factors going into a decision can be integrated into a simple optimal solution. However, by quantifying, analyzing, and summarizing as much of the elements of a problem as can practically be accomplished, the management scientists simplifies top management's job. The net benefit, in the long run, should be to enable top management to enhance the quality of its decisions and its batting average in guessing right.

There are few phases of business operation that cannot benefit from the aid of management science. While top management decisions are an initial illustration of the place of such science, most of the applications and techniques will take place in lower echelons of management, in production, engineering, development, marketing, and sales, and it is with these areas that most of the examples in this book are concerned.

Conclusion

It is admittedly unfair to criticize the management of this aircraft company on the basis of hindsight. This, however, is not the purpose of the chapter. Rather, we wish to demonstrate how modern management-science approaches might have helped the firm. From failures of the type in this case history, there has come the growing realization that we live in an age of rapid innovation technologically, with repercussions requiring an extremely alert management. Quantitative methods, when properly nurtured and maintained within an organization, aid management in its endeavors of staying alert and foresighted.

TABLE 3-1

PRICE CHANGES

(Index Numbers, 1952 = 100)

	Years				
Item studied	1952	1953	1954	1955	1956
Raw materials cost	100	103	104	122	127
Labor cost per hour	100	116	123	128	132
Average engine selling price	100	101	96	77	72

TABLE 3-2

MEASURES OF PERFORMANCE, 1951 TO 1958

(Index Numbers, 1951 = 100)

	Years		
Performance Measures	1951	1956	1958
Sales dollars	100	437	188
Average number employed	100	154	76
Sales per employe	100	284	250
Market share	100	200	86
Profit as a percent of sales	100	171	124
Profit margin	100	536	268

▶ ▶ ▶ ▶ **4**

Introducing
Operations Research Techniques
in an Organization

While, on the one hand, operations research is a tool designed to aid management, on the other hand, it also requires considerable management effort to introduce operations research techniques successfully in an existing organization. With regard to these managerial aspects, the observations by Robert A. Hammond, an associate with the well-known consulting firm of McKinsey & Company, Inc., may be of special interest.[1]

General

In recent years, OR established itself as a remarkably potent tool for solving business problems. Its potential increases as research produces new technical developments and as business feels the pressure to sharpen the impact of planning and decision-making procedures. At the same time, business executives have become increasingly receptive to trying out and adopting these new methods and, as a result, OR has been accepted by many companies.

Yet, despite the warm reception OR has enjoyed and despite many success stories, praise for it is not unanimous. A canvass of any representative sample of companies would reveal a large number of disillusioned rather than enthusiastic managements, and discontinued rather than flourishing programs.

Why has OR been successful in some companies and not in others? In carrying out such projects, what are the most common obstacles to the profitable solution of assignments? How can manage-

---

[1]The material in this chapter is adapted from "Making OR Effective for Management" by Robert A. Hammond, an undated brochure published by McKinsey & Company, Inc.

31

ment deal with these obstacles to ensure adequate returns on its
investment in OR? Can more managements profitably use this
powerful technique?

This chapter will serve to analyze these questions and seek to
explain how companies have obtained maximum benefit from OR.
From this, some guide lines will be developed for use by: (1) management responsible for organizing and directing OR in a company,
(2) operating management, the ultimate users of OR, and (3) the OR
staff.

Problems in Effectiveness

Management needs first of all a yardstick with which to measure
whether or not an OR project has been a success or failure so that it
can focus attention on specific problems in the effective use of OR.
Any one of several criteria can, of course, be used to measure OR
achievement. The technical quality of the analysis and solution, for
example, is one possible yardstick. Another is the improvement
in management's understanding of the problem. The expected profit
improvement or cost reduction is still another.

A more fundamental criterion than any of these is necessary,
however, and can be found in the one element common to all three
possibilities: the best solution of the business problem must be
effectively implemented. In this lies the measure of OR success.
Using effective implementation as a criterion provides a starting
point for determining what obstacles most frequently delay, or total-
ly prevent, the success of an OR project.

A review of many companies' experience in the management of
OR shows that there are many impediments to the effective completion of an OR project. Of these, four seem to be particularly
detrimental: (1) overemphasis on technique, (2) poor communication
between the OR team and management, (3) failure to make use of the
experience and judgment of operating managers, and (4) inadequate
participation of management in the project.

Technique

The lack of suitable mathematical techniques is rarely a problem
in OR studies. In fact, the availability of numerous methods and
computer hardware may in itself become a problem; the significance,
and novelty, of these techniques misdirects OR teams and managers
into enthusiasm for the mechanics rather than for the end product.

As a result, OR teams have at times taken up insignificant problems, or have attempted to solve important problems incorrectly, merely because a computer is available or a technique known.

Recently, for example, a paper company studied ways of scheduling orders on a papermaking machine so that waste (called "trim loss") would be minimized. The operations research team developed a linear-programing model to select orders in a way that minimized waste. The model proved difficult to use, however, because last-minute changes in production (not at all unusual in the paper industry) required frequent reruns on the computer. A later reappraisal of marketing needs and production scheduling showed that maintaining a finished-goods inventory of popular sizes provided the flexibility needed to schedule accurately without a computer. The decision to use linear programing not only cost the company money unnecessarily, but also left management's real problem unsolved.

In another instance, a heavy-equipment manufacturer undertook a lengthy study to improve production planning. The study was a very satisfactory scientific endeavor, which produced a complicated scheduling model. The cost reduction achieved, however, was insignificant compared with the cost of developing the model. In fact, the model produced results only slightly better than would have been achieved by using a series of simple decision rules derived from existing practice. This company lost sight of the true objective of the study: to determine better decision rules theoretically possible. Unquestionably, mathematical techniques and computers are pivotal in this field, and extensive technical research is essential for continued OR progress. Too often, however, technique dominates the selection of problems to be studied, the approach to be used, and the emphasis of the study.

Communication

No matter how effective the technique used to solve a problem, the technical group is always faced with the task of communicating the results of its study to operating management, in terms that can be fully understood and accepted.

A manufacturing company, interested in improving forecasts of the annual demand for its products, ran aground on a communications problem. After studying the problem, the OR team had developed a correlation method; this showed, by analysis of past data, the best relationship between product demand and a set of economic factors.

To the uninitiated, these factors — gross national product, average level of population, and average family income — appeared to have little direct connection with the company.

In presenting the forecasting method to marketing management, the team dwelt at length on technical points: how the method had been developed and the mathematical relationships between the economic factors and product demand. The practical application, however, went almost unmentioned. Consequently, management assumed, incorrectly, that the OR results were an explanation of how each factor affected demand, rather than a means of determining what action to take. The method, which was perfectly sound, was never accepted because the operations research team failed to interpret the results in operational terms for managers who had a marketing orientation.

It is frequently difficult for people with different technical backgrounds or functional responsibilities to come to agreement and understanding on a common problem. Yet it is in these interfunctional problems that OR can offer its greatest benefits to management. The OR research team is almost certain to encounter communication problems if it presents recommendations and results in an overly technical manner or does not specify the assumptions and limitations of the work. In companies with a successful operations research record, the OR team has been willing to expend considerable effort to ensure that its presentations are easily understandable and in terms that are meaningful to management.

Experience and Judgment

Many studies are unsuccessful because the OR team does not stay in close touch with the line managers to draw on their experience and judgment. From the outset of a project, these managers can offer guidance and know-how to the technical staff. They can assist in defining realistic objectives and suggest solutions that may otherwise be overlooked. Their knowledge can often be incorporated in the model as inputs or, at least, be used in formulating assumptions and constraints for it.

An OR team in an airlines company neglected this valuable approach and, in consequence, worked out a solution that, while technically sound, proved to be virtually useless. During the first few months of the introduction of a new jet aircraft into its fleet, the company experienced serious spare-parts problems. Aircraft components were failing much more rapidly than expected, and a policy of low initial stocking of spares made the difficulties more severe.

The OR team tackled the problem without more than the most casual contact with purchasing and inventory management. The team worked out a complete simulation model, which determined the total requirement for spare parts and the allocation of parts to field stores. Before a computer run could be planned, this model required data on the expected failure rate of each part and the expected schedule of planes. In fact, to use the simulation model would have required a major reorganization and change of approach in the purchasing department. Unfortunately, the model did not give the company's purchasing department a means of analyzing requirements on an item-by-item basis or of using the existing procurement facilities for rapid initial ordering. Thus, the model was a complete waste of effort because the OR work was treated as a research project with no appreciation of the urgency of the situation or the practical contributions that purchasing management could have made.

Success depends on the OR team's ability to use the experience of the decision makers and utilize all relevant information, both internal information about the firm and — just as important — external information, such as political, economic, and competitive factors. Management information on external factors is particularly significant for operations research to be successful in solving long-range problems, which require judgment on the future, problems, involving profitability, and problems of marketing strategy that, for example, could involve consideration of competition.

Management Participation

There is still another reason why OR programs fail to gain acceptance and full implementation: inadequate participation by management, especially the management level that must act on the recommendations.

When OR achievements of a leading manufacturing company were recently reviewed, the record showed that, although several models of processing operations had been built, the company was lagging far behind its competitors in applying operations research. In fact, few of the models had been successfully used. In tracing the causes for this failure, the review committee found that the OR group believed its responsibility ended when the mathematical model was completed. But even more important, the group was under the control of a functional head whose responsibilities were unrelated to the broad scope of OR work. Because of this organizational arrangement, the OR group did not have access to top management and was seriously handicapped in its study of interfunctional problems.

The effectiveness of an operations research team depends on obtaining the cooperation and participation of the level of management responsible for all of the functions involved in the study and affected by its recommendations. Thus, in a study of inventory, in which both marketing and production are involved, the executive responsible for both marketing and production must participate. Without his acceptance of the implementation program, the interfunctional problem cannot effectively be resolved.

Furthermore, it is important to enlist the participation of operating management, as well as of management responsible for functions involved. By contributing to an OR study, operating managers may be more profoundly persuaded of its validity and usefulness. That they be thus persuaded is essential to the full implementation of any operations research solution. For among most frequent obstacles to successful completion of a project are operating managers' prejudices against the use of quantitative solutions, their unwillingness to accept the computer as an aid to decision making, their understandable resentment of outside interference in their decision areas, and their suspicion of centralized decision-making authority, which may not provide the same degree of flexibility currently available in their decision areas.

Guidelines for Success

The OR experience of a wide range of companies of varying size and in different industries shows that the total effectiveness of OR, judged by the success of implementation, can be improved by careful planning and by close coordination between the operations research problem solvers and the solution implementers. Four important guidelines will help management and the operations staff carry projects through to their practical and profitable use: (1) solve problems rather than apply techniques, (2) organize for problem solving, (3) select projects carefully, and (4) use a planned approach to operations research studies.

Solving Problems The management point of view that is most likely to promote successful use of operations research is one that views operations research as an approach to problem solving and planning rather than as a collection of techniques. It is an extension of problem-solving and planning methods used by management. The results of operations research studies must be practical and capable of being put into operation in decision making or planning.

The best way to prevent a study from getting too deeply involved in merely application of technique is for the OR team and operating management to define clearly from the outset the objective and scope of the study and the approach to be used. It is also necessary to consider early in the study the value and impact that achieving the objectives will have for operating management. And throughout, management and the OR team must pursue with singleness of purpose the main objective of the study: to solve the problem. To achieve this prime requisite, the method employed is secondary, whether it is linear programming, simple algebra, or merely a sound process of improving existing practical decision rules.

If, as suggested, successful application of operations research depends on placing emphasis on problem solving and planning, then what are the specific benefits of the operations research approach? Four of them follow:

1. Some industries have problems that cannot be solved effectively or efficiently by relying solely on past experience in similar situations. This may be because there are many courses of action, with no standard solutions, or many interrelated variables. Therefore, the development of a mathematical model and analysis of alternatives, often with the aid of a computer, becomes the most profitable way of solving the problem. Operations research not only provides significantly better answers in thse cases but occasionally makes a solution other than a judgmental solution possible.

2. When developing planning methods and decision rules involving more than one functional area, OR often provides an approach to analysis of these problems, which leads to quantitative solutions that are thus removed to some extent from the gray areas of discretion.

3. The use of an approach to problem solving that requires a precisely defined objective and detailed resolution of significant factors and alternatives in many cases provides both

a better diagnosis of the problem and a quantitative justi-
fication for a program of corrective action.

4. In some cases the OR approach provides a solution of more
lasting value than a short-term judgmental solution. For
example, a manufacturing firm experienced a rapid increase
in its finished-goods inventory when production was not
reduced after a cut in a competitor's price caused a sudden
drop in sales. Inventories grew so rapidly that, when production finally acted, it was necessary to lay off part of the
work force. The layoff caused union grievances and a strike
was threatened. Inventories were slowly reduced by placing
the work force on a part-time basis and, at the same time,
a start was made on a long-term solution of the inventory
problem by setting up an operations research study on
inventory and production control. This study resulted in a
set of dynamic decision rules of long-term value — because
they could easily be updated as conditions changed — that
allowed management to plan production, work force, and
inventory levels.

Although the prime use of an OR study is to solve a specific
business problem, there are occasions when OR can also be used to
analyze an entire business system to provide information for decisions, or, in fact, to locate the real problem affecting the operation
of the company. In addition, where detailed analysis is not possible,
an OR approach can be used to evaluate the sensitivity of alternative
decisions to a range of possible future conditions.

Organizing for Problem Solving

Whatever the technical means used in an OR study, its success
depends in large measure on the organization and staffing of the OR
activity. Management, in fact, is concerned with the organization
and staffing of two kinds of OR activities: teams temporarily set up
to study a specific management problem or planning process, and the
permanent, specialized OR staff.

If a team is to solve specific business problems, it must consist of
both OR technicians competent in developing mathematical solutions,
and planners familiar with existing practices in making management
decisions. Furthermore, the team members must be skillful in

communicating conclusions and recommendations to management. They should be able to inspire management's confidence in the abilities of the team to understand and interpret the business situation and in the solution derived from the team's mathematical skills.

In organizing this kind of team it is particularly important that provision be made for drawing on management's experience. In a study of forecasting procedures, for example, a marketing manager's knowledge of the growth and decay of demand for a new product may be a key factor. Therefore, although the OR team is using exponential smoothing (a method of forecasting using weighted averages of past sales), it should take account of management's knowledge of the growth pattern and the impact of promotional efforts, to obtain the most useful forecasting procedure.

The only way of effectively incorporating such background knowledge and experience is to have members of operating management serve on the study team. Their participation prevents the last-minute realization that some practical and significant business facts have been omitted from consideration, thus invalidating the work. At the same time, they act as a sounding board for recommendations before the results are presented to top management.

When the team is first established, the stage must be set, organizationally, for implementing the final recommendations. Thus, if the study crosses functional, departmental, or divisional lines, the results and recommendations of the study should be directed to the management responsible for all operations involved. If the study crosses all functional lines, as some studies do, the work should be designed for, and directed to, the chief executive.

Even though such temporary operations research teams are important, the keystone of successful OR work is the specialized staff. To solve management's problems, such an OR staff must combine technical excellence with an understanding of management's approach to decision making. They should bring the problem solving all the capabilities needed: creativity, analytical skill, an unbiased approach, and practical ideas and reasoning. In addition, companies with the most successful OR records have high-caliber OR leadership. The OR staff in such companies also takes on the important training functions of (1) developing competence in OR techniques, (2) developing interest and ability to recognize opportunities for using OR at all management levels, and (3) helping operating management to understand and use the results of OR studies.

As for the place of the OR staff in the company organization, experience shows that several locations have been successful, provided the activity is not restricted to one functional area. Further, the staff must have access to, and cooperation from, a level of management high enough in the organization to ensure implementation of results.

This does not necessarily require all of the OR staff to be completely centralized. In fact, many large companies, particularly those in the oil industry, have men with OR skills strategically distributed at divisional levels. These companies, however, maintain a small, high-caliber staff group to provide functional or technical guidance for the total operations research activity. The staff group maintains close contact with top management, ensures that OR is applied wherever benefits can be derived, determines when outside technical aid is needed, and provides the technical guidance for planning programs and developing techniques.

This decentralized arrangement with central technical guidance has several advantages. The most important one is that the OR teams work in closer contact with the managers responsible for implementing results. In addition, a great deal of excellent operations research work can be carried out by specialists in other areas. Economists, engineers, and electronic data processing (EDP) experts, for example, can, with technical assistance, produce the benefits of a successful OR application.

In small companies, the only people with OR skills may be two or three on the technical operations research staff. They must be high-caliber men and, because they cannot be expected to possess every skill, they should be analysts and planners rather than expert mathematicians. Therefore, in small companies there may be a greater need to seek consulting advice and technical assistance outside the company.

In summary, then, the essential characteristics of temporary study teams are, first, that team members be planners and problem solvers dedicated to seeking practical guides for management decision making, and second, that quality rather than quantity be the main requirement. The exact organizational location of the permanent operations research staff is not critical, but the staff must consist of people with fresh ideas, technical knowledge, ability to take an objective and systematic approach to problem solving, and, above all, ability to communicate with all levels of management.

Selecting Projects Carefully

With satisfactory organization and staffing, the effectiveness of operations research will depend on the selection of projects and on the approach used by the teams to plan the work and meet the study objectives.

The selection of projects is a twofold responsibility. The first part is management's responsibility to identify the key decisions and problem areas and, with the operations research staff, to evaluate the need for better problem solutions or planning methods. Top management, as well as operating management, should play a part in this identification process because much of the real benefit of operations research comes from studies in decision areas that cross functional boundaries.

The second part of the responsibility falls on the OR staff that must assist management in identification and ranking of projects by estimating the probability of success, the expected benefits and risks, and the possible work load and timetable. All of these important factors can be used later by the study team when the project is started.

The selection of operations research projects is particularly important for companies just starting OR work because the future of OR in the company will be determined by the short-term benefits derived from the first projects. Selection of projects with short-term payoff and low risk of not reaching successful implementation is the best way to establish the value of OR and gain management interest and confidence. For example, such projects may be in production or inventory control where a high degree of success has been obtained. With initial success as background, more extensive studies — usually with greater potential payoff — can be undertaken.

Because starting an operations research activity presents some problems, and because the selection and ranking of profitable operations research projects requires a diagnosis of management problems and a knowledge of the likely success of OR work, companies often seek outside consultant guidance in these areas. For some companies, specialized staffs trained in mathematics may not be necessary at all to obtain the fundamental benefits offered by OR.

Even in companies where operations research is well established, projects that embrace total company or corporate problems should not be started without first taking significant intermediate steps. The company can benefit from analyses of parts of the larger problem that lend themselves readily to such approaches and that can be successfully completed in a reasonable span of time. Nevertheless, the long-range objective of the OR staff should be the benefits of OR that are obtained when it contributes to improved decision making in problems that have significant profit impact, such as major marketing and financial decisions.

Using a Planned Approach

To deal with problems of conflicting goals, policies, and alternatives, the OR team should use a planned approach to the study. It is important to recognize that the prime function of OR in industry is to develop and apply a quantitative approach to specific problems, rather than carry out fundamental research. The required creativity will not be restricted by scheduling and planning the study, and the desired end result, the implementation of the selected solution, will be ensured.

Figure 4-1 illustrates the total operations research approach to problem solving and shows that the first step in an approach is to obtain the basic facts, opinions, and symptoms of the problem needed to define clearly management's real problem.

Next, the factors affecting the problem, the variables, and constraints, must be determined. The variable factors are those on which decisions have to be made, such as level of inventory, production rate, or amount and character of promotional effort. The constraints limit the solution of the problem, such as specific out-of-stock criteria, a constant employment policy, or a minimum cash requirement. Also, the assumptions to be made when solving the problem must be identified, for example, the constant product mix or price, the uniform market growth, or the maximum and minimum range of future sales.

The next important step in the problem-solving approach is to develop alternative courses of action or possible solutions to the problem, and clearly stated objectives by which the alternatives can be analyzed. These alternatives are then evaluated to select the optimum solution: the course of action, plan, or rule that will best achieve the objective. The last and the most important step of all is, of course, implementation.

These steps represent a formal approach to problem solving applicable to the solution of any problem, whether the technique used is

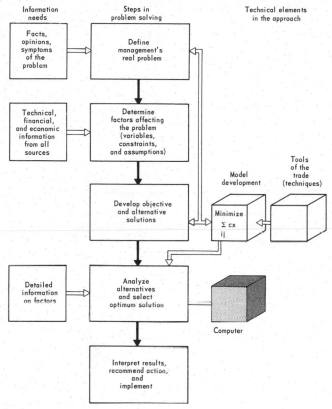

FIGURE 4-1. Operations research approach. The problem-solving steps to be followed by the O. R. team, leading to effective managerial implementation, are emphasized.

mathematical or nonmathematical. As Figure 4-1 shows, the technical elements of the operations research approach are concerned with developing alternative solutions and analyzing them to determine the optimum. This is usually done by the development of a mathematical model using appropriate tools of the trade (or techniques) to allow a computer to calculate the optimum solution. The important factor to consider when using the technical elements of the operations research approach is that the optimum solution of the model is not necessarily the course of action that management should take to solve their business problem. The model solution must be interpreted and evaluated in the context of the assumptions used and the total business environment, so that a detailed course of action for management is developed.

Conclusion

The company that gets more for its OR investment is one that successfully translates OR solutions into action. The responsibility for reaching this final result is threefold, resting in part on management, in part on permanent OR staff, and in part on the temporary study teams. Top management has the responsibility for (1) ensuring that the OR staff is advantageously located in the organization to facilitate communication and productive interchange of ideas, (2) initiating OR projects on key management problems, and (3) obtaining action based on accepted recommendations of OR teams. Operating management must seek advice on their problems, recognize opportunities for using OR, offer their experience, guidance, and direction to OR teams, and recognize the need for their participation in the problem-solving process.

The basis for success of operations research lies with the operations research staff, and in particular the head of this staff group. The group has the responsibility for (1) promoting the beneficial use of OR, (2) communicating with all levels of management on the objectives, benefits, limitations, and approach of OR to problem solving, (3) providing technical guidance and participation in studies, and (4) ensuring that the goal of seeking implementation is constantly upheld.

The temporary OR team, for its part, should concentrate on the underlying purpose of any study: finding better decision rules or better planning methods for the company, rather than the theoretical best rules. In defining the study, the team should choose the technique to fit the problem, not the problem to fit the technique. And in carrying out the study, the team should follow a planned approach in the search for practical answers to the problems on hand.

By retaining the objectivity of a consulting group, the team should cut through organizational red tape and personal prejudices. It should pull together conflicting points of view and methods, tap the company's fund of executive experience and judgment, and fuse all these with its own creativity and use of the OR techniques. By these means top management can look forward to significant profit contributions through action resulting from OR projects.

▶ ▶ ▶ ▶   **PART TWO**

Planning,

Programming,

and Program Review

▶ ▶ ▶ ▶ # 5
Linear Programming:
Graphic Method

Although linear programming (LP) was developed and discussed in publications only as recently as the early fifties,[1] it has rapidly found a large number of uses in the solution of a great variety of business problems. Probably, it is the method that has become most closely associated with modern management science and operations research.

Linear programming permits the selection of an optimum combination of factors from a series of interrelated alternatives, each subject to limitations. Many such problems exist in production, sales, and distribution. In order to be able to use LP, the problem to be solved must be capable of being expressed in terms of a linear relationship or function of the major variables involved, and the limitations applicable to each variable must again be in linear form. The illustrations to be presented in this chapter will illustrate the meaning of these specifications. The particular technique to be demonstrated is known as the "Simplex method."

Application to Sales-production Coordination

One of the most profitable applications of LP can often be found when a plant manufactures a relatively large number of products, models, or styles. Usually each such product is made by different combinations of machines and facilities. Furthermore, each product has a different market potential and profit margin. Often a product with a good profit margin may be relatively uneconomical to produce in large quantities because its productive requirements create bottlenecks in a department or on a critical machine, thereby dispropor-

---

[1]See Dantzig, G. B., "Application of the Simplex Method to a Transportation Problem" in T. C. Koopmans' *Activity Analysis of Production and Allocation.* New York: John Wiley & Sons, Inc., 1951.

tionately limiting the production of other products. Even though these other products may have less unit profit, yet in terms of total output they may contribute more to over-all profit.

Linear programming evaluates the various factors of sales and production in their combined effect to find that optimum combination of products and quantities which would yield maximum over-all profit for the company. This combination can then become the goal of selling and marketing activities and production planning.

Case History

For simplicity, only four products (K–N) and four processing departments (machining, coil winding, mounting, and testing) represent some 40 products and 12 processing stages of an electronic component manufacturer. Table 5-1 shows these products, the unit profit associated with each, and the productive requirements, as well as normal productive capacity.

In the early stages of the LP analysis, the sales manager doubted its value. He argued something like this: "You can see that we make the greatest profit on product K and the lowest profit on product N. We don't need LP to show us the most desirable products to sell. Our problem is that people won't buy much of K."

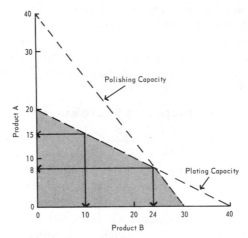

FIGURE 5-1. Graphic presentation of programming example of Table 5-2. Shaded area represents feasible production quantities of products A and B. Beyond this area, bottlenecks in polishing and plating prevent further production.

The production manager felt that some weight should be given to production balance. For example, while product K did indeed show a high unit profit, it was also likely to create a bottleneck in mounting. Mounting consumes a relatively large amount of time for this product. With bottlenecks occurring, some machines can not meet demand even at overtime runs, while other equipment stands idle at least part of the time. Therefore, unbalance was an important cost factor, which often would offset the gains from high unit profit.

Computer analysis using LP posed the question: "Which products in what quantities will result in an overall maximum profit for the company?"

A medium-sized computer can find the solution to such a problem in a matter of a few minutes even when a large number of styles and machines are involved. Line C of Table 5-1 shows the optimum product quantities that match sales potential with productive capacity. Line D shows that the profit that would result if this optimum can be attained is $3088 per week. No other combination of product quantities will result in a higher profit.

As usual, the analysis was very surprising. Product K, which the sales manager had been seeking to promote so vigorously, is a poor contributor to over-all profit. At the same time product N, with the lowest unit profit, is nevertheless the greatest contributor to over-all profit.

Company management gained a completely new perspective of its marketable products. In the actual analysis, which involved forty products, many past favorites lost out against previously overlooked items. In the future, sales and other promotional efforts could be directed far more intelligently and decisively. In addition to higher profits from increased sales the plant also gained in morale from a better balanced production, more even flow of work, and less overtime and part-time operations. It is of particular interest, in reviewing the scheduling information provided by line E of Table 5-1, that machining, mounting, and testing just use up available productive capacity, while in coil winding there is a slight (but unavoidable) slack.

Large-scale Problem

A large-scale problem will involve a great many factors and facets. Exhibit 5-1 lists these. Moreover, since the analysis takes but a few minutes on a computer, it should become a routine procedure.

In general, a weekly analysis is desirable, using the flow of information outlined in Exhibit 5-2.

In the long-run planning phase of management, the experience from the weekly short-term analyses and decisions will help in:

1. Considering the installation of new equipment in departments that may now be limiting over-all plant capacity
2. Planning to increase or trim managerial, administrative, staff, and operating personnel where this appears desirable
3. Preparing for long-term expectations as regards technological and market developments
4. Integrating a variety of other tools for quantitative analysis and control to work in harmony with the program

How to Program

The product-mix problem of a polishing and plating contractor is simple and typical (Table 5-2). At current prices, product A brings the higher profit. Although theoretically the capacity is enough to polish 40 gross of product A per week, plating can only produce 20

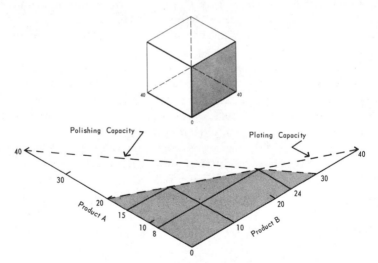

FIGURE 5-2. In order to show the profit (P) associated with various feasible quantities of products A and B that can be produced, we need a three-dimensional visualization. Figure 5-1 is now shown as the base of a cubic space (see small insert), preparatory to adding the third dimension (profit), to the diagram.

gross of product A and plating is therefore a bottleneck. Similarly, for product B, there is a bottleneck, but it is in polishing.

From line D it is apparent that if only product A is made, then 20 gross at a profit of $6 per gross will result in a weekly total profit of $120. If, instead, the lower unit-profit product B is made, profit will be realized on 30 gross at $5 each, amounting to a higher total of $150 per week. The fact that the two products have different bottlenecks suggests that, instead of making only A or B, a combination of the two products should be produced such as to balance the bottleneck factors.

To find the optimum combination make a graph with quantities of product A as ordinate and product B as abscissa (Figure 5-1). Connect the 40 on the *A* axis (representing capacity if only product A is polished) with 30 on the *B* axis (representing capacity if only product B is polished). Connect the 20 on *A* with 40 on *B*. Now we know that, because of bottlenecks, it is impractical to polish more than 20 gross of A or to plate more than 30 gross of B. Thus, only the shaded part

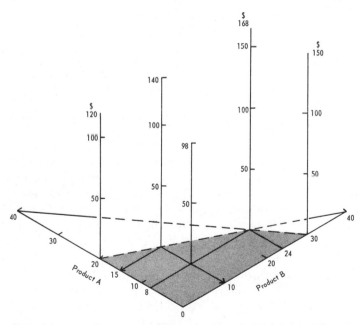

FIGURE 5-3. Typical examples of various profits from different quantities of products A and B are shown: If 20 gross of A only are produced, profit is 20 × $6 = $120, if 15 gross of A and 10 of B are produced, profit is $140 (15 × $6 + 10 × $5).

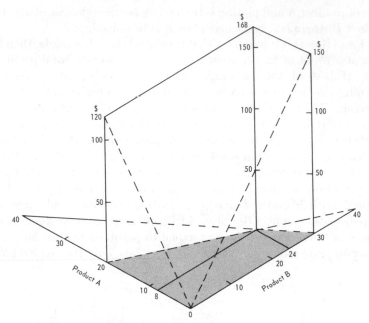

FIGURE 5-4.   Evaluation of the four corners of the base leads to
discovery of highest profit. The first corner, 0 production = 0 profit.
The second corner, 20 units of product A, at $6 per unit, yields $120;
the opposite corner, 30 units of product B at $5 per unit yields $150.
The farthest corner, for 8 units of A and 24 units of B yields the
highest profit of $168, (8 × $6 + 24 × $5).

of the graph represents feasible product combinations. For example,
if 10 gross of B and 15 gross of A are made, available plating capacity
is exhausted. Similarly, if 24 gross of B and 8 gross of A are produced,
both plating and polishing capacities are exhausted. The data in
Figure 5-1 may also be shown as depicted in Figure 5-2 a form that
permits addition of a further variable. The new variable will be the
profit that is associated with the various product combinations.

For the aforementioned 15 gross of A and 10 gross of B, total
profit will be 15 × $6 plus 10 × $5, or $140, as shown in Figure 5-3.
This amount is higher than the $120 for A alone, but less than the $150
for B alone. If we produce, say, 8 gross of A and 10 gross of B we will
not be using capacity (we are inside the shaded area, away from its
border lines) and profit will be only $98 per week (8 × $6 plus 10 × $5).
The trend of heights of the profit columns leads us to try the inter-

section point of the polishing and plating capacity, which corresponds to 8 gross of A and 24 gross of B, and which produces $168 profit ($6 × 8 plus $5 × 24), in Figure 5-4. Any movement away from this product combination yields lesser profit. We have found the optimum.

Essential Programming Principle

This simplified problem demonstrates an important principle, valid for all programming with linear relationships: in order to find the maximum profit, investigate the corners. By analyzing the points 0, 20, 30 and the intersection of the two capacity lines, we have not only succeeded in constructing the profit dimension but also have found the maximum profit point.

Maximum profit will not always involve a combination of both products. For example, if product A profit had been $11, then production of 20 gross of A would have resulted in $220 as against only $208 from 8 gross of A (8 × $11) plus 24 gross of B (24 × $5).

The principle of investigating corners is crucial to solving the type of problem described here. It is applicable for all linear relationships of products and profits, no matter how many products are involved. However, with each product, we add a dimension to the space structure to be investigated. Two products need three dimensions (a cube), three products need four dimensions. Ten products need 11 dimensions and 100 products call for 101. Since humans have ability to conceive only three-dimensional space, we must resort to mathematical investigation of corners in many-dimensional space.

Conclusion

The graphic method is, quite obviously, limited. For example, if in place of the two marketable products used in the graphic solution, we would have had three such products, we could not have shown these three on what is, after all, only two-dimensional paper. Isometrically, we were able to show a third dimension on which to plot profit. Had we used the three dimensions to show the three products, the essential further dimension to represent profit associated with each combination of products would have been missing.

The graphic method, then, is a useful device in visualizing the manner in which linear programming attacks an interlocking problem. Since actual problems involve many variables, we would theoretically need a many-dimensional model. While such a model cannot be constructed physically — beyond the actual three dimensions of our known world — nevertheless we can construct such a model mathematically. Through this means, we can again investigate all of the "corners" in this theoretical but extremely realistic construction, to find that corner which corresponds to the optimal solution. The procedure used is that of expressing all relationships and factors in the form of a set of equations and then solve by means of so-called matrix methods. This procedure will be shown in the next chapter.

EXHIBIT 5-1   Large-scale Programming Problems

1. *MARKETABLE PRODUCTS*

   Usually from 50 to 500 products are involved, but up to several thousand may be considered.

2. *PROCESSING DEPARTMENTS*

   Usually from 10 to 50 processing departments are involved. In place of processing departments, machine groups or individual machine types may be considered.

3. *PRODUCTION REQUIREMENTS AND CAPACITY LIMITATIONS*

   For each processing department, the following factors may be considered: machine-time, labor time, maintenance time, raw materials, supplies used, and skilled personnel needed.

4. *MARKET FACTORS*

   Among the market factors that may be included in the problem are: minimum product quantities for a "complete line," and maximum limits on marketability of other products, long-term sales contracts limiting productive capacity, possible production to inventory in "slack" periods, price-demand relations, and similar factors.

5. *OTHER FACTORS*

   Among these are considerations of "make or buy" on parts or completed components and assemblies, alternative production or sales programs, new equipment purchases, the profitability of preseason discount sales to large customers.

EXHIBIT 5-2   Flow chart for Programming Information

1. *PRODUCTS TO STRESS IN SALES PROGRAM*

Lists of the optimum quantities are taken from the computer section each weekend and are sent to the head office and regional sales offices.

TABLE 5-1

SOLUTION OF A TYPICAL LINEAR PROGRAMMING PROBLEM

	Marketable products				Productive capacity	
	K	L	M	N	Hours per week	Total
A. Profit (dollar per piece)	0.40	0.37	0.36	0.28		
B. Production time requirements (hours per 1000 pieces)						
Machining	30.6	30.6	32.6	22.4	250	
Coil winding	72.0	64.8	72.0	79.2	720	
Mounting	36.0	28.8	28.8	21.6	242	
Testing	18.0	26.0	24.0	29.0	260	
C. Optimum product quantities (pieces per week)	560	3790	0	5220		
D. Profit (dollars per week) $(= A \times C)$	224	1402	0	1462		3088[a]
E. Production time used by the optimum output, hours $(= B \times C/1000)$						
Machining	17	116	0	117		250
Coil winding	40	246	0	413		699[b]
Mounting	20	109	0	113		242
Testing	10	99	0	151		260

[a]This is the total profit found by adding the entries in line D. No other quantities of output than those shown in line C will give as high a profit.

[b]Comparison with corresponding productive capacity in lines B shows that coil winding is the only process not used to capacity.

2. *SALES AND PRODUCTION ADJUSTMENTS*

During the week, continuous adjustments are made for data on unsold stock on hand and uncommitted production expected by the end of the week, based on the progress of actual

TABLE 5-2

Simplified Programming Problem and its Solution

	Marketable products		Productive capacity (hours per week)	Total
	A	B		
A. Profit (dollars per gross)	6	5		
B. Production time requirements (hours per gross)				
Polishing	3	4	120	
plating	2	1	40	
C. Output if only product A or product B, but not both, are produced (gross per week)				
Polishing[a]	(40)	30[b]		
plating	20[b]	(40)		
D. Profit from output in C, found by multiplying A × C (dollars per week)	120	150		150[c]
E. Optimum product mix from Figure 5-1 (gross per week)	8	24		
F. Profit based on E, found by multiplying A × E, (dollars per week)				168[d]

[a]Productive capacity divided by requirements in line B. Thus 120/3 = 40. Since only 20 gross can be plated, the 40 gross in polishing can not be utilized beyond the plating bottleneck, and is therefore shown in parentheses.

[b]Bottleneck process for this product (A or B).

[c]Only product A or product B, but not both can be produced at this stage, so that the maximum profit equals the highest-profit product, which is Product B at $150.

[d]Maximum for optimum combination of both products. This $168 is $18 or roughly 10 percent better than the previous $150.

sales and production. The information is entered on computer tapes.

3. *PRICE AND COST ADJUSTMENTS*

Decisions on price changes and effects of changes in costs on unit profits are noted and recorded by the computer section, with appropriate revisions in stored data on prices, costs, and profits.

4. *OTHER ADJUSTMENTS*

Other pertinent developments allowed for in the planning of the computer program are recorded and entered. Revisions in computer programs may become necessary for new and previously unforeseen areas of development.

5. *NEW DATA*

During the weekend, the computer uses the information from steps 2 to 4, and prepares new data regarding stock on hand, sales records, and production expectations, as used routinely for sales and production purposes. These determinations will include a new LP analysis of the most desirable products and quantities to seek to sell, or to stress in the promotional program.

6. *NEW CYCLE*

With the preparation of the new data and analyses from step 5, a new cycle of sales promotion, production planning, and related business operations, can start.

Linear Programming:
Matrix Method

In practice, the large size of LP problems requires matrix algebra for solutions, whether they be obtained manually or on a computer. This approach will be illustrated using the problem of the polishing-plating contractor presented in the preceding chapter. The extension of this simple example to many more products and manufacturing processes than two each will be apparent.

Formulating a Model

The problem demonstrated in Table 5-2 can be expressed in the form of equations showing the goal or objective of management and the controlling factors involved. The procedure is demonstrated in Exhibit 6-1, that expresses the equations in symmetrical form. This pattern makes them suitable for transfer into a block of numbers, known as a "matrix," in Table 6-1. Having cast the data in matrix form, we solve for the optimum by following the matrix steps explained under each table.

Matrix Sequence

The first matrix shows that only the two imaginary products M and N should be produced (in quantities of 120 and 40 respectively as indicated under the result column), and that profit Z as expected will be zero! This first solution, then, represents the zero point of the diagram in Figure 5-4. The evaluation row Z–P of Table 6-1 also contains negative entries, meaning that we are far removed from the optimum. A second matrix must be investigated, as is done in Table 6-2, using the transformation procedure of Figure 6-1.

This new matrix recommends that 60 gross of imaginary product M and 20 gross of actual product A be produced, with a profit of $120. Note again the correspondence of this result with the identical finding

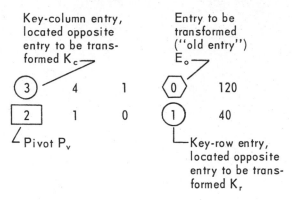

Formula for transformed entry E_t

$$E_t = \langle E_o \rangle - \frac{\textcircled{K_c} \times \textcircled{K_r}}{\boxed{P_v}}$$

$$E_t = 0 - \frac{3 \times 1}{2} = -3/2$$

FIGURE 6-1. Method of matrix transformation illustrated for one of the entries in the first matrix. The entire part of the matrix to be transformed, with key row and column is shown above.

at the A side of the structure in Figure 5-4. The matrix has investigated the corner represented by the product A line and the plating capacity line at the base. We are not yet at an optimum, since Z–P is negative for column B of the matrix.

The final third matrix (Table 6-3) yields the optimum solution of $168 for 24 gross of B, and 8 gross of A, corresponding exactly with the structure in the aforementioned Figure 5-4. This is the maximum profit for the problem conditions. Application of the model to more products and processes is illustrated in Table 6-4, using the problem of the electronic components manufacturer previously shown in Table 5-1.

Extended Models

The material presented so far gives the basic formulation for solving LP problems. Modifications, to meet a variety of requirements, are possible. The principal types of these will now be discussed.

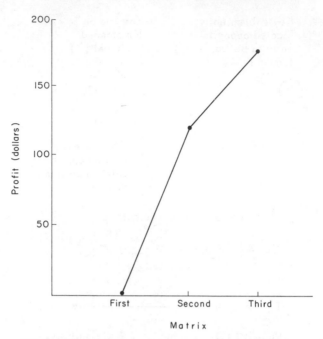

FIGURE 6-2. Systematic search towards optimum, starting with the zero plateau, as accomplished by successive matrix analyses.

Restrictions Regarding Minimums   For the polishing-plating problem, representing the key illustration of this chapter, we might have had a further restriction, such as: "In order to have a balanced product offering, such as to meet expected customer requirements, we must produce at least 10 gross of product A per week." Then, with symbol *A* representing the quantity of A to be produced per week, this restriction regarding minimum quantity would be written:

$$A \geq 10$$

Or in other words, the quantity of A produced must be equal to or greater than 10. Converting to equality sign, the inequality becomes:

$$A - S_1 = 10$$

This equation is parallel to prior formulations, with the letter S representing a slack variable of as yet unknown quantity. However, the equation cannot be used in the initial matrix, since it would produce a value of -1 in the identity portion. Yet, as was noted under Table 6-4, we need a row consisting only of 0s and a single positive 1. The resolution of this dilemma is simple, by adding a further so-called artificial variable U. The equation then becomes:

$$A - S_1 + U = 10$$

The U is entered, as though it were a slack variable, in the identity matrix.

Restrictions Involving an Equality   In order to illustrate this case, assume that the polishing-plating problem had involved the following requirement: "The amount of product B plus the amount of product A produced must equal 30 gross per week." In equation form, we would then write:

$$A + B = 30$$

For purposes of the initial matrix, we need a further variable to form the identity. It is best to use another U, say U_2, which results in:

$$A + B + U_2 = 30$$

Maximizing Equation   The objective function for the polisher-plater must express the goal of maximizing profit, based on unit profits of \$6 and \$5 for each gross of products A and B respectively. Originally, this was written:

$$6A + 5B = Z$$

Adding the slacks M and N, which may preferably be written S_m and S_n, and assigning zero value coefficients to each slack, we formed:

$$6A + 5B + 0S_m + 0S_n = Z$$

The zero value coefficients assured that products S_m and S_n, representing zero profits per unit of imaginary production, would be properly shown in the maximizing function. In the preceding discussion, we have collected the further artificial variables U, which might be more specifically labled U_1 and U_2. The variable $-S_1$ is a slack which, because of the minus sign, cannot be used in the identity, and must therefore go into the body. Collecting all these variables, we can now form the fully enlarged maximizing function:

$$6A + 5B + 0S_m + 0S_n - 0S_1 - MU_1 - MU_2 = Z$$

The coefficients M mean "very large number," and by assigning a negative value to them, we assure that in solving the matrix, they will not enter into the solution. Otherwise we would produce large quantities of a product with negative profit (that is, large loss) per unit, in seeking an optimum. As a further note, the entry $-0S_1$ above is usually written $+0S$, since -0 (minus zero) has no other meaning.

Inasmuch as a negative slack, such as the $-S_1$, is part of the body of a matrix, it is sometimes preferred to use the symbol $-t_1$, as a reminder that unlike positive slacks S, it does not go in the identity portion of the initial matrix. The restrictive equations and objective function, shown above, appear in matrix form in Table 6-5. The subsequent iterations follow the standard procedure shown.

Minimizing Equation   Instead of a maximum as a goal, we might have been seeking a minimum. For example, the dollar figures of 6 and 5 for products A and B respectively, might have represented costs rather than profits per gross. Cost minimization would then have been the objective. It is apparent that, when Z is a minimum rather than a maximum, the equation for Z just given must be modified. In particular, we wish to make sure that MU_1 and MU_2 become so large that they will not form part of the solution. By assigning positive magnitudes to M_1 and M_2, that is, by changing the minus to a plus sign in the equation, the function has been altered to reflect the new objective.

The matrix iteration procedures given with regard to maximization can still be used for a minimization objective, provided the function is multiplied first by -1. All variables then become negative, as follows (excepting that zeros are always plus):

$$-6A - 5B + 0S_m + 0S_n + 0S_1 - MU_1 - MU_2 = Z$$

Note that, while the maximizing equation also had a minus in front of MU_1 and MU_2, this sign became a plus for the minimization function. Multiplying through by -1 changes these MU's back to their original minus sign.

Matrix iteration now proceeds to look for a maximum. When this maximum is found, using the standard procedures given, it represents, in effect, a minimum. This result is the logical consequence of having reversed signs of the objective function. An equivalent procedure would have been not to reverse signs (by multiplication with

−1), but to use instead the highest $Z–C$ value for successive key columns in the matrix iteration steps. Either procedure will work and yield the same answer.

Conclusion

What is the significance of the matrix solution? For the small example given, it has very little value. True, the answer computed may in some cases be slightly more exact than an answer read from graph, and with experience a person can run through these few matrix

TABLE 6-1

FIRST MATRIX

Row	Profit P	Products				Result R	Evaluation R/A	Key Row
		A	B	M	N			
P		6	5	0	0			
M	0	3	4	1	0	120	120/3 = 40	
N	0	2	1	0	1	40	40/2 = 20	✓
Z		0	0	0	0	0		
Z–P		−6	−5	0	0			
Key Column		✓						

1. Columns A to R show the numerical coefficients of equations 1a to 3a for rows P to N. Column P shows the zero profits associated with the imaginary products M and N.
2. Row Z is the sum of the product quantities multiplied by their profits. For column A, 3 × 0 plus 2 × 0 totals 0.
3. Row Z–P is found by subtracting each entry in row P from row Z. Unless Z–P contains nonnegative entries in all columns, maximum profit has not been reached. In fact, column R shows that when 120 units of imaginary product M and 40 units of imaginary product N are produced, profit will be zero (row Z).
4. The key column is A, since it contains the lowest Z–P. By dividing each entry under R by its corresponding A, R/A is obtained. In row M, R is 120 and A is 3, so that R/A is 120/3 or 40. The key row is the one that contains the smallest positive R/A. In the present instance, both rows have a positive R/A, and row N, having the lowest ratio, is thus the key row.
5. The intersection of key column and key row is the intersection of A and N, which yields the pivot entry 2. This pivot, representing the lowest Z–P and the lowest R/A, is the basing point, from which a new matrix is formed next. This new matrix will seek to increase profits, until maximum profit is reached by successive "iterations" or matrix steps.

steps in a matter of minutes, thereby "beating" any trial-and-error approach. But the real significance is that one can readily expand the matrix to cover any number of products, and the procedural steps described will yield a solution.

The graphic method would fail here, and the trial-and-error approach would require a lifetime. Assume you had also desired to consider products C and D. All one needs to do is invent two further "imaginary" products, say K and L, add corresponding columns and rows to the first matrix, and start the matrix procedure rolling. After several iterations, the matrix that contains the optimum will be reached.

TABLE 6-2

SECOND MATRIX

	Profit	Product Columns				Result	Evaluation
Row	P	A	B	M	N	R	R/B
P		6	5	0	0		
M	0	0	5/2	1	-3/2	60	$60/(5/2) = 24$
A	6	1	1/2	0	1/2	20	$20/(1/2) = 40$
Z		6	3	0	3	120	
Z–P		0	-2	0	3		

1. Row M, columns B to R, is obtained from row M of the first matrix, using the transformation method shown in Figure 6-1. Column A, containing the pivot, becomes 0 for all product rows excepting the pivot row, where it becomes 1.
2. The other entries in row A are found from row N of the first matrix, by dividing each value in row N, from column A to R, by the pivot value 2. Under column P, the unit profit of $6 for product A is shown.
3. Rows Z and Z–P are found from the steps previously shown for the first matrix. For column B, for example, $Z = (5/2 \times 0) + (1/2 \times 6) = 3$. Next, $3 - 5 = -2$.
4. The lowest Z–P entry is -2 under column B, which is therefore the new key column. Evaluating the ratio R/B for rows M and A, we find the new key row, M, corresponding to the lowest value of the ratio. At the intersection of new key column M, and new key row A, is the entry 5/2, which is the new pivot.
5. Although the present matrix yields a profit of $120, based on production of 60 units of product M and 20 units of product A (column R, rows Z, M, and A respectively), it is not the maximum profit obtainable, since there is a negative value in the Z–P row. A third matrix must be formed, using the new pivot of 5/2.

Problems involving up to five processes and fifteen products can be solved with a desk calculator, and with experience, about a dozen hours of tedious calculations would be involved. For larger problems, such as the several hundred products in a realistic case, a relatively slow computer would grind out the solution in a matter of minutes.

Readers who find the formula for matrix transformation too much like a push-button procedure, and would like to investigate its theoretical foundation, will realize that rather advanced mathematics is involved. Nevertheless, a common-sense explanation can be given, as provided in the next chapter.

EXHIBIT 6-1   Equations of Production and Profit-optimizing Relationships

1. *OBJECTIVE EQUATION*

The over-all goal or objective is to maximize dollar profit Z. Since product A has a profit of $6 per gross and product B has a profit of $5 per gross, maximum profit will result from producing that quantity A for product A and that quantity B of product B which yields the highest Z, or:

$$6A + 5B = Z \qquad \text{Equation (1)}$$

2. *PRODUCTION EQUATIONS*

Production of products A and B is limited by the capacity of 120 hours-per-week in polishing and 40 hours in plating. At the production rates shown in Table 5-2, the quantities A and B of products A and B that can be produced are:

    a. In polishing: $3A + 4B \le 120$ Equation (2)

    b. In plating: $2A + 1B \le 40$ Equation (3)

The sign $\le$ means "equal to or smaller than," indicating that production cannot exceed capacity.

3. *SYMMETRICAL EQUATIONS*

The inequality signs in equations 2 and 3 are messy. But we can convert them to equal signs, by adding proper but as yet unknown magnitudes to the left-hand side of each equation. These magnitudes are known as "imaginary variables" representing imaginary production (of zero or greater quantity). Using "*M*" and "*N*" for these imaginaries and inserting zero values as shown below, we obtain symmetrical equations for the three expressions above:

$$6A + 5B + 0M + 0N = Z \qquad \text{Equation (1a)}$$

$$3A + 4B + 1M + 0N = 120 \qquad \text{Equation (2a)}$$

$$2A + 1B + 0M + 1N = 40 \qquad \text{Equation (3a)}$$

4. *SOLVING FOR THE OPTIMUM*

The equations 1a to 3a can now be rewritten in a block of numbers or matrix (Table 6-1), which is convenient for solving them for the optimum profit *Z*, sought.

TABLE 6-3

THIRD MATRIX

Row	Profit P	A	B	M	N	Result R
P		6	5	0	0	
B	5	0	1	2/5	−3/5	24
A	6	1	0	−1/5	4/5	8
Z		6	5	0.8	1.8	168
Z–P		0	0	0.8	1.8	

1. Row B, columns A to R, is obtained from M of the preceding matrix, by dividing each entry in row M by the pivot value 5/2.
2. Rows A, Z, and Z–P are found from the second matrix, using the transformation steps previously shown.
3. There are no negative values in the Z–P row. Therefore the profit of $168 shown is the maximum attainable. No further matrix will be needed. By producing 24 units of product B and 8 units of product A (column R, rows B and A), the $168 optimum profit results.[a]

[a]Note: For a graphic representation of the profits found from each successive matrix, Figure 6-2 may be examined.

TABLE 6-4

INITIAL MATRIX OF ELECTRONIC COMPONENT MANUFACTURER'S OPTIMIZATION PROBLEM

Row	Profit P	Products								Result R	Evaluation R/X_a	Key row
		X_a	X_b	X_c	X_d	S_a	S_b	S_c	S_d			
P		0.40	0.37	0.36	0.28							
S_a	0	30.6	30.6	32.6	22.4	1	0	0	0	250	250/30.6	
S_b	0	72.0	64.8	72.0	79.2	0	1	0	0	720	720/72.0	
S_c	0	36.0	28.8	28.8	21.6	0	0	1	0	242	242/36.0	
S_d	0	18.0	26.0	24.0	29.0	0	0	0	1	260	260/18.0	✓
Z												
Z-P		−0.40	−0.37	−0.36	−0.28							
Key column		✓										

1. The four actual products are shown by X_a X_b X_c, and X_d; while the imaginaries or slack variables are shown by S_a, S_b, S_c, and S_d.

2. The products section of the matrix consists of the body, X_c to X_d columns, and the identity, columns S_a to S_d. The identity consists of a block of zeroes surrounding a diagonal of ones. The row P is not a part of the body or the identity and merely represents the coefficients (labeled P for profit in this instance, but often labeled more generally as C for coefficients) associated with the variables of the objective function.

3. The pivot of 36.0 occurs at the intersection of key column and row, and is the starting point for the first iteration, which follows the procedural steps given in the prior tables in this chapter.

TABLE 6-5

POLISHER-PLATER PROBLEM, INITIAL MATRIX FOR EXPANDED FORMULATION

Row	Coefficient	Body		Products			Identity		Result R	R/A
	$C\rightarrow$	6	5	0	0	0	$-M$	$-M$		
		A	B	S_1	S_m	S_n	U_1	U_2		
S_m	0	3	4	0	1	0	0	0	120	120/3
S_n	0	2	1	0	0	1	0	0	40	40/2
U_1	$-M$	1	0	-1	0	0	1	0	10	10/1
U_2	$-M$	1	1	0	0	0	0	1	30	30/1
Z-C		$-2M-6$	$-M-5$	$+M$	0	0	0	0	0	

1. In order to handle this expanded formulation, it is convenient to show the coefficients C, first, followed by the variables (representing quantities of product, in this example) of A, B, $\cdots$, U_2.
2. Slack S_1 is in the body part, because of the negative value of -1.
3. Although we do not know the exact magnitude of M, we do know that in the Z-C row, $-2M - 6$ has the lowest value, forming the key column under A.
4. Row U_1, having the smallest positive magnitude of $10/1 = 10$ in the evaluation column (R/A), forms the key row, with 1 under A as the pivot.

7

Linear Programming:

Profitability Analysis

Having examined LP as a purely technical-geometric analysis, one may now view it from a still further viewpoint, as a comparison of the relative profitability of various alternative production schedules. Such an examination provides further insights into the reasoning of LP procedures.

Alternative Quantities

Using LP example of Chapter 6, begin with the First Matrix Table (Table 6-1), which represents the equations 1a to 3a of Exhibit 6-1. The matrix shows that if only products M and N (the imaginary products) are made, at quantities of 120 and 40 units respectively, capacity will be exhausted. But total profit will be zero. Thus starting with the least desirable position — imaginary products only, with no profit — one must look around to see what changes will lead to a better result.

In searching for the best direction toward an improvement, we examine the entries in rows M and N. Beginning with row M, we note that the first entry, under column A is 3. This 3 means in effect: "If you wish to polish one unit of product A, you must give up 3 hours of the imaginary product M, so as to obtain the requisite capacity." The adjoining entry calls for the surrender of 4 hours of M to obtain 1 unit of B. The entry 1 under column M indicates that M is a substitute for itself; that is, for each unit of M to be added, an old unit of M must be dropped. No production of M need be given up in order to polish an additional unit of N, since N does not need polishing, thus explaining the zero in the N column. The next row N is analyzed in a parallel manner, this time for the plating process.

Rows Z–P give for each product the loss resulting, per unit, because the product is not made. For example, $6 is lost for each unit of product A that is not produced. Since product A shows the highest loss per unit, it is desirable to seek an improvement by replacing some products M and N with product A. But how much?

Determining Quantities

The proper quantity of A is found from the Evaluation column. We note that 40 units of A can be polished, but only 20 units can be plated. Plating is the bottleneck process for product A.

We will investigate the effect of producing 20 units of A. Since this production exhausts plating capacity, we know that product A replaces N. Therefore, one must replace A for N in the matrix, and insert the unit profit of $6 in the Profit column. However, prior to inserting each entry for the Product columns and Results column, each entry must be divided by the pivot of 2. The reason for this division is as follows: since 2 hours of product N must be given up for each unit of product A added, the replacement of A for N means a change in the quantities of all entries by the ratio 1/2. The division by 2 or multiplication by 1/2 are equivalent. The latter value may be interpreted as the rate at which each unit of A is substituted for (the two units) of product N.

Product A, unlike product N, also needs polishing time. Product M must be reduced to permit this polishing. The formula in Figure 6-1 shows the amounts involved. This formula again represents a substitution effect, but this time there is a subtraction. The quantity to be subtracted is found in two steps. First, the corresponding key row entry is adjusted for the aforementioned substitution factor (multiplication by 1/2 in this example). Next, the resultant value is multiplied by an amount shown by the Key Column entry. The quantity thus subtracted represents the amount of production of M that must be given up to produce the 20 units of product A.

The Result column will be used as an example: for row M, the transformation is: $120 - (3 \times 40/2)$. The 120 represents present time used in producing product M. The ratio, 40/2 represents the 20 units of product A to be made, and the 3 represents the units of product M that must be given up for each unit of product A that is polished. Thus, 3 times 20 is 60, which subtracted from 120 gives the entry 60 found in the Second Matrix Table, (Table 6-2).

Determining Total Profit

The effect of substituting A for N in the Second Matrix Table results in an increase in profit total, from zero to $120. Yet, we know that we are not at a maximum as yet. Imaginary product M is using productive capacity to the extent of causing a loss of $2 per unit of potential production of product B. At least one more matrix is needed. Again we determine key column and row, find the pivot, make a substitution (this time row M is replaced with row B), and obtain the new third matrix. As can be seen, the introduction of B has resulted in production of 24 units of this product, but to accomplish this, the quantity of product A had to be decreased by 12 (from 20 to 8). Total profit is now $168, and the absence of negative values in the Z–P row indicates that no further substitutions can be made that would bring a higher profit. We have arrived at the optimum.

Conclusion

Linear programming has been examined from several aspects, representing graphical views, matrix algebra application, and, finally, an economist's approach of evaluating relative profits by means of comparative "rates of substitution," for the various alternatives available. In each case, we have come to the same optimum point, as a guide for management decision making.

▶ ▶ ▶ ▶ **8**
Simplex Programming:
A Case History

Illustrative material in the preceding chapters was presented primarily in conjunction with concepts, ideas, and procedures. The case history in this chapter supplements this material by bringing a more complete report of a successful installation of linear programming by means of the Simplex method.[1]

The Problem

The study encompassed an over-all examination of the operations of a textile mill, operated by the Pepperell Manufacturing Company and engaged in the production of blankets. It was hoped at the outset that application of the mathematical methods of operations research might yield findings and insights pointing to a potentially more profitable management of existing facilities. These hopes were subsequently amply fulfilled.

The complexity of the problem stems from the presence of interrelated restrictions. In particular, the numerous processes employed in the production of a great variety of blankets differing in raw material, yarn type, and weight, construction, size, and finish, as well as Jacquard design in some cases, are subject to capacity limitations. If we study a certain pattern of production and apply a single change, limitations of machine capacities will force us to alter some of the other items as well. Thus, if a loom, running at full produc-

---

[1]Adapted from Kurt Eiseman (Director, Computing Center, The Catholic University of America, Washington, D.C.) and William M. Young (Manager of Operations Research, RCA Defense Electronic Products, Burlington, Massachusetts), "Study of a textile mill with the aid of linear programming," presented at Middle Atlantic Conference, The American Society for Quality Control, at New York, February 1958.

tion, is capable of weaving blankets of type A, B, and C, any specified increase in the output of type A will require a reduction in the output of types B and C. In view of the forced changes in B and C, a limitation on some other machine will now cause further changes, and so on. Such propagation and interacting effects make changes in production pattern quite complicated to follow. It is fortunate that a scientific tool, enabling the mathematical representation and solution of such interdependent relations, exists in the form of "linear programming."

Linear Programming

The term "linear programming" denotes the following mathematical problem: Find the set of unknowns $x_1, x_2, \cdots, x_n$ that satisfies simultaneously:

$$\sum_j a_{ij} x_j \leq b_i \qquad (i = 1 \text{ to } m)$$
$$\text{all } x_j \geq o$$
$$f \equiv \sum_j c_j x_j = \text{maximum (or minimum)}$$

In words: For variables subject to certain simultaneous and interacting restrictions, find numerical values which will not only satisfy all restrictions, but which will do so at the highest possible profit (or lowest possible cost). This problem has been the subject of much investigation. Its marked importance derives chiefly from four facts:

1. A great many technical and industrial problems in a wide variety of fields can be represented in linear programming form.
2. In view of the interacting constraints, the propagations due to any change in the system are usually too complicated for common sense or trial-and-error examination.
3. Mathematical methods are available for systematic and complete solution.
4. Application to the operations of large companies has resulted, in some instances, in truly enormous economies.

Assembly of Data

A meaningful study of so complex a problem must rest on a solid foundation of accurate and reliable data. While data were available for the speed, productivity, and waste factor of each machine on each product, precise numerical values were also needed for the total effective capacities in terms of finished goods, after allowances for down time, separation of direct costs into fixed and variable components, and apportionment of indirect variable costs such as heat, light, and power. For the most part, such figures were not available in the required form and had to be laboriously derived from first principles. This phase of statistical compilation turned out to be both the most laborious and the most fruitful part of the analysis. The figures thus obtained established for the first time specific and reliable quantitative measures for the numerous operations performed in the mill, thereby providing management with valuable data. Even if no results had been obtained from the linear programming formulation, the numerical data gained by its motivation would have made the entire study well worth while.

One of the main obstacles consisted in the correct separation of fixed and variable costs. Of relevance to the problem was only that portion of the costs that would influence selection of an optimal product mix. The variable, or "out-of-pocket," costs are in this category. Obviously, fixed charges, such as depreciation on buildings, would have no relation to the product mix and were therefore not taken into consideration at any time. Left for numerical determination were only the variable costs pertaining to each item, which included costs of material, direct labor, and variable portions of general overhead such as heat, light, and power.

Some of the cost components varied with particular customers, depending on their specifications for binding, stitching, put-up, and ticketing. In order to provide a uniform basis, over-all averages were used, assuming current proportions to continue for some time into the future.

The common basis, in terms of which all figures were expressed, was yardage of finished blanket. This necessitated, in earlier production steps, inclusion of progressively higher quantities than required for net target figures of finished cloth, in order to allow for the numerous sources of waste along the way: card waste, waste yarns, napper flock, seconds, and rags and remnants. In this way, quantities and costs of waste were included from the outset in all figures for machine requirements and costs. Also included were allowances for down time.

During the compilation of numerical data, account had to be taken of the fact that the units of measurement in common usage differ from machine to machine. Thus the capacity of a card is expressed in pounds per hour, of a loom in picks per minute, and of a fly-frame or wool-spinning frame in pounds per spindle. This caused much conversion of units in order to express all figures in terms of the common basis of yards of finished product.

Sales Forecasts

Stipulations on volumes of production must be based on reliable sales forecasts. To assure realistic figures, the following procedure is in operation: detailed preliminary forecasts are made by the sales department in the wake of a market survey, item by item. These figures are then revised by the manufacturing department in the light of ratios of actual orders to forecasts from past years. Furthermore, curves are available for long-range trends. For each major item, three curves are plotted: a central curve indicating the trend, carefully prepared by means of statistical methods, flanked by two auxiliary curves at a distance of plus and minus two standard deviations. This provides a band within which 95 percent of the forecasts should fall. The revised forecasts are now compared with the trend curves. Any glaring discrepancies are then ironed out by consultation between the manufacturing and sales departments.

Simplifications

The first step of attack should, wherever possible, consist in simplifying the problem in a valid manner. In addition to bed blankets, the mill under consideration was also producing crib blankets. Since the over-all production pattern, however, was governed entirely by the former, it was felt appropriate to disregard the minor item, restricting the study to the production of bed blankets exclusively.

The demand for blankets being highly seasonal, fluctuations in demand are smoothed out in practice by setting as production goal a one month's moving average over forecasts for the coming three months. Ideally, account should be taken both of seasonal variations and of inventory policies. In the present instance, a more modest and feasible objective was posed by excluding considerations of inventory, and fixing as the basic time period a weekly average of yearly totals.

Also excluded from the study were considerations of sequencing and priorities.

Finally, all those processing steps for which excess capacity was clearly available were considered to be neither restrictive nor critical and were therefore omitted. These include opening, blending, binding, packaging, and other smaller operations.

There eventually remained for inclusion the limited, interlocking and governing cloth operations of picking, carding, drawing, winding, warping, slashing, spinning, weaving, dyeing, and napping.

Mathematical Formulation

In general terms, formulation of the problem within the framework of linear programming can be phrased as follows: within prescribed machine limitations and sales restrictions, what number of what types of blankets should be produced on what machines so as to maximize profit from over-all mill operations? Also, how sensitive is the answer to variations in cost (and therefore profit) of the most profitable item, and to variations in production goals (and therefore sales goals)? For illustrative purposes only, a greatly reduced and simplified version is shown numerically in Table 8-1.

Examining the mathematical relations in detail, we notice that the necessary figures embody the following data:

1. For each type of blanket, the types of machine required for successive production steps
2. The required time for processing each type of blanket on each machine (in hours per 100 yards of finished blanketing)
3. For each type of machine, the total availability (in hours per week)
4. Approximate sales forecast for each item
5. Contribution of each blanket, that is, the difference between sales price and total variable cost

Each unknown in the problem represented the quantity of a particular type of blanket as produced on a given set of machines.

Let us consider the case of a style which may be produced in several alternative ways. At one stage of process, we may have the option of spinning the filling on either wool spinning frames or fly frames, at another stage we may do the weaving on any of three types of looms, giving a total of six possible combinations of machines. We now treat each possibility as a distinct unknown with its own column in the table. From the point of view of the linear programming framework, each of the six columns employs a different set of machine processes and therefore denotes a different blanket, although the end product is the identical style. We may call such columns "vector blankets." Each style may therefore consist of several vector blankets, indistinguishable on the market but differentiated within the mill. (In the illustration of Table 8-1, columns 1 and 2 represent the same type of blanket, but woven on different looms. Similarly for columns 4 and 5 and 7 and 8).

Linear inequalities were then set up to represent the following:

1. Restrictions on total production time available on each machine
2. Restrictions on minimum and/or maximum volumes of production for various groups of blankets (based on sales forecast)

Finally, the function to be maximized was taken to be income minus variable costs, that is, gross revenue (before deduction of fixed costs).

The complete formulation of the actual basic problem resulted in a linear programming problem of 15 technological restrictions, plus up to eight volume limitations on 22 unknowns.

Solution

In view of the widespread occurrence of linear programming problems, standard machine codes are now available for the automatic solution of such problems on the major high-speed electronic computers on the market. An IBM 650 was used for solving several variants of the above problem as described below. For each problem, the machine required about 40 minutes for solution, as against an estimated 3 weeks by desk calculator, or 2 minutes on a larger and faster computer, such as an IBM 704.

The solutions all showed one striking feature in common: the profit attainable under optimal production was shown to be far higher than under current operations. It must be realized that the problem had been formulated under the assumption of ideal conditions and that no account had been taken of scheduling difficulties, changes in machine assignment, change-overs to the production of different styles, effect of machine breakdowns on subsequent processes, advantageous location of production facilities, considerations of inventory, seasonal variations, deviations of actual orders from forecasts, and similar realistic contingencies. Results pertaining to ideal conditions cannot, therefore, be implemented in every detail, but are sufficiently valid to constitute a valuable guide for broad policy decisions. In the present instance, the indicated differences were quite significant.

The computed optimal solutions showed how best to meet market restrictions within the available production capacity. In particular, the following indications could be gleaned:

1. Within the allowed range of volume for each product, the desirable specific quantity to be produced of each.
2. The advantageous machine allocations to be chosen from the available alternatives.
3. Within the imposed limitations, the maximum attainable profit.
4. Potential bottlenecks in production facilities as well as machines not fully utilized. This can provide valuable evidence to support selective expansion of equipment.
5. In the neighborhood of the current demand profile, the relative and absolute profitability of each item. This provided valuable clues as to the desirable selectivity of future sales efforts.

It may well happen that an item, which would be the most profitable one when taken by itself, appears in an optimal program in a rather small amount, or is even entirely excluded. This circumstance is due to the fact that the amount to be produced of each item for maximum revenue may not be maximized individually. Rather it is constrained in an interlocking fashion with all other items so as to satisfy simultaneously all sales forecasts and machine limitations, while striving for maximum profit.

In addition to the most profitable solution itself, two extremely useful by-products of a linear programming solution are the following:

1. Suppose we wish to depart from the theoretically optimum solution by retaining any one of the excluded styles. A decision of this nature may be based on considerations of customer good will, plant convenience, production policy, and the like. In order to ensure continuing satisfaction of all restrictions, the quantities of many other items have to be adjusted, thus altering their contribution to gross revenue. It is a particularly useful feature of linear programming that the resulting composite effect of all these adjustments on gross revenue is furnished. This provides the executive with a

useful guide for adapting a theoretically best production pattern to a realistic situation in the most advantageous manner.

2. A similar situation exists if we should wish to study the effect of relaxing any one of the imposed restrictions; a good many quantities may have to be adjusted as a result, in order to exploit the more liberal framework to best advantage. Again, linear programming summarizes the resultant over-all effect on gross revenue. If the inequality, whose relaxation we are considering, represents a sales restriction, we have at our disposal an immediate evaluation of a change in merchandising policy; if it represents a machine limitation, we have a comparative evaluation for the expansion of equipment.

Detailed examination of Table 8-2 will show that our abbreviated numerical example illustrates all of the above points. In particular, we notice the following:

1. Fly frames and wool spinning frames are utilized to capacity and represent a bottleneck.
2. The 112-inch looms are fully utilized, while 92-inch looms are used to 87 percent of capacity.
3. 44 percent of wool card availability remains completely idle.
4. As stated earlier, Styles 1 and 2 refer to the same type of blanket but woven on different looms, and similarly for styles 4 and 5 and 7 and 8. Table 8-2 shows that, of these alternatives, only styles 1, 4, and 7 should be produced, using the 92-inch rather than the 112-inch looms.
5. The 112-inch looms are best used for the production of style 6 exclusively.
6. For group 1, that is, styles 7, (8), and 9, only the minimum required number should be produced; then a moderate amount of style 1 plus a rather large quantity of group 2, that is, styles 4, (5), and 6.
7. Style 1, which brings in the highest contribution, should be produced in a comparatively moderate amount.
8. Of all styles using the wider loom, style 2, taken by itself, would yield the highest revenue. Yet, for highest total yield, it should not be produced at all.
9. Substantial savings could be achieved by removing the requirement of a minimum production volume for group 1.

10. With a knowledge of machine costs, the lower part of the table will immediately indicate which one of the saturated machine types — wool spinning frames, fly frames, or looms — would, when expanded, maximize returns on investment.

In our particular example we can clearly see that it would prove most rewarding, for this hypothetical company, to investigate thoroughly the reasons behind the minimum restriction on group 1. Is this group manufactured to meet a particular retail price range in order to present a complete line? Then it might well be profitable to offer a completely new blanket redesigned in terms of construction and material to fill this need. Or perhaps it is offered to one or more of its larger customers as a service? The results of the problem would then form a basis for a complete review of this merchandising policy.

Even an abbreviated project which does not go into the fine details is likely to throw considerable light on many aspects of the production and marketing areas. This would appear to be particularly true in the field of merchandising policies, which are not as amenable to ordinary quantitative analysis as is the production area.

Cases Run and Results

Let us now leave the illustrative example and return to the Pepperell pilot study. Solutions were obtained for several cases, each embodying sales forecasts and machine limitations jointly. The machine limitations, reflecting the extent of current facilities, were left identical for all cases, while the concurrently imposed sales restrictions were varied from case to case.

As would be expected from the nature of the linear programming approach, the change of a single restriction pertaining to one group of items affected not only the optimal quantities of those particular items, but caused compensating adjustments throughout the pattern of production. In this way, the linear programming procedure automatically took account of the entire framework of restrictions in order to absorb, within the system as a whole, the stipulated change to best over-all advantage.

The following cases were run:

1. Production volume for each item bounded by both a lower

and an upper bound (on the basis of sales forecasts). As already mentioned, a pronounced boost in attainable profit was uncovered.

2. A specified increase of 10 percent in the profit of the most profitable item. The resultant shift in production pattern utilized the existing machines in such a way that more of this item was produced at the cost of less profitable items. The consequent rise in over-all profit amounted to only a small percentage.

3. A specified decrease of 10 percent in the profit of the most profitable item. The consequent drop in over-all profit again represented only a small percentage. The possible improvement in operations was not, therefore, critically sensitive to moderate perturbations in the profit coefficient tested.

4. Removal of minimum production requirements only. This resulted in but slight profit increment.

5. Removal of maximum production requirements only. This caused a very pronounced shift in both pattern of production and achievable profit.

6. Removal of both minimum and maximum production stipulations. This particular formulation provided the most significant and illuminating information of the entire study. The further advance shown in the attainable profit pointed up the actual dollars and cents lost through failure to strive toward altering the composition of the sales profile.

Projected Extensions

As described, a model has been set up and several cases solved, the results of which have been useful in themselves and have already played a role in management decisions. The main accomplishment to date, however, has been the demonstration that the structure of our problem is amenable to treatment by linear programming techniques. Let us now look at some of the potential which linear programming holds in store for the Pepperell Manufacturing Company. To this end, we shall describe the projected program extension, which has already been approved in principle by the company's management.

In the first place, it is hoped to increase vastly the size of our problem. This will take place in three directions.

First, all productive processes involving possible machine

limitations will be included. The one important exception here will be that machine processes, such as warping, which top management would never allow to hold up production or become a bottleneck, will not be included. What processes should be counted in the latter category will be determined by consultation with management. This expansion will increase the number of rows in the table.

Second, many more sales restrictions will be taken into consideration and will be set up somewhat differently. Maximum and minimum sales restrictions will be set up for most of the styles individually, based on available forecasts, and with a much finer breakdown than in the first pilot study. In addition, several "cross restrictions" may also be set up, such as a restriction on the combined total of "king size" blankets of all styles. This would be done on the thinking that such blankets supply a limited market, in which the various styles are competing with one another. Quite probably these restrictions will be set up as a flat percentage range above and below the corresponding sales forecasts. The percentages would be determined by an examination of the historical variations of actual sales from forecasts. This expansion will further add to the rows of the table.

Third, as we have seen, one and the same style may be represented by more than one column of our table, whenever we have a choice among different machines at the same stage of process. It is planned to include henceforth all of the feasible combinations of machine selection. This will greatly expand the number of columns to be dealt with.

The extensions described above are expected to provide a very realistic picture of Pepperell's operations. The results should closely reflect the impact of all the factors included in the linear programming formulation.

So far we have dealt exclusively with the determination of optimum production goals within the restrictions imposed by mill equipment and market conditions. Let us now describe an additional benefit of the linear programming approach when applied to actual operations.

Suppose that on the basis of all realistic factors, such as seasonal fluctuations, inventory situation, deviation of orders received from the forecasts, and such, a definite production pattern has been decided upon for the coming month. This working program will differ from the one obtained as a yearly average target. We can now again set up a linear programming problem in which the total volume for each style is no longer allowed to vary in some range but is set equal to a fixed pre-established number, which will differ, in general, from the one which has resulted from the earlier general optimization. As before, different machine choices for the same style will be carried as separate columns in the table with correspondingly different profit coefficients.

Having prescribed a fixed, pre-established composition of mill output, a linear programming solution will now show up the best allocation of styles to machine combinations so as to accomplish the specified true mill output at a minimum total cost. Since all data on costs and machine productivities have already been collected for the earlier problem, the present optimization of actual mill operations would require only a minor amount of additional effort and machine time. It is therefore an outstanding example of the possible "side benefits."

There are further areas which must be investigated. One is the determination of sales restrictions which will adequately reflect each of the seasonal periods. Annual forecasts will provide us with only a general picture because of strong seasonal variations. These fluctuations differ for the various groups of blankets, namely, winter bed blankets, summer bed blankets, and crib blankets. It is likewise virtually certain that new areas will continue to be explored as they bring themselves to attention. Linear programming is headed for a long and eventful course before becoming stabilized.

Conclusion

In summary, a number of valuable lessons were learned from the results of the present study:

1. The establishment of quantitative data for operational characteristics proved an accomplishment in its own right.
2. The figures emerging from the linear programming solutions furnished quantitative measures for a highly complex system of interacting effects.
3. Critically limited processing steps as well as redundant capacity were clearly brought to light and gauged quantitatively.
4. Guiding lines were crystallized for increasing over-all profits by rendering future sales efforts more selective.

5. The linear programming approach was shown capable of furnishing guidance for setting up production targets, evaluating merchandising plans and capital investment, and improving efficiency in the utilization of machines for actual mill output.

6. Striking evidence was brought home of the great potential benefits to a manufacturing business from the services of an operations research team of mathematically trained and competent scientists.

The insights revealed through this study impressed management to the extent that definite plans were formulated for continuing such studies and extending their scope.

EXHIBIT 8-1   Product Mix Problem of Pepperell Expressed in Equation Form

1. Restrictions on machine hours and spindle hours:
   a. For 92-inch looms (subscripts on X denote style number).

$$15.8X_1 + 0X_2 + \cdots + 0X_9 + S_1 = 2900$$

   ... proceed in parallel manner for 112-inch looms, cards, and fly frames ...
   b. For spinning frames

$$550X_1 + 550X_2 \cdots + 0X_9 + S_5 = 20,000$$

2. Restrictions regarding maximum sales volume achievable per week:

$$X_7 + X_8 + X_9 + S_6 = 70$$

3. Restrictions regarding minimum quantity to be available in order to meet customer requirements:
   a. For styles number 4, 5, and 6

$$X_4 + X_5 + X_6 - S_7 + U_a = 7$$

   where S_7 is a slack with a negative coefficient of 1, and U_a is an artificial variable.

TABLE 8-1 PEPPERELL MANUFACTURING COMPANY, PRODUCT-MIX PROBLEM OF BLANKET MILL, EXPRESSED IN L.P. FORM

	Marketable blanket styles									Productive capacity per week	
	No. 1	No. 2	No. 3	No. 4	No. 5	No. 6	No. 7	No. 8	No. 9	Machine hours	Spindle hours
	Gross revenue (dollars per hundred yards sold)										
	101	98	60	68	65	81	55	52	58		
Time required to produce 100 yards of blankets (in hours) on:											
92-inch looms	15.8	0	17.6	18.9	0	0	15.6	0	0	2,900	
112-inch looms	0	20.2	0	0	21.6	21.6	0	17.9	17.9	900	
woolen cards	0.30	0.30	0.36	0.36	0.36	0.45	0.31	0.31	0.34	120	
fly frames	0	0	820	830	830	950	705	705	725		125,000
spinning frames	550	550	0	0	0	0	0	0	0		20,000
Maximum volume salable per week (100 yds.)							70				
Minimum volume needed per week (100 yds.)											
Group 1 styles				7							
Group 2 styles								15			

Note: Designating the quantities X of each of the styles 1, 2, 3, and such, by the corresponding subscripts, X_1, X_2, X_3, then a matrix reading of, for example, the "spinning frames" row would give: $550X_1 + 550X_2 = 20,000$.

TABLE 8-2

PEPPERELL MANUFACTURING COMPANY, OPTIMUM SOLUTION OF PRODUCT-MIX PROBLEM, THROUGH LP

	Marketable blanket styles (in 100s of yards)								
	No. 1	No. 2	No. 3	No. 4	No. 5	No. 6	No. 7	No. 8	No. 9
Quantity to be produced	36.36	0	0	90.17	0	41.67	15.00	0	0
Penalty for violation, (in dollars per 100 yards.)[a]		5.96	7.18		6.17			5.63	1.26
Shortage from max. limit of 70: Group 1[b]							55.0		
Excess over minimum limits of 15 and 7:									
Group 1, (15)[c]					124.84				
Group 2, (7)[d]								0	
Bonus for slackening, (in dollars per 100 yards)[e]								2.76	

TABLE 8-2 (*Continued*)

	Machine and spindle hours available, used and idle				
	92-inch looms	112-inch looms	Woolen cards	Fly-frame spindles	Spinning spindles
Available capacity	2900	900	120	125,000	20,000
Amount utilized	2512.77	900	66.77	125,000	20,000
Amount idle	387.23	0	52.23	0	0
Bonus for slackening, (in dollars per hour)[f]		0.15		0.08	0.18

[a]Penalty is the loss in total profit that occurs by producing a style that is not in the optimum, and adjusting other quantities so as to remain within all specified limits.

[b]The maximum salable, 70, minus the amount recommended, 15, is 55.

[c]The minimum called for, 15, equals the amount recommended, 15.

[d]The minimum called for, 7, deducted from the recommended 90.17 and 41.67, leaves a balance of 124.84.

[e,f]This represents the possible increase in over-all profit when the imposed restriction is relaxed, namely, no minimum must be produced or capacity of mill is increased.

Note: The equations and resulting initial matrix, leading to the solution shown here are given in Table 8-3 and Exhibit 8-1.

TABLE 8-3

PEPPERELL MANUFACTURING COMPANY, INITIAL MATRIX OF PRODUCT-MIX OPTIMIZATION PROBLEM

Row	Coefficient		Body						Identity					Result
	$C \rightarrow$	101	98	$\dots$	58	0	0	0	0	$\dots$	0	$-M$	$-M$	R
	$\downarrow$	X_1	X_2	$\dots$	X_9	S_7	S_8	S_1	S_2	$\dots$	S_6	U_a	U_b	
S_1	0	15.8	0	$\dots$	17.9	0	0	1	0	$\dots$	0	0	0	2900
S_2	0	0	20.2	$\dots$	0	0	0	0	1	$\dots$	0	0	0	900
S_6	0	0	0	$\dots$	1	-1	0	0	0	$\dots$	1	1	0	70
U_a	$-M$	0	0	$\dots$	0	0	0	0	0	$\dots$	0	1	0	7
U_b	$-M$	0	0	$\dots$	1	0	-1	0	0	$\dots$	0	0	1	15
$Z-C$		-101	-98	$\dots$	$-M$ -58	0	0	0	0	$\dots$	0	M	M	

The dotted parts identify products X_3 to X_8 and the corresponding slack variables, S_3 to S_5. The omission of this detail from the table serves to simplify the presentation. The full initial matrix would contain a full row for each of the six slacks S_1 to S_6 and the two fictitious products U_a and U_b or a total of eight such variables in the identity portion of the matrix.

b. For styles number 7, 8, 9

$$X_7 + X_8 + X_9 - S_8 + U_b = 15$$

with S_8 as a further slack with negative coefficient of 1, and U_b as a further artificial variable.

4. Objective equation, maximizing Z

$$101X_1 + 98X_2 \cdots + 58X_9 + 0S_7 + 0S_8 + 0S_1 \cdots + 0S_6 - MU_a$$
$$- MU_b = Z_{\text{maximum}}$$

with X_1 to S_8 forming the body, and S_1 to U_b forming the identity of the matrix.

▶ ▶ ▶ ▶ **9**

Linear Programming, Transportation Method

In certain instances, the so-called transportation method of linear programming can be used in place of the Simplex. Both techniques yield identical results, but the transportation method requires far less mathematics. Unfortunately, the transportation method is limited to problems with resources and requirements that are given in terms of only one kind of unit. Also interdependencies among resources, such as shown in the production-sales coordination example, can be handled only with the Simplex approach.

The term "transportation method" is misleading. Machine assignment, plant location, and product mix problems can be solved with it, so that the method is not really confined to transportation or distribution problems.

Example

The illustrative example following shows the weekly output of cattle feed supplement, in tons, as the by-product of alcohol distillation in two plants, A and B which is to go to four distributing warehouses 1, 2, 3, and 4, weekly. The transportation costs per ton are also shown in Table 9-1. For the purpose of solving this problem, we may place it in matrix form, as shown in Figure 9-1.

Matrix Terminology

The matrix used in the transportation method is comprised of squares or "cells" which when stacked form "columns" vertically and "rows" horizontally. The cell that is located by the intersection of a row and a column is designated by its row and column headings. Thus,

Warehouses

Plant	1	2	3	4	Output
A	3	4	9	2	23
B	6	5	8	8	27
Demand	12	13	15	10	50

FIGURE 9-1. Basic matrix. Unit costs, in dollars per ton of distributing feed from plants to warehouses 1, 2, 3 and 4, are shown in the small boxed inserts of each cell.

TABLE 9-1

WEEKLY OUTPUT AND DISTRIBUTION OF FEED SUPPLEMENT[a]

Plant	Warehouse 1	2	3	4	Output (in tons)[b]
A	3	4	9	2	23
B	6	5	8	8	27
Demand (in tons)[c]	12	13	15	10	50

[a]Entries show dollar costs per ton of distributing feed from plants A and B to the respective warehouses 1, 2, 3, 4.

[b]Output represents normal weekly production of feed supplement, as a by-product of distillation.

[c]Demand shows normal weekly customer requirements to be on hand at each of the four warehouses.

the intersection of row A with column 1 would locate the cell A1. Unit costs have been placed in the small squares located in the upper right-hand corner of each cell for convenience in working this problem.

Northwest Corner Rule

The first step in the transportation method is to load the basic matrix without worrying whether the solution being formed is optimal. Although it is not important in what sequence one loads the matrix, it is customary to use the northwest corner rule. This rule states that in making initial assignments one starts by loading the cell located in the upper left-hand corner of the matrix, and filling row requirements to the right and downward, until all of the requirements of the problem have been satisfied. This method was followed in arriving at the first feasible solution in Figure 9-2.

Plant A, with an output of 23 tons, first supplies warehouse 1 with its requirements of 12 tons, and then supplies warehouse 2 with the remaining 11 tons of output. But warehouse 2 requires 2 more tons to complete its requirements. Output of plant A, however, has been scheduled to its capacity. We are forced, therefore, to supply warehouse 2 with its 2 additional tons from plant B. We continue loading in this manner, until all of the output has been assigned, always being careful to observe the problem restrictions. These restrictions are given by the output column and demand row, which in effect say:

1. Do not assign output from the last column, showing plant capacity, in excess of this capacity.
2. Do not shortchange any warehouse demand by assigning less than the quantity required by each warehouse.

Had the problem involved, say, five rows (A to E) we would have

Warehouses

Plant	1	2	3	4	Output
A	3 12	4 11	9	2	23
B	6	5	8	8	27
		2	15	10	
Demand	12	13	15	10	50

FIGURE 9-2. First feasible solution. Cells received tons of plant A and B output in accordance with the demands for tons, beginning with the upper left-hand corner, filling row requirments to the right and downward, until all demands were satisfied from the available output.

first used up all of A's output, as done above, then B's, C's, proceeding in an orderly manner from the upper left-hand corner of the matrix, to the right and downward.

Cost Evaluation

The transportation costs involved in the first solution can be evaluated readily, by simply multiplying unit cost per ton, in dollars, times the number of tons shipped. In particular, see Table 9-2.

TABLE 9-2

Plant	Ware-house	Unit cost (in dollars)	Shipment (in tons)	Unit cost × tons = total cost (in dollars)
A	1	3	12	36
	2	4	11	44
B	2	5	2	10
	3	8	15	120
	4	8	10	80
Total				290

Evaluation of Empty Cells

In order to ascertain whether or not this first solution with a total shipping cost of $290 is optimal, the empty cells in the solution must be evaluated. In particular, we must investigate whether use of any of these empty cells would result in a lower cost than the present schedule. For instance, would it be better if some of plant Bs production were sent to warehouse 1?

The question just posed means that we ought to evaluate the effect of including empty cell B1 in a shipping program. Now, every additional ton shipped from plant B to warehouse 1 involves a cost of $6 extra. But, since plant B is scheduled to capacity, moving 1 ton from it to warehouse 1 would mean that one less ton could be sent to, say, warehouse 2, thus subtracting $5 of cost. But, this move would leave warehouse 2 short 1 ton and would require an additional ton from plant A, adding $4. This move in turn would overload plant A requiring that plant A ship one less ton to warehouse 1, thus subtracting $3 of cost. Therefore, the net effect of shipping 1 ton from plant B

Warehouses

Plant	1	2	3	4	Output
A	−3 11	+4 12	9	2	23
B	+6 1	−5 1	8 15	8 10	27
Demand	12	13	15	10	50

FIGURE 9-3. Evaluation of empty cell B1. Plus and minus signs in the unit-cost squares indicate the effect of the shifts: Adding one ton to B1 and A2 each, adds +6 and +4 in cost; removing one ton from B2 and A1 each, reduces costs by −3 and −5. The net effect is a raising of total cost by +6 +4 −3 −5 = $2. Thus, total costs cannot be reduced by adding a ton to B1.

to warehouse 1 would be $+6 - 5 + 4 - 3 = +\$2$, as shown graphically in Figure 9-3. Arrows have been inserted to show the route of the evaluation. Plus and minus signs indicate which cells either gained or lost a ton.

The following important points are brought out by the procedure used to evaluate the empty cell B1:

1. By shifting 1 ton from a loaded cell into the empty cell, we are actually comparing the cost of the original schedule with the cost of a new schedule involving the empty cell.
2. The loaded cell chosen to supply a ton to the empty was a special cell with two important characteristics:
   a. It is located in the same row or column as the empty cell being evaluated.
   b. It is so located that the route used for the evaluation would not require us to load more than one empty cell during the same evaluation. We could not, for example, have chosen to shift 1 ton from cell B3 into cell B1, which would have made it necessary to follow route $-B3 + B1 - A1 + A3$, and both B1 and A3 are empty cells. A similar analysis would prove that cell B4 is also unacceptable.

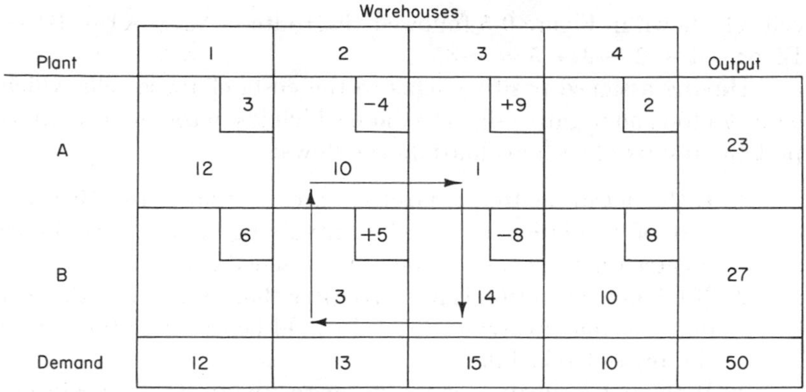

FIGURE 9-4. Evaluation of empty cell A3. In order to move a ton to A3, we remove a ton from A2. Next, to restore a ton to warehouse 2 and remove the extra ton from warehouse 3, we shift one ton from B3 to B2. The unit costs, in dollars, associated with these moves are: $-4 + 9 - 8 + 5 = +2$. Adding a ton to empty cell A3 would therefore increase, not reduce total costs.

3. The evaluation was not complete until enough tons had been shifted to satisfy the problem requirements of output and demand.

Further Evaluations

Evaluation of cell A3, shown in Figure 9-4, followed the route $-A2 + A3 - B3 + B2$ or $-4 + 9 - 8 + 5 = +\$2$. Evaluation of

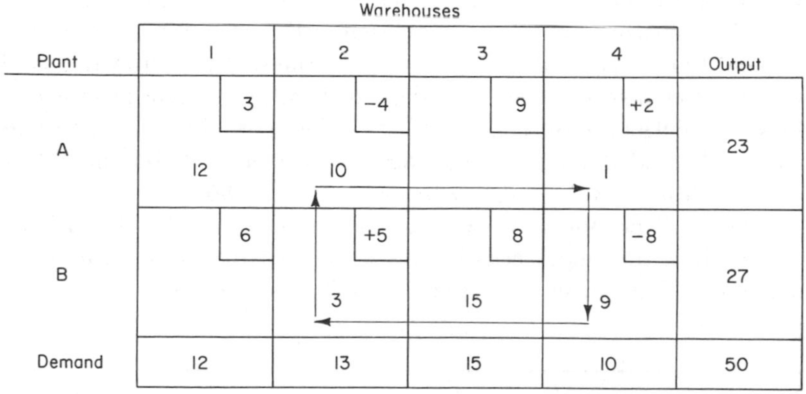

FIGURE 9-5. Evaluation of empty cell A4. It is not permissible to add to (or remove from) an empty cell (such as A3) other than the empty cell being evaluated. Therefore, to avoid any additions or removals in cell A3, the evaluation arrow skips column 3, ending in cell B2.

cell A4, shown in Figure 9-5 followed the route $-$A2 $+$ A4 $-$ B4 $+$ B2 or $-4 + 2 - 8 + 5 = -\$5$.

Having assigned positive signs to the costs of those cells which gained a ton and negative signs to those which lost a ton, we can interpret the results of each evaluation as follows:

1. If the net evaluation is positive (greater than zero), then the cost of a solution or schedule involving this cell would be greater than the cost of the present schedule.
2. If the net evaluation is negative (less than zero), then the cost of a schedule involving this cell would be less than the cost of the present schedule.
3. If the net evaluation is exactly zero, then total cost will not change by using this empty cell. We have the option of using a schedule involving the empty cell, or using the present schedule.

Second Feasible Solution

By applying the reasoning above to the results of the evaluations, it is seen that the first feasible solution is not optimal. For each ton that is placed in cell A4, $5 will be saved. Therefore, one would try to shift as many tons as possible into cell A4. But, as shown in the evaluation of cell A4, for every ton moved into that cell, 1 ton must be moved out of both A2 and B4. (The negative cost signs indicating that these two each lost a ton.) Obviously, we cannot move more tons out of a cell than are actually in that cell. Therefore, the largest amount that can be shifted is governed by the smallest entry in any of the cells that lose a ton. The smallest such entry, as shown in the first feasible solution, is 10 tons, in cell B4. Therefore, by adding 10 tons to cells A4 and B2, and subtracting 10 tons from cells B4 and B2 we arrive at the second feasible solution in Figure 9-6.

We still do not know whether or not this solution is optimal. Again all of the empty cells in the second feasible solution must be evaluated. This evaluation gives the following results:

TABLE 9-3

Empty cell	Route	Evaluation (in dollars)
A3	$-$A2 $+$A3 $-$B3 $+$B2	$-4 + 9 - 8 + 5 = +2$
B1	$-$B2 $+$B1 $-$A1 $+$A2	$-5 + 6 - 3 + 4 = +2$
B4	$-$B2 $+$B4 $-$A4 $+$A2	$-5 + 8 - 2 + 4 = +5$

Warehouses

Plant	1	2	3	4	Output
A	3 12	4 1	9	2 10	23
B	6	5 12	8 15	8	27
Demand	12	13	15	10	50

FIGURE 9-6.   Second feasible solution. Evaluation of empty cells shows it to be optimal, involving the lowest possible total transportation cost.

The net evaluations for all empty cells involve costs greater than zero. Therefore, any change in this solution would increase total costs. The solution is thus optimal.

Had the cell evaluations revealed any negative costs, this would have indicated that a further matrix, with a third feasible solution is needed. The process of matrix formation and evaluation is completed only when all evaluations are positive, thereby indicating that an optimal schedule has been found.

Degeneracy

Frequently linear programming problems become "degenerate." This means that the solution has reached a point where full evaluation of the problem is impossible because there are not enough loaded cells available to complete the evaluation of all empty cells. And, loading more than one empty cell during one cell evaluation is not permissible.

A simple test can be used before attempting to solve any transportation problem to see if the problem is degenerate. Check that the number of cells in which an entry has been made is not less than $m + n - 1$, where m is the number of rows, and n is number of columns in the matrix. In the example used, m is 2, and n is 4. Therefore, if at any time the solution had had less than 5 loaded cells, it would have been impossible to solve the problem using the method given.

One can get around a degenerate situation by assigning very small, fictitious loads to enough empty cells to bring the number of loaded cells up to $m + n - 1$. These fictitious loads are usually indicated by the Greek letter ϵ, a small epsilon. Subscripts are used when more than one such letter is required. Evaluation of the remaining empty cells then proceeds in the ususl manner, moving the ϵ's until all of the empty cells have been evaluated.

Unbalance

In the illustrative example, total output equaled total demand. In practice, resources (such as the outputs) and requirements (such as warehouse demands) will not be precisely balanced. If there is excess capacity, resources will exceed demands. In such instances an additional column of fictitious demand by a fictitious warehouse can be added. Excess capacity then is planned to be "shipped" to this imaginary warehouse. The purpose of this scheme is merely to balance the matrix. No actual shipment would be occurring for the fictitious column. An illustration of how this unbalance is handled in practice will be given in the case history of the next chapter.

Speeding up Calculations

It is sometimes possible to reduce the amount of work required in reaching an optimum by arranging rows and columns so that the lowest costs tend to cluster in the northwest corner of the first matrix. For example, in Figure 9-1, it might have been desirable to interchange columns 3 and 4. Both have the same costs for shipment from plant B, but for plant A, warehouse 4 has a cost of only $2 per ton, while warehouse 3 has a cost of $9. The northwest corner rule might result in a speed-up of calculations — fewer iterations of matrix steps — if warehouse 4 preceded warehouse 3.

For the small problem given for illustrative purposes, it is of course not of any real value to make such shifts. However, even a modest size matrix, with five rows and five columns, would benefit noticeably in most instances.[1]

Conclusion

One might ask: "What happens if a cell is evaluated erroneously?" If a cell is evaluated to be negative, when it should have been positive, this may mean that further needless iterations are followed.

---

[1]A similar approach is to ignore the northwest corner rule for the first or initial matrix, and instead assigning the initial solution by judgment as good as seems possible.

But the optimum will still be found. On the other hand, if a cell is evaluated to be positive, when actually it is negative, this may mean that a solution is called "optimal" when actually it is not.

The methods of linear programming, brought in the preceding chapters do not exhaust the commonly used techniques of LP for business problems. Only the two principal techniques, the Simplex matrix and the transportation method, have been shown. The graphic demonstration was really just a visual presentation of the Simplex approach. With the methods shown, however, the reader will not only know the principal techniques of LP analysis; but he will also be in a good position to understand other LP techniques, with which he may be confronted in special situations requiring other than the common approaches. In order to demonstrate the usefulness of the transportation method further, a case history will be presented in the next chapter.

10

Linear Programming,

Transportation Method:

A Case History

For the purpose of demonstrating how the transportation method of linear programming works, relatively simple data were used. In this chapter, an actual case history will be examined.[1]

Background

Company management was interested in LP and its possible uses. A staff group was asked to illustrate to management the applications of this tool with a plant problem. After several areas had been considered, a problem involving the determination of optimal pump replacements was selected for study, since it fulfilled all of the following requirements:

1. A relatively simple LP solution could be applied.
2. The solution would lend itself to ease and clarity of management presentation.
3. Worthwhile practical improvement would result.

Dope-metering pumps are used in the extrusion of synthetic filament. A mixture of polymer and a solvent, commonly called "dope," is extruded through extremely fine holes in an extrusion die. Then the solvent is evaporated and the filament is formed as the end product. Weight per unit length or "denier" of the product depends upon the amount of dope extruded in a given time period. In order to assure a constant supply and delivery of this dope, metering pumps are needed. The pumps must perform with a high degree of precision and uni-

---

[1]Data adapted from J. W. Cowdery, "An application of linear programming to metering pump replacement," a paper presented before the Statistics Section, Virginia Academy of Science, at Roanoke, Virginia, May 9, 1958.

formity. And relatively frequent failures occur. When a pump fails, it costs $5 to replace it.

A multiplicity of extrusion machines and pumps is involved. By changing pump revolutions and making other adjustments, a machine may be made to produce different items or products. The particular plant studied produced ten such different products.

The three different types of pumps, S_1, S_2, and S_3, had different rates of dope delivery. Replacement rates also varied for each of the ten products, P_1, P_2, $\cdots$, P_{10} made, because each required a different dope throughput. Higher throughput means faster pumping and earlier failure of equipment.

Formulating the Model

It was realized that data would have to be obtained for each of the replacement rates R shown schematically in the matrix of Table 10-3. Later, the number of pumps, $x_{i,j}$ to be assigned to each product, would appear in a similar matrix as the optimal solution. In particular, if subscript i represents pump types 1, 2, and 3, and subscript j represents the products 1, 2, $\cdots$, 10 produced, then the total cost of replacement C can be obtained from the expression below with Σ representing sum of and c representing the cost of an individual replacement:

$$C = c \sum\nolimits_{j=1}^{10} \sum\nolimits_{i=1}^{3} X_{ij}R_{ij} \qquad \text{Equation (1)}$$

The objective is to minimize this total cost C.

Data Gathering

Pump-replacement rates were obtained from a study of past records, and are listed in Table 10-4. Blank spaces represent missing data. Although each pump is capable of producing each product, it turned out that some pumps had never been assigned to all items.

At first, it seemed as though the problem could not be continued because of missing data. Then, however, it was decided to go ahead anyway and, if necessary, to fill in blank spots with estimates based on engineering judgment. Product requirements were similarly obtained by examination of past records and sales forecasts. This phase of the study was limited to a quarterly basis, with the intention of making new evaluations each quarter. The product requirements are listed below in terms of machine weeks:

TABLE 10-1

Product	Machine weeks	Product	Machine weeks
P_1	153	P_6	63
P_2	33	P_7	3
P_3	24	P_8	36
P_4	14	P_9	50
P_5	98	P_{10}	110

Thus, for product P_1, for example, quarterly production requirements to meet anticipated sales volume is 153 machine weeks.

Replacement cost per pump was found to be $5 regardless of type.

The following represents data concerning the number of pumps available:

TABLE 10-2

Pump Type	No.
S_1	338
S_2	97
S_3	194

The information gathered can now be combined as shown in Table 10-5. Since the number of pumps available exceeds the production requirements, an imaginary product Q has been added as a column. We may look at Q as "zero production" from 45 "idle pumps," representing the excess of the available 629 pumps over the 584 required pumps needed.

Solving the Problem

The objective now is to find that pump assignment which will minimize cost C of pump replacement, using as our cost model equation (1). Since resources, represented by the available pumps, and requirements, represented by the pumps needed to produce the output demanded, are in like units (to wit, pumps,) it is apparent that the transportation method of LP can be used.

The first matrix, in Table 10-6, yields an initial solution, involving a total replacement of 2403.66 pumps at a unit cost of $5 each, or a total cost of $12,018.30. This solution is, of course, not the lowest-cost assignment. Several matrix iterations are required, until the optimum — in Table 10-7 — is reached. This shows that 1469.51 pumps at a total cost of $7347.55 will need to be replaced during the quarter, using the optimal assignment.

TABLE 10-3

METERING-PUMP ASSIGNMENT PROBLEM, SCHEMATIC REPRESENTATION

Pump types available	Products									
	P_1	P_2	P_3	P_4	P_5	P_6	P_7	P_8	P_9	P_{10}
S_1	$R_{1,1}$	$R_{1,2}$								
S_2	$R_{2,1}$	$R_{2,2}$								
S_3										

The entries $R_{i,j}$ represent the replacement rates, expressed as failures per machine week. The first subscript i refers to the pump type or row with i equal to 1, 2, or 3. The second subscript j refers to the product extruded or column with j equal to 1, 2, 3, $\cdots$, 10. Thus $R_{1,2}$ represents the replacement rate of pump S_1 when extruding product P_2.

TABLE 10-4

METERING-PUMP ASSIGNMENT PROBLEM, PUMP REPLACEMENT RATES

(Pump failure means pump replacement. Rates are shown on a basis of failures per 1000 hours of operation)

Pump Type	Products									
	P_1	P_2	P_3	P_4	P_5	P_6	P_7	P_8	P_9	P_{10}
S_1	3.36	0.84	2.87	6.72	11.34	1.68	0.91	1.47	1.12	4.76
S_2					5.81	0.21		0.84	0.70	3.08
S_3	0.70	2.10	0.70	0.77	6.37	0.77	0.91	0.98		4.34

Blank spaces mean that no data were available, or else only inadequate data were recorded.

Practical Installation

The solution shown was not completely adaptable to plant use, because of lack of complete flexibility in pump assignment. Not all of the extrusion machines are capable of extruding each of the ten products. The cost of changing pumps from one machine to another exceeds any possible savings in replacement rates. It is also impractical to stop a machine in operation to make a product change, and at any one time the production volume on each style may not be exactly as anticipated from forecasts of customer demands. With varying customer requirements, changes in product must occasionally be made.

For these reasons, a set of guide rules was developed for shop use, based on the LP solution, but not requiring blind adherence to that solution. The following are these rules:

1. Use S_2 pumps on product P_5. If an excess of these pumps is available, use it on product P_{10}. Should there not be enough S_2 pumps available to meet the requirements for P_5, then use S_1 pumps.
2. Use S_3 pumps on products P_1, P_2, P_3, and P_4. If production requirements cannot be fulfilled, meet these needs by using

TABLE 10-5

METERING PUMP ASSIGNMENT PROBLEM, PUMPS AVAILABLE AND REQUIRED

Pump type	Products											Pumps available
	P_1	P_2	P_3	P_4	P_5	P_6	P_7	P_8	P_9	P_{10}	Q	
S_1												338
S_2												97
S_3												194
Pumps required[a]	153	33	24	14	98	63	3	36	50	110	45	629

[a]Pumps required represents the pump weeks needed to produce the various products P_1, P_2 $\cdots$ P_{10} for which there is expected to be customer demand during the coming quarter. For example, to meet demand for product P_1, 153 pump weeks of production will be needed during the quarter.

S_1 on the lower numbered products. If an excess of S_3 pumps is available, use them on the higher numbered products.
3. Complete any additional requirement with S_1 pumps.

An evaluation was made of the effect of operation of the plant under these three operating rules. A review of past operations showed that the rules, if used, would have resulted in a replacement cost of $7400. Actual replacement costs for this period were $10,400. Thus, a saving of about $3000 per quarter was demonstrated as attainable.

A further, more important, gain from the application of LP was that it provided new insights and answers in many production and sales areas where prior approaches had failed to yield optimality.

TABLE 10-6

METERING PUMP ASSIGNMENT PROBLEM, FIRST SOLUTION[c]

Pump type	Products											Pumps available
	P_1	P_2	P_3	P_4	P_5	P_6	P_7	P_8	P_9	P_{10}	Q	
S_1	153	33	24	14	98	16[a]						338
S_2						47	3[b]	36	11			97
S_3									39[b]	110	45	194
Pumps required	153	33	24	14	98	63	3	36	50	110	45	

[a]We proceed following the northwest corner rule. The top row S_1 can be filled from pumps S_1 for products P_1 to P_5, but there are not enough pumps to use more than 16 of S_1 for product P_6. Yet 63 pump-weeks are required. Therefore, we must use 47 pumps S_2. Proceeding similarly, the entire matrix is filled.
[b]Although missing from the original data, these two values had to be filled in from engineering estimates. It is of interest to note that in the final solution, these two cells were not used.
[c]To find the cost of this assignment, multiply the number of pumps in each cell by the failure rate of Table 10-4. Add the results and then multiply the sum by the replacement cost per pump, $5. This yields the total cost of the first solution:

Step 1: $(153 \times 3.36) + (33 \times .84) + (24 \times 2.87) + (14 \times 6.72)$
$+ (98 \times 11.34) + (16 \times 1.68) + (47 \times .21) + (3 \times .91) + (36 \times .84)$
$+ (11 \times .70) + (39 \times .84) + (110 \times 4.34) + (45 \times 0) = 2,403.66$
pumps to be replaced.

Step 2: C = \$5.00 × 2,403.66 = \$12,018.30[d].

[d]An evaluation of empty cells quickly reveals that we are far from an optimum. Further matrix steps are required.

TABLE 10-7

CELANESE CORPORATION

METERING PUMP ASSIGNMENT, OPTIMUM SOLUTION[a,b]

Pump type	P_1	P_2	P_3	P_4	P_5	P_6	P_7	P_8	P_9	P_{10}	Q	Pumps available
S_1		33				63	3	36	50	108	45	338
S_2					95					2		97
S_3	153		24	14	3							194
Pumps required	153	33	24	14	98	63	3	36	50	110	45	629[c]

[a]This final matrix contains the optimum assignment of the three types of metering pumps to the ten products.

[b]The cost of replacement involved in this optimal solution is \$7347.55 an approximately 40 percent improvement over the original solution of \$12,018.30.

[c]To find the total cost associated with the assignment of the pumps, we proceed as before:

Step 1: Multiply the number of pumps in each cell by the failure rate in Table 10-4, and add:

$$(33 \times 0.84) + (63 \times 1.68) + (3 \times 0.91) + (36 \times 1.47)$$
$$+ (50 \times 1.12) + (108 \times 4.76) + (45 \times 0) + (95 \times 5.81)$$
$$+ (2 \times 0.70) + (153 \times 0.70) + (24 \times 0.70) + (14 \times 0.77)$$
$$+ (3 \times 6.37) = 1469.51$$

Step 2: C = \$5 × 1469.51 = \$7347.55 = Minimum cost assignment

▶ ▶ ▶ ▶ **11**

Planning of
Capital Improvements and
Other Long-term Investments

That one of the thorniest problems management must tackle is the choice of investment alternatives: whether to buy or not to buy, and if to buy, which purchase is best, is said by John G. McLean, Vice President of Continental Oil Company, a firm that invests over a million dollars each week. The record of the past years shows that modern industrial management is on the alert for new products, new processes, and new equipment, and will not flinch from taking sound risks and high investments when necessary. There is, however, also evidence that in those instances where quantitative aids towards investment planning are not routine, profitable investment opportunities are often passed up. Losses in terms of higher costs, less saleable products, and missed markets are the price paid for less than optimal capital investment policies. In this chapter the principal quantitative tools for investment decision making will be considered.

Framework of Management Planning

Routine planning for capital expenditures requires an organizational structure, such as outlined in Figure 11-1. From a consideration of the factors affecting the worth of an investment (Exhibit 11-1), it is apparent that the details of investment planning affect all important areas of management. Moreover, the extent to which all personnel — management, staff and supervision — play a role in the assembly of vital data and decisions is brought out by a consideration of the many factors that must be checked when planning individual equipment acquisitions (Exhibit 11-2).

The degree to which the various phases of scientific investment planning can be integrated within an organization determines the

107

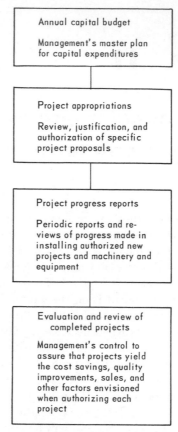

FIGURE 11-1. Schematic of management planning and control responsibilities with regard to capital outlays.

long-run success in keeping up to date on modernization, and in assuring that earnings will be adequate to continue modernization in the future. "Innovate or be inundated" is an admonition which is especially valid in a highly competitive industry.

Quantitative Aids

Investment planning requires facts and figures, and this in turn spotlights attention to quantitative methods.

To answer the question, "How long will it take until this investment has paid off," the "payback-period method" is used as a quick but crude guide (Exhibit 11-3). A more complete evaluation is afforded by the analysis of expected earnings, using the "rate of return method" shown in Exhibit 11-4. In recent years, this method has come in for heavy criticism, since it ignores the time at which various earnings are received. Yet, a dollar "today" is far more valuable than a dollar expected some years from now; especially at an age when high interest rates and creeping inflation are very much to be considered. In order to ascertain a "true rate of return," which allows or "discounts" for the fact that earnings from an investment will stretch over a relatively long period of time, the "discounted cash flowback method" must be used. Exhibit 11-5 illustrates the procedures, using the data in Table 11-2. A simplification, using an assumed decrease in cash flow, based on the expected life of the project

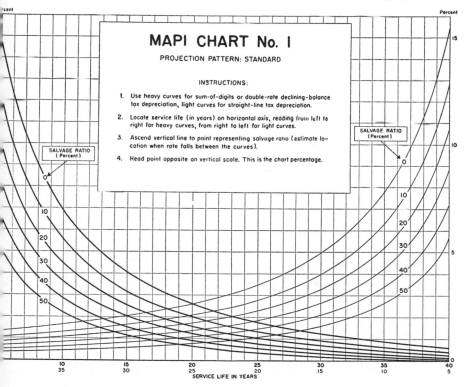

FIGURE 11-2. Mapi chart. Courtesy Machinery and Allied Products Institute.

and the first year's cash flow, is the Mapi system, developed by the Machinery and Allied Products Institute. Exhibit 11-6 and Figure 11-2 illustrate the application of this system, which has gained considerable favor throughout industry.

Conclusion

Industry has entered the age of scientific-quantitative methods, automation, and computerization of operations. Modern quantitative methods for evaluating alternative investment opportunities, based on the concepts of discounted cash flow, will play an increasing role in helping to finance and accelerate this new age. Quantitative investment evaluation is a tool which will permit management to pick and choose sound capital expenditures with confidence.

EXHIBIT 11-1   Factors Affecting Worth of an Investment

1. *DETERIORATION*

Expected costs increasing with age and usage of equipment:
a. Maintenance work
b. Repair parts

2. *OBSOLESCENCE*

a. Reduced efficiency and more downtime as machine ages
b. New, lower-cost machines which may become available in the future, and which may also involve greater efficiency and service value
c. Style changes, rise of substitute products, and other market developments may reduce over-all demand for the products produced by the equipment

3. *TAX CONSIDERATIONS*

a. Effect of different tax depreciation allowances applicable.
b. Tax deductibility of interest-payments on borrowed money
c. "Leasing" versus "owning" in its effect on tax

4. *PRESENT AND FUTURE SALVAGE VALUES*

Present salvage value of facilities to be retired and the future salvage value of equipment to be acquired

5. *RANKING*

Evaluation of various opportunities by relative degree of desirability

EXHIBIT 11-2   Factors to Check when Evaluating New Equipment

1. *TRIAL RUNS*

Wherever possible, sample equipment should be run in the plant on regular production and stock. Carefully maintained records will reveal such important factors as:

a. How maintainable is the machine?
b. What are the other running conditions like on this machine and in subsequent processing?
c. Are there any signs that the equipment tends to deteriorate rapidly?
d. What production efficiency, speed, waste, scrap and product quality are being obtained?

2. *DESIGN*

Design and production engineers should carefully evaluate the technological aspects of the machine regarding:

a. Is the construction sturdy and reliable?
b. Is the equipment likely to perform well under high speeds, long runs, and under heavy abuse?
c. Are bearings, rolls, and other parts arranged so as to minimize likelihood of chokes, breaks, poor quality, or safety hazards?
d. Are replacement parts readily obtainable?

3. *COST*

Cost factors must be reviewed with great care.

a. How does the equipment compare with competitive machinery?
b. What will be the savings in labor, productivity, waste and quality (fewer seconds)?
c. What will be the cost of maintenance, repair parts, eventual scrap, or salvage value?
d. Is the anticipated cash flowback, discounted at appropriate rate of return, satisfactory?

EXHIBIT 11-3   Payback Period as a Measure of Worth of Investment

PRINCIPLE

This method answers the question: "How many years will it take to get the invested cash back?" using the formula:

$$\text{Pay back period (in years)} = \frac{\text{Net investment made (in dollars)}}{\text{Annual after-tax earnings (in dollars)}}$$

EXAMPLE

New equipment will cost $120,000 installed. Old equipment can be sold for $20,000. Net investment will be $120,000 less $20,000, or $100,000. Higher quality and productivity of new equipment will yield about $50,000 per year. At 50 percent corporate income tax rate, the after-tax earnings will be 50 percent of $50,000, or $25,000. Therefore:

$$\text{Pay back period (in years)} = 100,000/25,000 = 4$$

Refinements may be introduced to take account of further factors, such as previously listed, but profitability beyond the payback period does not enter into the formula.

ADVANTAGES

1. The quantities involved are readily measurable, easy to compute and quickly understood.
2. In an age of intense needs for large amounts of working capital, the length of pay back period is an important factor to consider in making capital investments.
3. In a dynamic economy, marked by frequent innovations, new products, radical substitutes, and changes in market conditions, knowledge of the pay back period aids in evaluating the risk of an investment. The longer the pay back time, the greater the risk.

DRAWBACKS

1. Liquidity may be overemphasized
2. The life-pattern of earnings is ignored, thus penalizing new equipment with long pay off period but high long-run profits

EXHIBIT 11-4   Rate-of-return Accounting as a Measure of Worth of Investment

PRINCIPLE

Average annual net income, after taxes and depreciation, is expressed as a percent of capital outlay. The formula is:

$$\text{Rate of return}^a, \text{ (in percent)} = \frac{100 \times \text{After-tax, after-depreciation earnings per Year (in dollars)}}{\text{Net investment made (in dollars)}}$$

The after-tax, after-depreciation earnings per year represent an average expectation, calculated by accounting methods.[a]

EXAMPLE

Net investment for new equipment is $100,000. Based on a ten-year expectation, average earnings per year, after taxes and depreciation are estimated at $20,000. Then:

Rate of return (in percent) = $100 \times \$20,000/\$100,000 = 20$ percent

Methods to determine average annual earnings vary considerably, and rely largely on forecasts of sales, prices and costs.

ADVANTAGES

1. The method yields values that are consistent with the firm's accounting methods. Proposals involving similar factors and earning patterns can be compared readily.
2. It is a good supplement to the pay back period figure, by showing overall profitability.

DRAWBACK

1. The method ignores the fact that earning rates on new investment may vary over the years. Such earnings should then not be averaged, since $1 earned a year hence is worth more than $1 earned 10 years hence. For example, a dollar invested in a 7 percent bond would double in 10 years, while $1 earned 10 years hence is still just $1. In short, future earnings are not discounted.

---

[a]Sometimes, "rate of return" is considered simply the reciprocal of the pay-back period.

EXHIBIT 11-5   Discounted Cash Flowback as a Measure of Worth of Investment

PRINCIPLE

The true rate of return offered by a new project is evaluated, based on the "discounted" or present value of future earnings.

EXAMPLE

Net investment is $100,000, cash flowbacks (after allowing for taxes due on earnings and taxes saved on depreciation) are expected as is shown in Table 11-1. Desired rate of return on risk capital is 20 percent. Present values, based on 20 percent interest per annum, are read off tables, such as Table 11-2.

TABLE 11-1

CALCULATION OF TOTAL PRESENT VALUE OF INVESTMENT

(A) End of year	(B) Inflow of cash (in dollars)	(C) Present value of one dollar (in dollars)	(D) Present value of cash inflow, $(B \times C)$ (in dollars, rounded)
1	30,000	0.83	24,900
2	29,000	0.69	20,000
3	28,000	0.58	16,200
4	27,000	0.48	13,000
5	26,000	0.40	10,400
6	25,000	0.33	8,300
7	24,000	0.28	6,700
8	22,000	0.23	5,100
9	20,000	0.19	3,800
10	18,000	0.16	2,900
Total	200,000		111,300
average	20,000		

The total present value of the investment, evaluated for its expected life of 10 years, is $111,300. This is above the presently proposed investment of $100,000. Therefore, the project is slightly better than the firm's standard of 20 percent of discounted return on risk investments.

ADVANTAGE

Liquidity, time effects and true rate of return are included in the evaluation of the proposed project.

DRAWBACKS

Validity of calculations depends upon reliability of cash-flow estimates. Calculations required are complex.

EXHIBIT 11-6 Machinery and Allied Products Institute Method of Investment Study, Illustrative Example

PROBLEM DATA

Installed equipment will cost $120,000. Old equipment will be sold at $20,000. Net cost of installed new equipment will thus be $100,000.

Expected earnings in first year of operation of new equipment, based on lower labor costs, higher out-put rate, improved quality and marketability, will be 50 percent of $100,000 or $50,000.

Expected life of new equipment is 10 years. Thereafter it will have a salvage value of 10 percent of 120,000 or 12 percent of $100,000. For tax purposes, the declining-balance method of depreciation is used.

PROCEDURE

1. After-tax return

   For the first year of operation, using a 50 percent corporate income tax rate, applied to the expected earnings of $50,000, yields 50 percent of $50,000 = $25,000.
2. Mapi chart allowance

   For a 12 percent salvage ratio and declining balance depreciation, the Mapi chart shows an allowance of $5\frac{1}{2}$ percent. Applied to the original installed net investment of $100,000, this results in $5,500.
3. Return on investment

   Based on the original net investment of $100,000 an after-tax return of $25,000 and the Mapi chart Allowance of $5,500:

Return on investment = ($25,000 − $5,500) / $100,000 = $19\frac{1}{2}$

The Mapi estimated rate of return or profitability of the investment is therefore 19½ percent.

TABLE 11-2

PRESENT VALUE OF ONE DOLLAR TO BE RECEIVED N YEARS HENCE
AT VARIOUS ANNUAL INTEREST RATES

(values given in cents)

Number of years (N)	Interest rate (in percent)											
	1	3	5	6	8	10	12	15	20	25	30	40
1	99	97	95	94	93	91	89	87	83	80	77	71
2	98	94	91	89	86	83	80	76	69	64	59	51
3	97	92	86	84	79	75	71	66	58	51	46	36
4	96	89	82	79	74	68	64	57	48	41	35	26
5	95	86	78	74	68	62	57	50	40	33	27	19
6	94	84	75	71	63	56	51	43	33	26	21	13
7	93	81	71	67	58	51	45	38	28	21	16	9
8	92	79	68	63	54	47	40	33	23	17	12	7
9	91	77	64	59	50	42	36	28	19	13	9	5
10	91	74	61	56	46	39	32	25	16	11	7	3
12	89	70	56	50	40	32	26	19	11	7	4	2
15	86	64	48	42	32	24	18	12	6	4	2	
20	82	55	38	31	21	15	10	6	3	1		
25	78	48	30	23	15	9	6	3	1			

1. There are blank places in the table because the particular values are less than a full cent.
2. Present value P in cents, after N years, at interest rate i, expressed as a decimal, is found from:

$$P = 100/(1 + i)^N$$

Example:

Given $500 to be received 10 years hence, assuming that money is worth 30 percent per annum. Find the present value.

Then, entering the table at the level N of 10 and proceeding horizontally to an interest rate of 30 percent, we find the present value of $0.07, for $1.

The present value of the $500 is therefore 0.07×500, or $35.

12

Capital Investment:
Further Aspects of
Discounting Future Earnings

In Chapter 11 the importance of discounting future earnings as a means of sound investment analysis was brought out. The method of discounting involves the determination of the present value of a future amount. For such purposes, we may simply use a table, such as Table 11-2. Some persons will, however, be interested in how this table was derived, and this in turn leads to a discussion of compound interest problems.

Compound Interest

Compound interest arises from the following series of events in making a loan or investment:

1. A given monetary amount or "principal" earns interest at certain stated intervals, or "interest periods."
2. At the end of the first interval, the interest earned is added to the principal.
3. During each subsequent interval, the interest earned is computed on the basis of the original principal plus the interest added thereto in prior periods.
4. After a particular number of interest periods have been completed, the sum by which the original principal has increased is the "compound interest." The original principal plus the compound interest represents the "compound amount."

Compound Amount

The "compound amount" S, using a given principal P, "annual rate of interest" j, and yearly frequency m of "compounding" or

117

adding interest to the principal, after a number of k "years," is given by the expression below.[1]

$$S = P(1 + j/m)^{mk} \qquad \text{Equation (1)}$$

Thus, given a principal of $200 at annual rate of interest of 8 percent (or 0.08 as a decimal), compounded quarterly (or four times per year), for 3 years, we obtain:

$$S = \$200 \ (1 + 0.08/4)^{4 \times 3} = \$253.64$$

The ratio j/m represents the interest "rate per interest period" and mk represents the "number of interest periods" in k years. By subtracting P from S, or $253.64 minus $200.00, we obtain the compound interest of $53.64.

Nominal and Effective Rates

The annual rate of interest j illustrated above is considered a "nominal rate." It is the rate usually quoted. However, unless interest is compounded annually, the nominal rate will not represent the "percentage rate per year at which the investment grows." This growth rate is the "effective interest rate" i. Note that for $m = 1$, $j = i$. For a given nominal rate j, the effective rate i can be readily determined. It is usually convenient to base calculations on a principal of $1 and interest accumulation of one year. At the end of the year, the compound amount will be given by:

$$S = 1 + i \qquad \text{Equation (2)}$$

S is also found from the expression below, based on Equation (1), omitting P and k since their magnitude is 1, unless otherwise stated:

$$S = (1 + j/m)^m \qquad \text{Equation (1a)}$$

From Equations (2) and (1a), we obtain:

$$1 + i = (1 + j/m)^m \qquad \text{Equation (3)}$$

so that

$$i = (1 + j/m)^m - 1 \qquad \text{Equation (4)}$$

---

[1]Note that if m becomes indefinitely large and P and j equals 1.0, then the expression in Equation (1) will approach ($\leq$) the value $e = 2.7183$, which is the base of the natural logarithms. Also, e is the transcendental limit of the series $1 + 1/1! + 1/2! + 1/3! \cdots 1/n!$, where n is indefinitely large.

For the example above, with $j = 0.08$ and $m = 4$, Equation (4) yields:

$$i = (1.02)^4 - 1 = 0.0824 = 8.24 \text{ percent}$$

The effective rate i of 8.24 percent thus corresponds to the nominal rate of 8 percent compounded quarterly.

Present Value of Compound Amount

Up to now, the problem was to determine the compound amount, with a given interest rate and principal. In many investment problems however, the compound amount as well as the interest rate is given and it is the principal that must be found. This principal P is known as the "present value" of the compound amount S. The pertinent formula is derived by simple transposition of (1), so that:

$$P = S/(1 + j/m)^{mk} \qquad \text{Equation (5)}$$

For example, to find the present value of the compound amount $253.64, due at the end of three years, at an interest rate of 8 percent, compounded quarterly, we set:

$$P = \$253.64/(1 + 0.08/4)^{4 \times 3} = \$200$$

In problems of this type, the interest period is known as the "conversion period." Note that there are 4×3, or 12 conversion periods. By definition, the "discount" on a compound amount S is the difference between S and present value P at a date occurring mk conversion periods prior to the time that S is due. Thus, for the example just given, the discount is found from:

$$\text{Discount} = S - P \qquad \text{Equation (6)}$$

and therefore,

$$\text{Discount} = \$253.64 - \$200 = \$53.64$$

Present Value of Compound Amount, Further Example

A further example of the determination of present value is given below, based on these "given" data:

1. Compound amount S of $1000
2. Interest rate j of 2 percent or 0.02
3. Conversion period of 6 months, representing a compounding frequency per year of $m = 2$
4. Due date for payment of compound amount is $3\frac{1}{2}$ years from hence, so that $k = 3\frac{1}{2}$

To find present value of compound amount of $1000, we will now proceed as follows:

1. Use formula Equation (5), substituting the appropriate values:

$$P = \$1000/(1 + 0.02/2)^{2 \times 3.5}$$

$$= \$1000/(1.01)^7$$

2. $\log\ P = \log\ 1000 - (7 \times \log 1.01)$

$$= 3.0 - (7 \times 0.00432)$$

$$= 3.0 - 0.03024$$

$$= 2.96976$$

3. antilog $2.96976 = 932.74$

4. The present value is therefore $932.74

From the present value data in Table 11-2, using $N = 7$, and $i = 1$ percent, a present value of $0.93 per $1 would have been obtained. Multiplied by the compound amount of $1000, this value yields $930 as the approximate (rounded) present value. It may also be observed that the reciprocals of the tabulated present values yield compound amounts.

Annuities

An annuity is a sequence of equal payments made at periodic "payment intervals" during the "term" of the annuity. In "ordinary annuities," all payments are made at the end of each period. The "term" of an annuity represents the time from the beginning of the first payment interval to the end of the last payment interval. The total of the payments made within a year is the "annual rent." Thus an annuity of $1000, payable annually for five years represents a payment interval of 12 months, an annual rent of $1000 and a five-year term. If the annuity had been in the amount of $83.33, payable monthly, the payment interval would have been one month and the annual rate would have been 12 × $83.33 or $1000 rounded.

For a given rate of interest, the "present value of an annuity" is the sum of the present values of all payments made under the annuity. The "compound amount of an annuity" is the total of the amounts that will accrue by the end of the term if annuity payments are left to accumulate at interest.

Present Value of Annuity

Assume an annuity of $1000 payable annually for four years with interest at the rate of 4 percent compounded annually. Then, from Equation (5) it is apparent that at the beginning of the first year the present value of the first annuity payment is:

$$\$1000/(1.04)^1 = \$961.54$$

By proceeding in a similar fashion for all years, we obtain a total present value of the annuity, of $3629.90. The steps are shown below.

TABLE 12-1

Annuity payment due at end of year	Present value of annuity payment	
	Formula	Amount (in dollars)
1	$1000/(1.04)^1$	961.54
2	$1000/(1.04)^2$	924.56
3	$1000/(1.04)^3$	889.00
4	$1000/(1.05)^4$	854.80
Total		$3629.90

A special mathematical formula has been developed, which obviates the need for lengthy calculations. This formula states that the present value P_k of an annuity at annual interest rate i per period and k annual payments R is:

$$P_k = [1 - 1/(1 + i)^k] \times (R/i) \qquad \text{Equation (7)}$$

For the present example,

$$P_k = (1 - 1/1.04^4) \times (1000/0.04)$$
$$= \$3629.90$$

This result checks with the answer found by the long but direct calculations given above.

Compound Amount of Annuity

Using the data from the example just given, it is now a simple matter to demonstrate the compound amount S of an annuity. The compound amount is the result of nonwithdrawal of the successive annuity payments, so that compound interest is accumulated on each. Thus, at the end of the first year, a payment of $1000 is due. If this payment is permitted to remain "on deposit" at 4 percent interest per year, then at the conclusion of the four years representing the term of the annuity, there will have elapsed $4 - 1 = 3$ years from the onset of the first payment under the annuity. Therefore, from formula (1), we have, based on the first year:

$$S = \$1000 \times (1.04)^3$$

$$= \$1124.90$$

Proceeding similarly for all of the years under consideration, yields the total compound amount S of $4246.50, as shown below:

TABLE 12-2

Annuity payment due at end of year	Compound amount at end of term accruing at 4 percent interest compounded annually	
	Formula	Amount (in dollars)
1	$\$1000 \times (1.04)^3$	1124.90
2	$\$1000 \times (1.04)^2$	1081.60
3	$\$1000 \times (1.04)^1$	1040.00
4	$\$1000 \times (1.04)^0$	1000.00
Total		$4246.50

Again, a formula has been developed. This states that the compound amount of an annuity for k interest periods at interest rate i per period, with annual payments R is:

$$S_k = [(1 + i)^k - 1] \times (R/i) \qquad \text{Equation (8)}$$

For the illustration above, we obtain:

$$S_k = (1.04^4 - 1) \times (1000/0.04) = 4246.50$$

This result checks with the answer found above.

Amortization

A debt is being amortized at a particular rate of interest if it is discharged by a series of periodic payments, consisting partly of interest and partly of repayment on the principal. Usually, the periods are equally spaced with equal amounts paid at the end of each period. Thus, the payments form an annuity with present value P equal to the amount of the debt originally incurred.

For example, $100,000 amortized at annual interest rate of 4 percent in five annual payments represents an annuity with present value $P = \$100,000$. The amount of the annual payments, R, can be found by reference to Equation (7); in particular:

$$P = (1 - 1/1.04^5) \times R/0.04$$

and, since P is $100,000, we can readily transpose to find

$$R = 0.04 \times \$100,000/(1 - 1/1.04^5)$$
$$= \$22,463$$

Thus, annual payments of $22,463 at the end of each of the five years will amortize the original amount of $100,000. It will be a simple matter to prepare an amortization schedule showing, for the end of each year the interest due on the unpaid balance, the debt reduction and the debt outstanding. Thus, at the end of the first year, the interest due on 4 percent of 100,000 will be $4000. Deducting this from the annuity payment of $22,463 leaves $18,463 as a payment in reduction of the debt. $100,000 less $18,463 leaves $81,537 as the debt remaining or "outstanding." At the end of the next year, interest of 4 percent on $18,463 will be only $3261, so that $19,202 can be applied against the debt, leaving a new balance outstanding of $62,335. At the end of five years, this process leaves a zero balance, meaning that the debt has been fully amortized.

Sinking Fund

A debt may be paid off by means of a "sinking fund" in a series of periodic payments, consisting of the following:

1. Simple interest on the principal
2. Payment to the sinking fund

For example, the $100,000 borrowed may be repaid in five equal annual deposits into the sinking fund, with 6 percent simple interest per year on the amount of the loan, while the amount in the sinking fund earns 4 percent, compounded annually. To find the annuity payment per year R, reference is made to Equation 8. In particular,

$$\$100{,}000 = (1.04^5 - 1) \times (R/0.04)$$

$$= 0.2167\ R/0.04$$

$$R = \$4000/0.2167 = \$18{,}459$$

The \$18,459 represents the annual annuity payment. This amount must be increased by the interest charge of 6 percent of \$100,000 or \$6000, to yield \$24,459 as the total annual payment. The payment of \$18,459 to the sinking fund represents a reduction of the book value of the debt, from \$100,000 to \$81,541. In subsequent years, the reduction of the debt will proceed more rapidly, since the sinking fund increases by the 4 percent interest compounded annually on the amounts in the fund.

Conclusion

It will be noted that for annual interest rates, compounded yearly (Equation (1)) can also assume a form of the more general type:

$$Y = AB^X \qquad \qquad \text{Equation (9)}$$

Where m is assumed to be 1 and the following symbol replacements occur: Y for S, A for P, B for $(1 + j)$, and X for k. This expression describes a curve known as the "exponential curve," but also called "compound interest curve." An important characteristic of this curve is that logarithms of the Y-values will form a straight line, since

$$\text{Log } Y = \log A + (\log B) \times X \qquad \text{Equation (10)}$$

Distributions of certain operational characteristics, such as servicing times for queued-up items, (see Chapter 20) often follow in approximate form a negative exponential distribution, e^{-x}, or the equivalent $1/e^x$, as will be discussed further. When A is 1, and B is e, Equation (9) is known as the exponential function. It is the only function that is exactly the same as its derivative.

▶ ▶ ▶ ▶ **13**

Program Evaluation
and Review Techniques
(Pert)

The name Pert refers to a recently developed method, "Program Evaluation and Review Technique," which can be used effectively for management planning and control activities. From a general viewpoint, Pert aids the manager in guiding and directing team efforts more effectively. It permits advance planning, indicates current progress, and warns of potential future trouble spots when there may still be time to avoid them. More specifically, Pert shows its value most strikingly when special projects of a new kind are undertaken. Management must then have an aid in handling the uncertainties regarding time schedules, coordination of many activities, and control of the costs involved. Pert is such a tool.

Applicability of Pert

A few illustrations will indicate the types of activities in which Pert is of value:

1. An electronics producer is setting up his own metal stamping, machining, and heat-treating facilities and must estimate costs, time factors, and anticipated completion dates.
2. An aircraft manufacturer must submit bids on a spacecraft contract, including not only prices but also well-supported estimates of anticipated completion dates for various phases of the project.
3. A commercial manufacturer is planning a new model which must be ready in time for the new season or for other special market demands.

In a highly competitive situation, unless time schedules can be estimated with confidence and costs can be predicted within narrow margins for error, considerable losses will inevitably occur. For example, late entry of a new model may encounter a market that has been largely pre-empted by a competitor. Or, by overestimating the costs of a project, management may decide against an undertaking, and then watch a competitor forge ahead in a similar project.

A Case History

One firm which used Pert to plan and control the building, equipping, staffing, and initial production of a new plant, credited this approach with accomplishing good co-ordination of schedules, avoidance of many overlaps of sub-projects, reduction of project interferences, and an over-all cut in project time of seven to ten months. Considering investment capital in such a relatively high-risk undertaking as a new plant to be worth 15 percent per year, then on an investment of two million to three million dollars, the saving of seven to ten months is worth from 200 to 300 thousand dollars, in terms of investment costs alone.

Illustrative Example

For purposes of illustration, a simplified version of relatively modest Pert application will be presented, concerned with a silver-

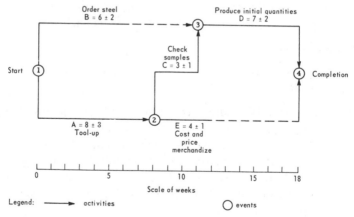

FIGURE 13-1. Pert diagram. Activity arrows are dimensioned according to normally expected number of weeks. Dotted lines mean slack periods or waiting periods. For example, activity E can be finished by the 13th week, but a wait occurs because activity D will not be completed until the 18th week. (Dimensioning of arrows, while helpful for visualization of time factors, is not really needed.)

ware manufacturer's development of a new line of flatware. The following were the steps involved:

1. Prepare a Pert diagram, showing the major activities envisioned in developing the new line, as illustrated in Figure 13-1.
2. Analyze the program, using the steps shown in Tables 13-1 and Exhibit 13-1.
ᐧ 3. Review the Pert diagram, based on the analysis made. Plan changes and revisions of the program accordingly.

Using the Pert approach, management gained the following useful and beneficial data:

1. From Table 13-1, line P, it was learned that one could expect at a 95.5 percent confidence level, that the program would be completed within the 20 weeks allowable.
2. From line H of Table 13-1 and the dotted lines in Figure 13-1, management was able to spot slack segments. This in turn led to a tightening of the schedule through rearrangement of activities. Instead of waiting until after tooling up to cost and price the merchandise, this activity was moved from its present position, *F* to follow *B*, thereby occurring in the slack time preceding event 3. Activity *A* was revealed as the most critical time-losing activity. Further study showed that by skillful rescheduling in the die room, tooling-up could be accomplished in less time. As a result, the combined time for activities A and C was reduced from 11 to 9 weeks. It was not possible to order the steel earlier because of market and style factors.

As a result of analyses, such as just specified, it was possible to cut over-all development time from 18 to 15 weeks. This in turn meant reduced development costs and a significant speedup in providing samples to the salesmen. They in turn were now earlier and "ahead" in showing samples to the trade. A larger volume of sales, coupled with earlier orders, were the net advantage derived.

Pert as a Management Tool

Many a manager may point out with regard to the illustrative discussion that he would not have needed Pert. He could have carried out the Pert analysis in his head. It should be borne in mind,

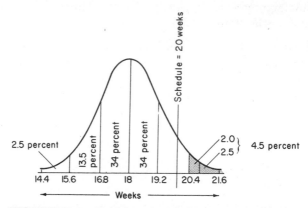

FIGURE 13-2.   Relation of critical path time, 18 weeks, to maximum time allowed by the schedule for completion of project, 20 weeks.   The shaded area, representing 4.5 percent shows the probability that the schedule may be exceeded.   Therefore, 100 minus 4.5 or 95.5 percent represents the probability of fulfilling the 20-week schedule or requiring less than 20 weeks.

however, that we have brought a highly simplified illustration, designed primarily to show how Pert works. In practice, problems are more complex. Also, while the manager may have his program well planned in his own mind, he still needs a tool to assure that those who work with him will also have a full, correct and adequate time and cost-proportioned visualization of the program.

Pert analysis does not replace progress charts, production control boards, or production scheduling graphs. These tools will continue to be of great value in monitoring, expediting, and controlling routine operations. But when special projects come along, these older management tools are not adequate. Moreover, Pert can be applied readily and often without resort to computer analysis. For large projects, the procedures of Exhibit 13-1 are best handled on a computer. Rented computer time at low-cost rates is available to any plant.

Pert does its job by helping management to better understand and plan for the needs of its programs. It provides a systematic way to evaluate and review such programs. From such evaluation and review, an optimum program schedule is developed. Pert will rarely prove to be as dramatic as in the development of the Polaris

TABLE 13-1. PERT ANALYSIS OF A PRODUCT DEVELOPMENT

(Time data in weeks)	Activities (Arrows)					
	A	B	C	D	E	Total
A. Activity time (T_a)	8	6	3	7	4	
B. Expected error	±3	±2	±1	±2	±1	
C. Event (circled) shown by arrow	2	3	3	4	4	
D. Shortest feasible route to the event	A	B	A + C	(A + C) + D	A + E	
E. Earliest expected time	8	6	8 + 3	11 + 7	8 + 4	
(based on shortest route)	= 8	= 6	= 11	= 18	= 12	
F. Longest route	A	A + C	A + C	(A + C) + D	(A + C) + D	
G. Latest expected time	8	8 + 3	8 + 3	11 + 7	11 + 7	
(based on longest route)	= 8	= 11	= 11	= 18	= 18	
H. Slack Time, (= G − E)	0	5	0	0	6	
I. Critical path, (= zeroes)	A		C	D		
J. Time of critical path T_c	8 · · · +		3 · · · +	7 · · ·		= 18
(= T_a for all H of 0)						
K. Error squared (= B^2)	9 · · · +		1 · · · +	4 · · ·		= 14
L. Over-all error = $\sqrt{14}$						= ±3.7
M. Standard deviation						= 1.2
(L/3.0ª = 3.7/3.0)						
N. Time scheduled (T_s)						20
O. Ratio: ($T_s - T_c$)/(standard deviation)						1.7
= (20 − 18)/1.2						
P. Probability P of fullfilling schedule						95.5
(from normal curve in percent)						

ªThe constant 3 is taken from Normal Curve Table 13-2.

missile where it saved almost two years. However it will be of value whenever a research, development, design, installation, re-equipment or other special project needs to be tackled efficiently.

Conclusion

Present indications are that Pert, Pert-cost applications and critical path analysis (sometimes referred to as "CPM" for critical path method) will become increasingly important management planning aids. Large buyers, such as the government and many private organizations, insist on a realistic appraisal of quality, reliability, cost, and completion dates for any major construction, building, or research and development contract. Without a Pert-cost analysis by a bidder, showing how he expects to meet specifications for product quality and reliability, within realistically estimated costs and with reasonable assurance of fulfilling completion-time deadlines, it is many times impossible, today, for a contract to be awarded.

In short, the buyer today demands a superior product regarding three major items: quality-reliability, cost, and delivery date. Pert is a technique that contributes primarily to the delivery-date phase of a contract. In aiding in the planning of time factors, however, it also helps with cost and quality-reliability factors. When production runs on schedule, excess costs for emergency speedups shrink and the tendency to "pass" inferior goods, because of time pressures, is diminished.

EXHIBIT 13-1   Procedures of Pert Analysis

Steps 1 to 16 below correspond to lines A to P of Table 13-1 in step-by-step and row-by-row sequence.

1. Enter the estimated time required to complete each of the activities, A, B, C, D, and E, as evaluated by the supervisors and managers concerned with each activity.
2. Enter the expected error in the estimate, representing the most optimistic and the most pessimistic possibilities envisioned. For example, activity A is expected normally to be completed in 8 weeks, but with unusual "luck," it might

be completed 3 weeks earlier. Also, with an unusual amount of bad luck (things going wrong) it may not be completed until 3 weeks later. (In this illustration, the + and − errors happen to be symmetrical, but in actual practice this need not be the case.)

3. Show the event indicated by each activity arrow.

4. Indicate the shortest route to each event. For example, activity B leads to event 3, which event is reached most quickly through activity B = 6 weeks. Activity E leads to event 4, which is reached most quickly through Activities A and E = 8 + 4 = 12. One might try the route BD, representing 6 + 7 or 13 weeks. But this is longer than AE at 12 weeks. Moreover, route BD is not a feasible route, since there is a delay (or slack) of 5 weeks until activity D can start.

5. Earliest expected time is the number of weeks corresponding to the shortest route. For example, activity D leads to the final event 4, which is reached best through *ACD*. Since length A + C is shown to require 8 + 3 = 11 weeks, (see C column), therefore, the total time span is $(8 + 3) + 7$, where the length 7 represents the weeks in D. We find: $(8 + 3) + 7 = 11 + 7 = 18$.

6. Find the longest routes. Sometimes, such as for activity D, leading to event 4, the longest and shortest routes are the same. At other instances, such as for activity E, there is a difference in time required.

7. Express the routes in terms of weeks, thus yielding "Latest Expected Time," by methods parallel to step 5.

8. Slack time is the difference found for Latest Expected Time minus Earliest Expected Time. For B, for example, 11 minus 6 yields 5 as the slack time. An activity with slack time is one that has extra resources, not needed to meet the schedule of the program from an over-all viewpoint. Sometimes, these extra resources may be reused or rescheduled to assist in shortening some of the more critical activities.

9. Slack time values of zero indicate critical paths, which are represented by activities A, C, and D.

10. The critical path requires the following activity times, as obtained by reference to line A: A, C, and D = 8 + 3 + 7 = 18. This 18 weeks represents the amount of time to be ex-

pected to complete the program, provided the shortest route is used.

11. As a computational step, we square the error terms in Line B and add them, yielding $3^2 + 1^2 + 1^2 = 14$. Only the error terms associated with the critical path concern us, since this is the route that governs the expected time to complete the program.

12. The over-all error, in weeks, àssociated with the expected time of 18 weeks, is the square root of the sum of the squares of the individual errors. Since the sums of the squares is 14 (line K under Total), the over-all error is found from the square root of 14 which is ± 3.7.

13. The estimated standard deviation is found by dividing the over-all error, ± 3.7 by the factor of 3, which is a constant obtained from the normal curve. Thus, $3.7/3 = 1.2$. For reasons of custom, the $\pm$ sign is dropped when writing the standard deviation.

14. The scheduled time is the time allowed for completion of the program, as established by management in setting various schedules of operation.

15. The ratio of the scheduled time (20 weeks minus the critical Path Time of 18 weeks, or 2 weeks) divided by the standard deviation, 1.2, yields 1.7. This magnitude, often labeled "t," is used to enter a table of areas of the normal curve.

16. Table 13-2 of Normal Curve Probabilities shows that a value of 1.7 standard deviations includes 95.5 percent, representing the probability of meeting management's schedule of 20 weeks. There remains a 4.5 percent probability that the actual program will require more than 20 weeks for completion. Figure 15-2 illustrates how the probability shown is derived.

RESULT: For a critical path of 18 weeks, an over-all estimating error of 3.7 weeks, and a scheduled time of 20 weeks, we may expect to meet the schedule with a 95.5 percent probability of success.

TABLE 13-2

Normal Curve Probabilities[c]

Ratio (t)	Probability that schedule will be fulfilled[a] (in percent)	Probability that schedule will be exceeded[b] (in percent)
1.0	84.	16.
1.1	86.	14.
1.2	88.	12.
1.3	90.	10.
1.4	92.	8.
1.5	93.	7.
1.6	94.5	5.5
1.7	95.5	4.5
1.8	96.	4.
1.9	97.	3.
2.0	98.	2.
2.3	99.	1.
2.6	99.5	0.5
3.0	99.9	Nil

"*t*" is: (Scheduled Time − Critical Time)/Standard Deviation. Scheduled time is the program time allowed. Critical time represents the minimum critical path time of the Pert diagram.

[a]The probability that the program will be fulfilled includes being ahead of schedule.

[b]The probability of exceeding the schedule is the chance that the program may fall behind the scheduled time allowed.

[c]The use of normal probability distribution curves in evaluating Pert estimates is a simplifying assumption. It is often the simplest and thus most practical assumption to use, with relatively small gain from more refined but also more complex approaches. Chapter 24 brings further material on the Normal Curve and associated Standard Deviation.

▶ ▶ ▶ ▶ **14**

Pert in Large-scale Projects

When program evaluation and review techniques (Pert) are to serve in large-scale projects, equal emphasis must be placed on both time and cost factors. How this is accomplished will be described with reference to a Pert-cost application provided by the National Aeronautics and Space Administration.[1] An over-all view of the project with its work breakdown structure is given in Figure 14-1, while the glossary in Exhibit 14-1 explains the various terms used. From an analysis of the over-all project, functional phases regarding design, manufacturing, inspection, and testing, can be attained, as depicted in simplified form in Figure 14-2. Pert planning thus proceeds from the major phases to the subdivisions and functional phases. For a further illustration of this principle, Figure 14-3 may be examined, showing how one major phase, the power subsystem, can be broken down into various subdivisions of work (SOW) regarding distribution, fuel cell, and solar array. It is apparent that for each such subdivision, the elements of direct labor, materials, and overhead cost can be evaluated. In this manner, time and cost factors can be evaluated and controlled jointly.

Master Plans

Master schedules, related to cost and financial plans, are the key elements of a large scale Pert project with an associated cost system. Assessment of actual against planned progress and com-

---

[1]Data and diagrams in this chapter were taken from *Pert and Companion Cost Systems Handbook*. Washington, D.C., National Aeronautics and Space Administration, October 30, 1962, (pamphlet, irregular paging).

134

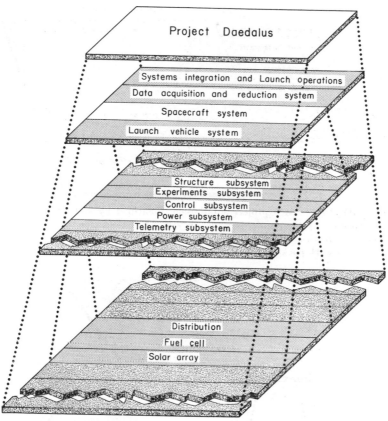

FIGURE 14-1.   Over-all view of project, showing planning and breakdown of work from the top down.

munication of the status of various project phases is thereby facilitated.

A typical master schedule is given in Figure 14-4, based on the symbols in Figure 14-5, and covering the fiscal years (FY) shown on the time schedule at the top of Figure 14-6. This schedule is derived from the detailed Pert networks supporting each of the work subsystems. Among the factors considered in arriving at a master schedule are (1) availability of manpower, equipment, and facilities, (2) overtime work on some subphases and idle time on others, while waiting and slack may occur, (3) financial and funding limitations, and (4) best estimates of appropriate time allowances for all parts of

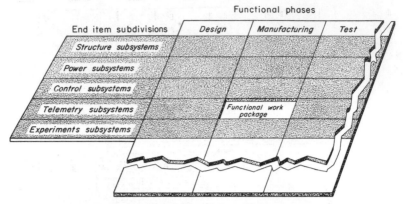

FIGURE 14-2. Each project subdivision, identified by end item, such as structure sub-system, power sub-system, etc., can be identified by its various functional phases, such as design, manufacturing, and testing. As a result, functional work packages are identified.

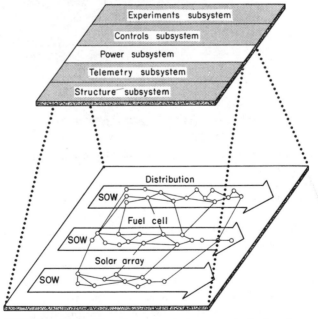

FIGURE 14-3. Plans for each subsystem can be broken down into smaller subdivisions-of-work (SOW), each with its own Pert network. Note that individual networks are connected at various points. For example, assembly of certain solar array parts depends upon completion of related fuel-cell components.

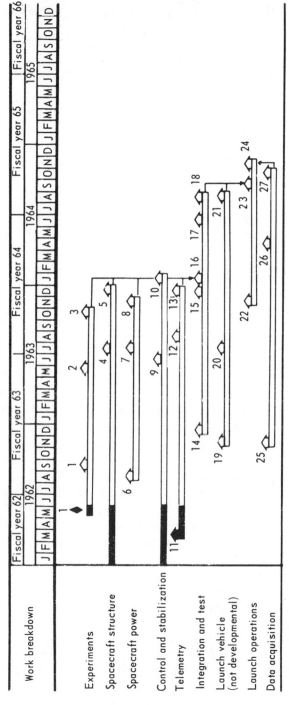

FIGURE 14-4. Project master schedule, showing scheduled and completed events or "milestones." A separate list identifies the numbered events, from 1 to 27. For example, event 1 denotes "all contracts awarded," while event 27 denotes "facility operational."

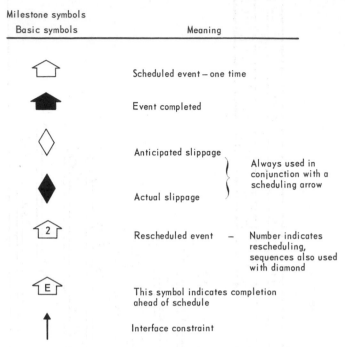

FIGURE 14-5.   Scheduling symbols and their meaning.

the work. Only after reviewing these factors in detail can firm dates for anticipated completions be established. Moreover, the accuracy of time estimates for completion of each individual event or "milestone" will often have a significant bearing on related milestones. For example, completion of testing cannot be done until after certain phases of manufacturing are completed. Because plans are only estimates, schedules need revision in the course of time. Figure 14-6 shows some typical scheduling situations of this nature.

Corresponding to the time schedule, financial plans are controlled by means of the type of graph shown in Figure 14-7. This shows the following information as of the date of the report, indicated by the vertical line: (1) funding plan in terms of fiscal year increments, (2) cost plan as approved, (3) commitments based on actual accounting records, (4) actual costs accrued, (5) expected further costs, and (6) current commitments required to cover expected costs and deviations of actual from plans. The illustrative example shows for the reporting date of May 30, 1962, that actual funding is some $100,000

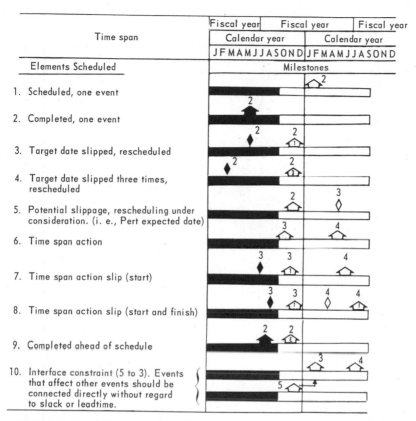

FIGURE 14-6. Typical scheduling situations. The events depicted represent the following: 2: First-stage contract, 3: Start static test program, 4: Complete static test program, and 5: Complete static test facility.

below plans, actual costs are slightly above plan, and that at completion of the project actual costs are now expected to be somewhat above original plan.

The utilization of the master schedules fits well into the principles of general managerial analysis and control, as depicted in Figure 14-8. Moreover, the correlation of time-span data to cost elements of a project, forming the basis of the dual control cycle shown, is illustrated in Figure 14-9.

Pert-cost management in a long-term project with considerable complexities has thus been shown in its major outlines.

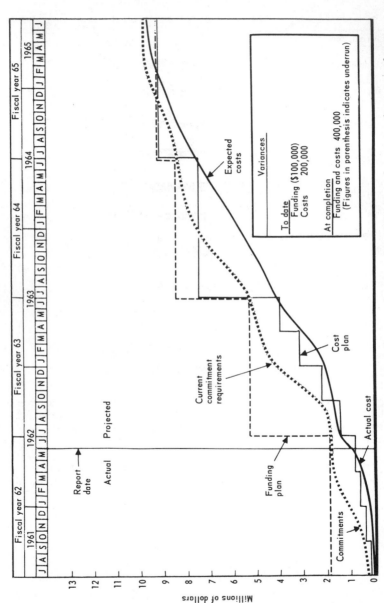

FIGURE 14-7.   Master financial plan, showing actual and projected funding plans, commitments and costs.

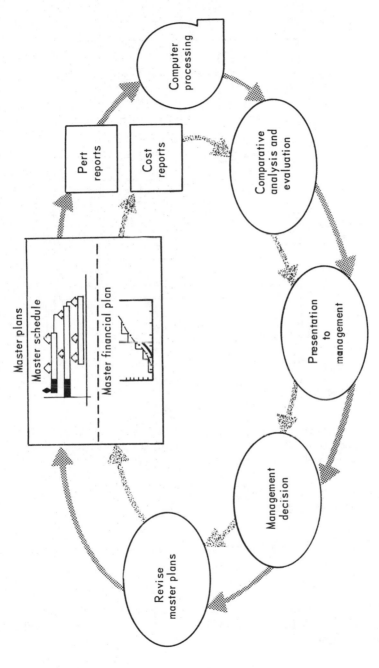

FIGURE 14-8. Pert-cost information flow for analysis and management decisions.

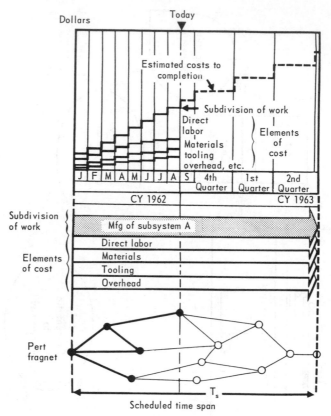

FIGURE 14-9.   Pert-cost progress chart. The time span
involved in each individual Pert fragnet (project network)
can be correlated with all pertinent cost elements, from start
to completion.

EXHIBIT 14-1   Pert-cost Glossary (Abbreviated)

ACTIVITY

A time-consuming element occurring between two events and
shown in a network by an arrow. The time of the activity is usually
expressed in weeks.

CRITICAL PATH

In a network, the path with the smallest amount of positive slack or largest amount of negative slack. The most rigorous time constraint.

EVENT

A meaningful accomplishment or "milestone," usually represented by a small circle or box in a network.

FRAGNET

A portion of a project network.

INTERFACE

The relationship existing between events and activities that constrains completion of events and activities between two or more fragnets.

NEGATIVE SLACK

The amount of time which is not available to perform the series of activities in a particular slack path and still meet the required completion date.

NETWORK

A flow plan containing the pertinent activities and events.

POSITIVE SLACK

The amount of additional time which is available to perform the series of activities in a particular slack path and still meet the required completion date.

▶ ▶ ▶ ▶ **15**

Line-of-Balance
(LOB)
Systems

Many project planning and monitoring systems, similar to Pert, are in use. Of such controls, Line-of-Balance or "LOB" has been selected. It is illustrated from data relating to an application with regard to production and assembly of a product identified as "Hydropack."[1]

LOB Flow Chart

The first step in LOB control is the preparation of a flow chart, such as in Figure 15-1, incorporating the following principal features:

1. Events are numbered, beginning with the earliest "No. 1" for procuring rod end to "No. 27," ship, in this example.
2. Labeling the final event, "No. 27" as zero, a schedule of working days from right to left is drawn.
3. Activities are drawn in, with the length of each activity line corresponding to its expected working time. (Note that in Pert, scaling is permitted but not really required).

While the starting points for each subassembly are identified briefly, such as "Event 11" representing "(Procure) Sleeve Actuator," for the most part it is desirable to have a separate list, showing the nature of each event. There is simply not enough space on the flow chart to show detailed identifications.

---

[1]Case data due to Melvin Silverman, Program Manager, Kearfott Division, General Precision, Inc., Little Falls, N.J.   Diagrams reprinted from *Product Engineering*, for October 15, 1962, pp. 76–78.   Copyright © 1962 by McGraw-Hill Publishing Co., Inc.

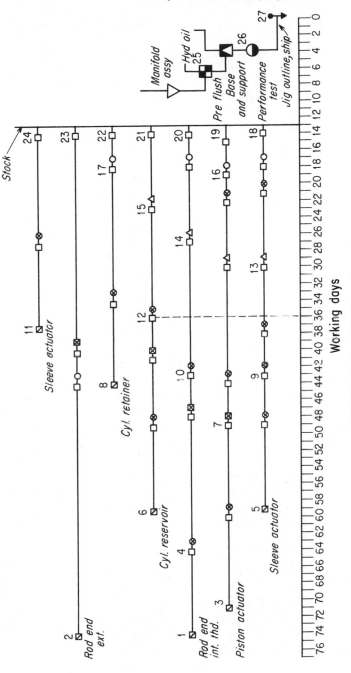

FIGURE 15-1. LOB Flow chart.

LOB Production report—Hydropack

Project number <u>135</u>   Date: <u>23 March</u>

Event number	Description	LOB Required	Actual	Hold up and or corrective action
2	Procure Rod End Ext.	60	58	2 pieces due in on 3/24
4	Insp. Rod End Int.	60	55	5 pcs. in process
9	Insp. Mach. Sleeve Act.	60	53	7 pcs. in process
10	Insp. H. T. Rod End	60	50	Vendor delay; 15 pcs. exp. 3/24
12	Insp. H. T. Cyl. Res.	53	23	Vendor delay; 40 pcs. exp. 3/24
15	Insp. Mach. Cyl. Res.	40	20	Hold up at Event 12
21	Cyl. Res. Into Stock	28	17	Hold up at Event 12

FIGURE 15-2. LOB production report. Events representing delays are listed and explained. Corrective action taken is indicated.

Production Progress Reports

Weekly progress reports by supervisors may be assembled for each project, as shown in Figure 15-2, supplemented by the cumulative lines of actual versus scheduled deliveries in Figure 15-3. Differences between actual and scheduled production (namely, delivery of subassemblies) are represented by the vertical differences of the two lines, while differences in production rates are gleaned from divergencies in the two slopes of the lines.

A further means of visualizing progress of production, actual versus LOB expectation, is afforded by means of bar charts. Figure 15-4, for example, shows the LOB as of March 23. It thereby amplifies the information in Figures 15-1 to 15-3, as just discussed.

Financial LOB

Application of LOB is not confined to production. For example, assume that a diagram corresponding to the chart in Figure 15-3 had shown accrued costs, which on March 23 were slightly above schedule. In view of the slightly advanced actual production ("actual" line ahead of the "scheduled" line), a cost accrual slightly higher than anticipated is normal. For example, if production is three percent

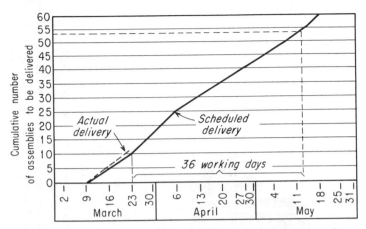

FIGURE 15-3. LOB production and delivery schedule. Actual production and delivery of subassemblies are shown to be ahead of schedule at the March 23 reporting date.

ahead of schedule, such as due to early delivery of raw stock, then it is only natural that accrued costs should similarly be three percent ahead of schedule.

A good LOB system that serves management usefully will, just as Pert, show both time-span and cost-accrual information at regular periods throughout the life of the project. Management action, based on original plans and actual performance records, can then be taken promptly. Moreover, the activities of all personnel involved in a project can be well coordinated.

Project Planning and Control Systems — Conclusion

From the customer's viewpoint, whether he be a private company or a government agency, the factors of importance in purchasing from a vendor are threefold: quality, delivery, and price. Increasingly, it is the quality-to-price ratio that receives attention when selecting among suppliers, but also delivery-on-time is important. This is why the government and many other organizations require Pert, LOB, or other data from a prospective supplier, to assure that they will receive the goods "on time and up to the quality contracted." Modern needs in the space age cannot be met in less than the best-planned efforts.

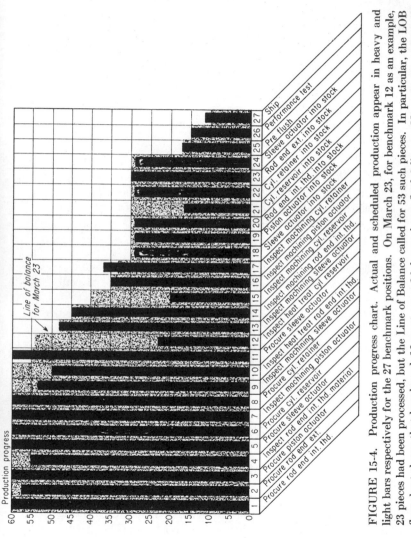

FIGURE 15-4.   Production progress chart.   Actual and scheduled production appear in heavy and light bars respectively for the 27 benchmark positions.   On March 23, for benchmark 12 as an example, 23 pieces had been processed, but the Line of Balance called for 53 such pieces.   In particular, the LOB flow chart shows that benchmark 12 must occur 36 days prior to final delivery.   Now, 36 days added to March 23 brings us to May 13, at which date the LOB schedule in Figure 15-3 calls for 53 assemblies to be delivered.   Thus the gap, on March 23, between the 53 needed by the LOB and the 23 pieces actually processed.

PART THREE

Management
of Inventories
and Waiting Lines

▶ ▶ ▶ ▶ # 16

Principles
of Inventory Management

The complexity and size of modern business operations, even in many so-called small organizations have reached such proportions in our high-technology, management-science age, that it is no longer advisable to make inventory decisions unaided by quantitative evaluation of the factors involved. Business organizations who have installed modern tools of management science in various phases of their operations often find that the most readily applicable and often the most profitable areas are those concerned with control and optimization of inventories. An idea of the potential of savings to be gained may be gleaned from the data in Table 16-1, showing that even a small plant may have from 1 to 10 million dollars invested in inventory over the span of a year. Often from 5 to 15 percent of this is misplaced.

A misplaced inventory may be either inadequate or excessive. For example, in one small plant, the owner kept insisting that he was losing too much money in maintaining large bank loans to finance inventory in process. Yet, in many instances of machine down time, maintenance trouble and quality problems were traceable to running out of stock or not having the right parts and supplies to keep machinery in proper operation. Actually, misplaced emphasis in inventory activity will occur in both large and small organizations (Exhibit 16-1 gives some typical examples) unless a scientific and quantitative approach is used to aid management in its evaluation, judgment, and decision making. The case of the management-science versus the purely intuitive approach of "experienced judgment" is dramatized (possibly somewhat unfairly) in Figures 16-1 and 16-2. The illustration refers to the control of supplies inventories. However, a similar case could be made for finished goods inventories, in a plant that must produce and stock in anticipation of peak-season demands. Overestimating because of undue optimism based on early-season

151

MANAGEMENT-INTUITION APPROACH

Illustrated from Control of Supplies Inventories

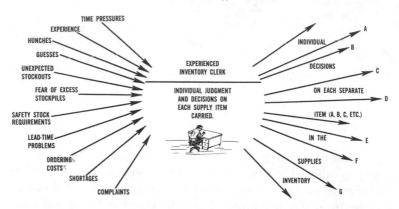

FIGURE 16-1. Management-intuition approach. Each individual item requires a separate decision on reordering point, lead-time allowance, and quantity to order. Conflicting and below-optimum decisions will occur.

MANAGEMENT-SCIENCE APPROACH

Illustrated from Control of Supplies Inventories

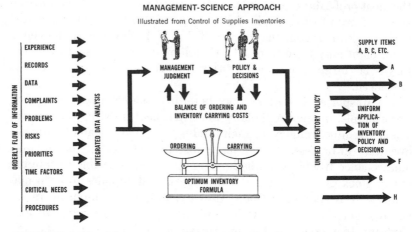

FIGURE 16-2. Management-science approach. Inventory policy is laid down by management once, based on integrated data analysis, optimum inventory formula, and managerial judgment. A unified inventory policy, applied uniformly, results. Management experiences fewer stockouts and overstocking; management personnel is freed to devote time to more meaningful tasks and decisions.

inquiries, or excess pessimism, when a few days of "slack" are experienced, may result in overproduction or underproduction, with consequent "distress goods" on some lines and shortages on others.

The management-science approach cannot avoid losses from errors in anticipation of market demands or requirements. It does, however, help management by providing useful information, abstracted and summarized from the detailed data that accumulates in ordinary business operations. It is this information, digested through simple formulas for weighing the cost factors present in the data, which together with management judgment comprises the modern management-science approach to decision making. Experience has shown that an organization thereby reduces risks and thus lessens possible errors in planning and controlling inventories.

TABLE 16-1

AREAS REQUIRING OPTIMAL INVENTORY POLICIES

Illustrative Data from Several Small Plants

Category	Annual range of cost, (in dollars)	Potential[a] savings, (in percent)
1. Supplies and repair parts	200,000 to 600,000	10 to 20
2. Raw stock and purchased parts	500,000 to 5,000,000	1 to 3
3. Stock in process	250,000 to 1,000,000	1 to 2
4. Intermediate product inventories	250,000 to 3,000,000	5 to 15
5. Finished product	250,000 to 2,000,000	5 to 20
6. Overall (rounded)	1,000,000 to 10,000,000	5 to 15

[a]Figures are very approximate, based on experience in plants who had not as yet installed management-science methods of inventory control. Note that an optimal inventory is not the lowest-cost inventory, but that inventory which best balances the costs of carrying inventory against losses that would result from inadequate inventory in terms of stock-outs, back-orders and lost customers.

EXHIBIT 16-1   Errors under Rule-of-thumb Inventory Control

1. *ERRORS IN ORDER-QUANTITY*

    a. Ordering inadequate quantities of low-cost items. As a result, costs of excessively frequent ordering and risk of running out of stock are incurred.
    b. Ordering excessive quantities of high-cost items, thereby running risks of obsolescence and undue costs of carrying excessively high inventories.

2. *ERRORS IN DELIVERY TIME*

    a. Ordering too far in advance of actual need, when an item normally involves relatively short delivery. Such items will usually be received soon after ordering. They then take up storage space, inflate inventories, and may spoil while waiting to be used.
    b. Ordering too late when an item is likely to involve relatively long delivery. Quantities ordered may then arrive too late, interfering with sales and production schedules. Bottlenecks, tie ups, back-ordering customer irritation and other losses result.

3. *ERRORS IN PRODUCTION RUNS*

    a. Ordering small runs on items requiring large set-up costs. Since the cost of setups — such as cleaning machinery, making special adjustments in settings, gearing, speeds and product flow — must be apportioned to the production lot, small lots mean high setup costs.
    b. Ordering large runs on items requiring minor setup costs. Undue inventories will then pile up, with the usual carrying costs, until the lot has been sold and shipped.

4. *ERRORS IN GENERAL*

    Lot sizes, production runs, order quantities, and frequencies that do not optimize the factors involved.

▶ ▶ ▶ ▶ # 17
Economic Lot Sizes

Management conscious of interest charges and other costs of carrying inventory is always seeking to minimize inventories of all types. Yet, as has been noted, carrying unduly small inventories involves other costs. When supplies inventories are too low, for example, excessive ordering is needed. The costs of such ordering may soon exceed the savings in inventory-carrying charges.

The "economic" or optimum lot size is that quantity which balances the costs of carrying inventory and costs of purchasing or ordering, as itemized in Tables 17-1 and 17-2.

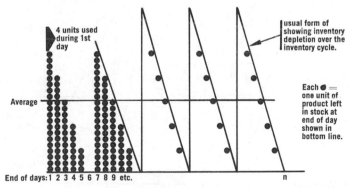

FIGURE 17-1. Theoretical inventory cycle. The illustration shows the position of inventory at the end of each of six days, based on a starting inventory of 24 units and a consumption of 4 units per day. At the end of the first day, there are 24 minus 4 = 20 units in stock; at the end of the sixth day, there are 24 minus 6 times 4 = 0 units in stock. Stock is replenished in the interval between the last day of the six-day cycle and the first day of the new cycle. The average inventory (based on start of each day) is the total number of units at start of cycle divided by 2, or 24/2 = 12.

Inventory Cycles

Basic to inventory problems amenable to optimum-lot size evaluation is the concept of inventory cycles, as appearing in theoretical form in Figure 17-1. In practice, the intervals between receipts of shipments and usage of receipts, or between completion of production and sale of merchandise produced, will vary, as is shown in Figure 17-2. Many further deviations occur in practice, such as erratic rather than smooth inventory withdrawals from day-to-day. Nevertheless, it has been found generally feasible to make the simple assumption that in any cycle average stock is half the difference between inventory peak and safety level floor. How this assumption leads to an optimum lot size formula is shown in Exhibit 17-1, using the definitions of Table 17-3.

Best Lot Size, Illustration

The illustrative example in Table 17-3 is based on a supplies-inventory control.

Further demonstration of how the optimum lot size formula will yield minimum cost is provided graphically in Figure 17-3, with the points of the curves derived in Table 17-4.

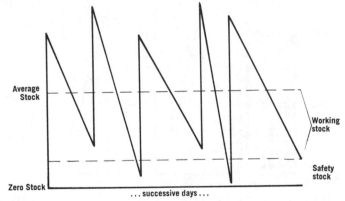

FIGURE 17-2. Practical inventory cycle. Because of variations in the rate of use of units in stock and variations in time of receipt of shipments of new stock, a safety stock is needed. The differences in length of the inventory cycles 1–5 are explained as follows: (1) slow use permitted stock buildup; (2) late shipment, depleted stocks; (3) again, slow use; (4) rapid use because of rush-order production depleted stocks; (5) early receipt of new stock and slow use brought inventory back to normal.

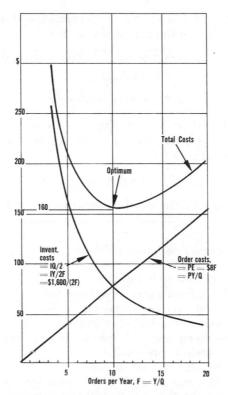

FIGURE 17-3. Inventory carrying costs and ordering costs in their combined effect on total cost. The point of minimum cost, corresponding to the optimum lot size $Q_{optimum}$ occurs when $F = 10$. For symbols and example-data see Table 17-4.

Practical Uses

In daily routine usage, slight deviations from the theoretical optimum lot size will become necessary. The why and how of such practical modifications will become apparent from the typical cases discussed in Exhibit 17-2.

As has been mentioned, the optimum lot size formula is applicable to a large variety of situations. In place of the supplies inventory problem, the problem of a dye-lot size for a plastic part might have been solved for the following data: expected yearly sales of 24,000 gross; set-up costs per lot $100, including cleaning, adjustment and dye liquor losses, interest charge of 10 percent, and dyed-parts costs per gross of $3. The optimum lot size is then:

$$Q_{\text{optimum}} = \sqrt{2 \times \$3 \times 24{,}000 \times \$100/0.1}$$
$$= \sqrt{\$144{,}000{,}000}$$
$$= \$12{,}000 \text{ or } 4000 \text{ gross.}$$

Thus, to the extent that management's cost, demand, and sales estimates are correct, will the optimum lot size be found to have practical value and validity.

TABLE 17-1

FACTORS COMPRISING INVENTORY CARRYING COSTS

Category, description, and basis	Typical annual percentages[a]
1. Interest on money tied up in inventory Current rate for borrowing from a bank or other lending institution. A firm who has exhausted its borrowing capacity, but has large anticipated earnings opportunities from expanded operations, will sometimes use a rate based on these earnings opportunities.	10 ± 5
2. Obsolescence, depreciation, and spoilage Engineering and cost estimates. Depreciation charges need not correspond to rates prescribed for tax accounting.	5 ± 3
3. Storage and handling Floorspace and related costs of caring for stock in storage.	3 ± 2
4. Insurance Coverage should include fire, windstorm, theft, and other insurable risks.	2 ± 1
5. Taxes Taxes on stock in inventory vary with localities, but are usually below 1 percent.	1 ± 1
6. Total $(= 1 + 2 + 3 \cdots + 5)$	21 ± 12

[a]Data represent rough guides only. Inventory carrying costs must be assessed individually for each company. Also, the base from which to measure percentages, will vary. Replacement cost, market value, or market price are often used, but the determination of such base values is often difficult. A policy to use actual cost as the basis for calculating inventory carrying costs, as a percent per annum, may be the simplest and, in the long run, most satisfactory approach.

TABLE 17-2

FACTORS COMPRISING PURCHASING COSTS

Step and procedures involved	Proportion of total cost (in percent)[a]
1. Requisitioning Select supplier, identify item, check catalog, provide blueprint, specify shipping, provide supplementary detail.	20
2. Preparation of purchase order Recheck requisition, verify questionable items, insert tolerances where required, specify detail concerning delivery, inspection and guarantees.	15
3. Order placement and follow up	10
4. Receipt of shipment Check quality and prepare inspection report, verify quantity and prepare receiving report.	20
5. Movement to store room Identification of shelf location, shelf placement, part number verification, inventory card and record entry, issuance to production.	25
6. Accounting Verification of invoice, clearance for payment, issuance of check, payment of carrier, manual or machine posting to proper ledgers and accounts, clearing of cancelled checks.	10

[a]Total cost per order varies from \$2 to \$20 per type of order. Data represent approximate proportions of total cost. Total cost of ordering, being made up of the six items shown, will be 100 percent. When material comes from another unit within the same company, all of the purchasing costs shown here will still occur.

EXHIBIT 17-1 Derivation of Formula for Optimum Lot Size $Q_{optimum}$

(This material is not needed for practical applications)

1. Costs that increase with increasing frequency of ordering, F, are the ordering costs per year, PF.
2. Costs that decrease with increasing frequency of ordering, F, are the costs of carrying inventory throughout the year, $IQ/2$.

3. The two opposing costs PF and $IQ/2$ will be balanced and therefore at a combined minimum when

$$PF = IQ/2$$

4. In order to solve step 3 for Q, we may substitute for PF the quantity PY/Q. We now have

$$PY/Q = IQ/2 \text{ ; or } IQ/2 = PY/Q$$

TABLE 17-3

BASIC QUANTITIES USED IN OPTIMUM LOT SIZE CALCULATIONS

Symbol	Value[a]	Description and example
Q	In dollars	Lot size, such as the size of a purchase or a production order. The most economical lot size or optimum lot size is usually found from the relationship $Q_{optimum} = \sqrt{(2PY)/I}$. P, Y, and I are defined below.
Y	In dollars	Yearly cost of goods sold or yearly consumption of supplies. For example, yearly use of grinding wheels may be \$16,000.
P	In dollars	Purchase or production order costs. For example, it may cost \$8 each time to issues and follow through on an order. When special setups are needed to produce a lot, then P should include such costs.
I	Decimal	Inventory carrying costs as a decimal fraction of inventory value. For example, if it costs 10 percent annually to store a wheel, then $I = 0.10$. (In this example, wheel cost is set equal to its value.)
F	Numbers	Frequency of ordering, the number of times a year an item is ordered such as the number of times wheels are ordered. F is at an optimum when $F = Y/Q_{optimum}$.
$Q/2$	In dollars	Average annual inventory on hand.
$IQ/2$	In dollars	Inventory carrying cost in dollars. This cost decreases as F increases, since $F = Y/Q$ and therefore $Q = Y/F$, so that smaller inventories are carried.
PF	In dollars	Ordering cost per year. This cost increases with F, since $F = Y/Q$ and therefore $PF = PY/Q$.

[a]Units in which quantities shown are expressed. Note that the last three quantities listed are derived from the prior magnitudes Q, Y, P, I, and F.

5. The following simple algebra may now be applied:
   A. Multiplying both sides of step 4 by $2Q$, yields

$$IQ^2 = 2PY$$

   B. Shifting I and taking square roots,

$$Q = \sqrt{2PY/I}$$

The Q found is $Q_{optimum}$, since it gives a minimum total for the two types of cost combined.

TABLE 17-4

CALCULATION OF POINTS FOR ILLUSTRATIVE COST CURVES[a]

(A) Number of orders per year, F	(B) Lot size, $Q = Y/F$ $= 16,000/F$ (in dollars)	(C) Inventory cost, $IQ/2$ $= (0.10/2)Q$ (in dollars)	(D) Ordering cost, PF $= \$8 \times F$ (in dollars)	(E) Combined cost $(c) + (d)$ (in dollars)
1	16,000	800	8	808
5	3,200	160	40	200
10	1,600	80	80	160[b]
16	1,000	50	128	178
20	800	40	160	200
40	400	20	320	340

[a]Based on the prior example $Y = \$16,000$, $I = 10$ percent, $P = \$8$.
[b]Optimum lot size is $1600, with 10 orders per year at a cost of $160 each. Inventory and ordering cost are equal at this point. The $Q_{optimum}$ of $1600 could have also been found directly from the relationship:

$$Q_{optimum} = \sqrt{2PY/I} = \sqrt{2 \times \$8 \times \$16,000/0.10} = \$1600$$

EXHIBIT 17-2 Overcoming Practical Problems of Optimum Lot Sizes

1. *ROUNDING OF QUANTITIES*

When optimum lot sizes are uneven, rounding is permissible, and often necessary. For example, one can not order $3\frac{1}{2}$ electric motors. The order quantity would be 3 or 4.

2. ALLOWING FOR PRODUCTION ECONOMIES

If the optimum dye-lot quantity is calculated to be 180 gross, but the dye vat holds 200, it will usually be to advantage to process 200 gross lots. Decisions of this nature can usually be overcome readily without separate calculations.

3. ALLOWING FOR SHIPPING QUANTITIES

If the optimum order quantity for a purchased item is 4 dozen, but normal shipping containers and quantities involve 5 dozen then it will usually be desirable to order 5 dozen. Requests for special packing involve extra costs and greater chances of error in shipping or packing.

4. ALLOWING FOR DISCOUNTS

Quantity discounts are no longer as prevalent as they used to be, once an economical minimum has been satisfied. Moreover, for many routinely purchased items, most suppliers will quote an annual quantity discount (based on a guaranteed annual volume of purchases), rather than on each individual shipment. Yet, there are some items, such as belting, lighting equipment, and other supplies, where quantity discounts apply to each individual shipment. For such items, management should first calculate the optimum order quantity without discount. Next, the total annual cost of ordering at the discount quantities may be considered. There are usually only two or three quantity categories at which various discounts apply (such as 10 percent discount for one quantity, 15 percent for a larger quantity and 20 percent for a still larger amount). The quantity which, after study of all discount categories, yields the lowest total cost, is then selected.

5. USING JUDGMENT

When optimum lot sizes involve considerations going beyond those factors that can be put in the optimum lot size formula, it will be judgment and not the formula that should win out in the final decision. The formula is no substitute for common sense.

►►►► 18

Proper
Reorder
Points

In the management of inventories, "reorder point" refers to the level of inventory at which action must be taken to replenish supplies. In the case of raw stock, supplies, and replacement parts obtained through purchase, reordering will occur with regard to outside suppliers. However, when in-process inventories are involved, reordering will be with regard to within-plant or within-organization goods. Whether stock is purchased from the outside or produced within the organization, the principles of optimal reorder point and safety stock discussed in this chapter will apply.

Need for Reorder Point

If management were to wait with the reordering of needed quantities of an item until the inventory had fallen to zero, considerable losses from stockouts as listed in Exhibit 18-1 would be incurred.

Provision must therefore be made for reordering in advance of anticipated stockout, based on the leadtime involved. Moreover, since there are normally fluctuations in leadtime, usage, and demand of any inventory item, provision must be made for a safety stock, which should be accounted for in developing a proper reordering point.

Calculation of Reorder Point, Stockout Cost, and Safety Stock

The calculation procedures for finding safety stock and related quantities are illustrated in Table 18-1. The following principal results are noted:

1. After considering leadtime, usage, delivery lead, and demand of an item, the expected combined effect of fluctuations in

163

these factors must be evaluated. A useful and simple statistical measure is the standard deviation.

2. Safety stock is calculated on the basis of this standard deviation, allowable risk of stockout (Table 18-2), and unit cost involved.
3. The quantities so determined yield the reorder point, which also establishes a yearly stockout cost and a safety stock carrying cost.

It is apparent that there is conflict of costs. With large safety stocks (earlier reorder point) the risk of stockout and resultant yearly stockout cost will be lower, but larger safety stocks increase inventory carrying costs.

Because of the problem of calculating the optimum between these two opposing costs, many organizations establish fixed risks for various types of items; such as an 1 percent risk for very critical items (stockout causes great trouble and expense), 2 percent risk for the average item (moderate trouble and cost if stockout occurs) and 5 to 10 percent risk for noncritical items (little trouble or cost from stockout).

While not very "scientific," such general rules for use of risks are of great practical value in all those instances where it is difficult to estimate the costs of stockout.

Evaluation of Optimal Risk

When detailed cost-accounting data permit relative precision in evaluating the cost of a stockout, the risk is evaluated as shown in the illustration of Table 18-3. Unfortunately, a series of trial calculations must be used. There is no direct formula that can be summoned for aid.

When a large number of items is to be analyzed for optimal stockout risk, yielding a minimal combined cost of safety stock and yearly stockout, computer calculations on owned or inexpensively-rented computer time are needed.

A frequent finding from calculations such as the ones just shown is that rule-of-thumb safety stocks and reorder points on critical items have been too low. The quantitative approach to inventory control permits a more satisfactory and more consistent application of management goals.

TABLE 18-1

QUANTITIES USED TO FIND REORDER POINT,
STOCKOUT COST AND SAFETY STOCK

Symbol	Basis	Description and example
L	Months	Leadtime. Time lapse between order placement and receipt. Example: leadtime to receive grinding wheels, 0.5 months.
U	Units	Usage per month. Example: Shop uses an average of 200 wheels monthly.
D	Units	Delivery lead. $D = U \times L$. For the example data above $D = 200 \times 0.5 = 100$ wheels.
d	Units	Demand. Example: An average of 5 wheels are requisitioned at one time; $d = 5$.
σ_c	Units	Standard deviation, a statistical measure of normally expected fluctuations in delivery lead D, usage during leadtime, also D, and demand d. $$\sigma_c = \sqrt{2D + d} = \text{(for our example) } \sqrt{(2 \times 100) + 5} = 14$$
Q_u	Units	Quantity of safety stock. Depends on the risk used (r percent) from Table 18-2. For $r = 2$ percent and $\sigma_c = 14$, $t = 2.1$. $$Q_u = 2.1\sigma_c = 2.1 \times 14 - 29.4 \text{ or } 30 \text{ (rounded)}.$$
Q_v	In dollars	Value of safety stock. Depends on unit cost of an item. For cost of \$10 per wheel, $Q_v = Q_u \times \$10 = 30 \times \$10 = \$300$.
R	Units	Reorder point. Quantity level of inventory when reordering becomes necessary. $R = D + Q_u$, which for the example data is $100 + 30$ or 130, at a 2 percent risk of stockout.
C_i	In dollars	Stockout cost per occurrence. For wheels C_i was estimated at \$70.
C	In dollars	Yearly stockout cost. Using a risk r of 2 percent ordering frequency F of 10 per year, and $C_i = \$70$ $$C = r \text{ percent} \times F \times C_i = 2 \text{ percent} \times 10 \times \$70 = \$14$$
IQ_v	In dollars	Safety stock carrying cost per year, at a rate $I = 10$ percent. $IQ_v = 10$ percent $\times \$300 = \$30$

NOTE: Predominant practice is to calculate the standard deviation σ_c merely from $\sqrt{D} = \sqrt{100}$ or 10 in this example. A more conservative approach, used above, is to allow also for variations in usage during the time of delivery lead, thus resulting in $2D$, plus an allowance for the quantity d requisitioned each time there is a demand.

EXHIBIT 18-1 Costs of Ordering after a Stockout Has Occurred

1. Man-hours lost in various processing departments while a) waiting for supplies, b) relying on make-shift arrangements, and c) not replacing worn parts, such as rolls, tapes, and gears when needed.
2. Quality losses from deficiencies in supply.
3. Long-distance phone calls to "expedite" shipment.
4. Shipping charges for air-freight, special handling, and similar "rush" costs.
5. Inadequate time to inspect shipments before giving stock out to processing departments. Losses in quality and quantity may occur.

TABLE 18-2

PROBABILITY FACTORS (t) FOR EVALUATING RISKS (r PERCENT), OF STOCK-OUT

Based on normal curve data

Risk (r,) of a stockout (in percent)	Approximate odds against a stockout (ratio)[a]	Normal curve probability factor (t)
0.1	1000 to 1	3.1
0.5	200 to 1	2.6
1.0	100 to 1	2.3
2.0	50 to 1	2.1
2.3	42 to 1	2.0[b]
3.0	32 to 1	1.9
4.0	24 to 1	1.75
5.0	19 to 1	1.65
10.0	9 to 1	1.3
16.0	5 to 1	1.0
20.0	4 to 1	0.85
40.0	1.5 to 1	0.25
50.0	1 to 1	0.0

[a]More exactly, since stockout odds ratio $= (100/r) - 1$ to one, the first four ratios would read 999,199,99 and 49.

[b]Most frequently used. Note that the validity of these probability values depends upon the degree to which stockout risks conform to the normal curve. In practice, some inaccuracies will occur.

6. Premium prices for special rush orders. Losses from discounts not taken.
7. Extra pick-up labor and trucking costs.
8. Generally confused method of doing business, resulting in disorganized procedures, lowered morale of personnel, frayed tempers, fretting over late deliveries, and inability to meet promise-dates to customers.

Note that especially large losses can sometimes be found in plants located in the vicinity of many supply houses. The false sense of security so created results in neglect of safety stocks, with attendant frequent runouts.

TABLE 18-3

EVALUATION OF LOWEST COST OF CARRYING SAFETY-STOCK

(Based on example of grinding wheels)

Costs (in dollars)	Stockout Risk (r percent)					
	0.1	0.5	1.0	2.0	3.0	4.0
1. Probability factor t, from Table 18-2	3.1	2.6	2.3	2.1	1.9	1.75
2. Quantity of safety stock, $Q_u = t\sigma_c = t \times 14$	43.4	36.4	32.2	29.4	26.6	24.50
3. Value of safety stock Q_v = unit cost, $10 \times Q_u$,	434	364	322	294	266	245
4. Safety stock carrying cost $IQ_v = 10$ percent $\times Q_v$	43.40	36.40	32.20	29.40	26.60	24.50
5. Yearly stockout cost $C = r$ percent $\times F \times C_i$ = r percent $\times 10 \times \$70$	0.70	3.50	7.00	14.00	21.00	28.00
6. Total cost = Line 4 + Line 5	44.10	39.90	39.20[a]	43.40	47.60	52.50

[a]Lowest total cost

Inventories
to Smooth
Market Fluctuations

"Our sales department is either elated or depressed, never 'normal,'" said the manager of manufacturing. "When a few large orders have come in, sales predicts a top season and expect overtime production to build up inventories. But when things have been slack for a few days, they want us to close down the plants." The problem, faced by many firms who produce for a seasonal market, was to know just how much inventory should be built up of each model during the slack months. Failure to build up enough inventory at that time causes lost sales in the peak months when the plants cannot possibly keep up with current orders. On the other hand, overextension of inventories leads to leftover goods, sales at "distress" prices, and excessive inventory carrying costs. Management needs a systematic approach for coordinating production with sound sales forecasts, so as to keep inventories at an optimum.

Seasonal Inventory Build-up

The technique described here is applicable in instances where production must be planned in advance of actual receipt of orders, so that during the peak season the built-up inventories can be used to supplement current production in meeting customer demands. In many types of business, such stock build-up is unavoidable, regardless of how management may generally feel about production to inventory. The particular illustration described was credited with having accomplished the savings quoted in Exhibit 19-1. It involved the following steps:

1. Monthly general forecasts of total sales, with revisions as needed. The type of source-information materials in Exhibit 19-2 are very helpful.

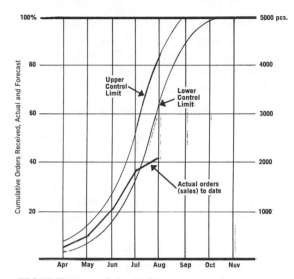

FIGURE 19-1.   Sales build-up curve. In August,
actual cumulative sales had fallen below lower control limit, indicating need to revise forecast of 5,000
pieces.
NOTE: Control limits are smoothed curves based on
points in Table. 19-1.

2. Individual forecasts for each product line.
3. Development of pattern buildup curves and control limits, as
   illustrated in Figure 19-1 and Table 19-1, for each product line,
   using the methods shown.
4. Gearing of production to sales and inventory, as illustrated in
   Table 19-2.

All of the product lines were charted. As long as actual sales
orders remained within the control limits, this generally indicated that
business for the product was developing within the previous pattern
and in approximate accordance with the predicted total. On the
other hand, a departure of actual sales from the pattern beyond the
control limits was a signal for the sales department to review the forecast. An off-standard trend below the lower control limit indicated
that earlier estimates of business were excessive and that production and inventory build-up should be reduced. At other times,
an off-standard trend above the upper control limit indicates that
earlier expectations were really too low, and inventory build-up

should be accelerated. Application of the exception principle of management meant that only styles with out-of-control trends are reviewed. It was thus possible for management to spend adequate time on styles needing attention, while not bothering with styles whose trends were within normal fluctuations.

Contract Business V. "Spot" Inventories

Often a plant has an option of whether to produce to contract orders only, or whether to "take a chance" on having "spot" goods. Theoretically, spot goods — merchandise produced in advance and on hand for immediate delivery — should bring higher prices. However, a plant that has an excess of spot goods in a declining market may well find a "squeeze" situation, in which spot goods must be sold at a loss.

No system can remove the "chance" from a decision to produce spot merchandise. The forecasting principles described above are applicable, but less reliably, to spot goods problems. A profitability analysis based on such forecasts, as shown in Table 19-4, will be of value to management in deciding whether or not to produce for inventory, and which models or lines are most likely to yield results.

Again, a control chart approach will be of value, but the method needed may be somewhat different, such as illustrated in Figure 19-2, based on the calculations in Table 19-5.

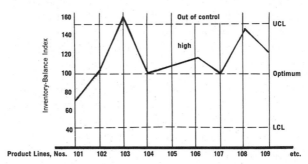

FIGURE 19-2.   Inventory-balance control chart.   Line 103 is in need of corrective action (out-of-control at present) because of excess scheduled production.   Line 108 is nearing an "out-of-control" state and should be investigated.

LCL and UCL = Lower and Upper Control Limits; Level of 100 = optimal level of inventory-balance index.

TABLE 19-1

PATTERN OF INVENTORY BUILD-UP FOR FALL SEASON FOR A PRODUCT LINE

Month	Monthly pieces sold			Cumulative pieces sold			Cumulative sales (percent)			Range	Average	Control	
	1961	1962	1963	1961	1962	1963	1961	1962	1963			Upper	Lower
April	40	100	120	40	100	120	4	4	6	2	5	7	3
May	50	170	160	90	270	280	9	11	14	5	11	16	6
June	80	240	160	170	510	440	17	22	22	5	20	25	15
July	180	400	440	350	910	880	35	36	44	9	39	48	30
August	380	1000	690	730	1910	1570	73	77	79	6	76	82	70
September	190	510	340	920	2420	1910	92	97	96	5	95	100	90
October	60	70	80	980	2490	1990	98	99	99	1	99	100	98
November	20	10	10	1000	2500	2000	100	100	100	0	100	100	100

1. Range = difference between highest and lowest value, thus for April, $6 - 4 = 2$.
2. Average = total/number of years. For April, $(4 + 4 + 6)/3 = 5$ (rounded).
3. 5 percent-risk control limit = average $\pm$ range $\times F_c$, with F_c from Table 19-3.
For example, for April: $5 \pm 2 \times 0.97 = 7$ and 3 (rounded).
The average is used as an estimate of seasonal pattern of sales in percent.

Conclusion

Inventories of product for sale involve problems of forecasting, control, and production-sales coordination. Management judgment is an indispensable ingredient of proper inventory decisions in these areas. The mathematical and graphic tools illustrated serve to help sharpen that judgment and to remove needless detail from the routine chores of the executive.

TABLE 19-2

GEARING PRODUCTION TO SALES AND INVENTORY[a]

One product line	Number of pieces	Number of weeks	Number of machines
a. Stock on hand	200		
b. Desired safety stock	150		
c. Working inventory (a − b)	50		
d. Length of season		40	
e. Length of peak of season		15	
f. Time remaining of peak		10	
g. Expected sales during peak, from forecast	850		
h. Shipped to date	300		
i. Production required during next 10 weeks (g − h − c)	500		
h. Production rate required per week (i/f) = 500/10	50		
i. Production per machine per week	2.5		
j. Number of machines to put on this product (h/i) = 50/2.5			20

[a]Forecasts and schedules are up-dated weekly.

Result: In order to meet expected demand, after considering inventory on hand and production rate of this product, 20 machines should be assigned. In this manner, production will be planned to meet expected demand.

TABLE 19-3

CONTROL LIMIT FACTORS FOR VARIOUS RISKS OF ERROR

Sample size (number of years used)	Factor, F_d[a] for converting range R to estimated standard deviation, σ	Control Limit Factors, F_c, for the following risks of error (in percent)				
		5	10	15	25	33⅓
		Found from normal curve factor t[b] of:				
		1.645	1.282	1.035	0.675	0.431
2	0.8865	1.46	1.14	0.92	0.60	0.38
3	0.5907	0.97	0.76	0.61	0.40	0.25
4	0.4857	0.80	0.62	0.50	0.33	0.21
5	0.4299	0.71	0.55	0.44	0.29	0.19
6	0.3946	0.65	0.51	0.41	0.27	0.17
8	0.3512	0.58	0.45	0.36	0.24	0.15
10	0.3249	0.53	0.42	0.34	0.22	0.14

[a] Reciprocal of factors d_2 given by Tippett, L. H. C., "On the Extreme Individuals and the Range of Samples Taken from Normal Population," Biometrika, (1925) 17 : 364–387.

[b] *Technical Note:* Factors t (from Table 18-2) represent risk of an erroneous out-of-control point, with regard to *either* the upper *or* the lower control limit. Risks with regard to *both* upper *and* lower limits are found by simply doubling the percentages under F_c above.

Formula for control limit CL

= Past pattern ± range $(F_d \times t)$

= Past pattern ± range × F_c, note that $F_c = tF_d$

Example:

Given: Past pattern indicates 30 pieces sold in a particular month. Range is 5 based on 3 years' data. Risk, chosen by management, is 5 percent.

Then: $CL = 30 ± (5 \times 0.97) = 35$ and 25 pieces.

EXHIBIT 19-1 Savings from the First Year of Finished Product Inventory Control, Coordinated with Sales Forecasting and Production Planning

Excerpts from a report by the company president

We have been able to achieve a 40 percent saving in interest payments, and when we will have completed our current fiscal year,

TABLE 19-4

	Product Lines			
Estimates and calculations[a]	1001	1002	1003	1004
a. Manufacturing cost, (dollars per piece)	0.50	0.40	0.60	0.80
b. Spot goods inventory, 1000 pieces	90	60	50	100
c. Value of inventory (a × b) $1000	45	24	30	80
d. Differential of spot goods price minus contract price, (dollars per piece)	0.05	0.02	0.03	0.02
e. Potential gain, (b × d) $100	45	12	15	20
f. Spot goods carrying cost per year (based on c) (in percent)	24	24	24	24
g. Average length goods are in stock (in months)	3	2	1	1
h. Effective spot goods carrying cost (c × f × g)/(12 months per year), $100	27	10	6	16
i. Allowance for losses from distress sale of left-over stock, 1 percent of c, $100 (rounded)	5	2	3	8
j. Net GAIN (+) or LOSS (−) expected (e − h − i) $100	+13	0	+6	−4

[a]Of necessity, estimates represent forecasts of anticipated sales, sales rate, and prices which are subject to revision as the season progresses. Spot goods carrying costs and allowances for losses represent past experience summarized from accounting data.

Result: Lines 1001 and 1003 appear profitable for spot-goods production, lines 1002 and 1004 are likely to be unprofitable.

we will have saved at least $100,000 in interest expense alone, arising primarily out of our inventory control system.

Earlier this year, our finishing plant built a new finished goods storage warehouse. Because control reduced the size of our inventories, the new warehouse was considerably smaller.

We were able to eliminate completely rental charges on outside storage facilities.

Insurance premiums on inventory were reduced.

Losses arising from the closing out of undesirable merchandise were minimized.

TABLE 19-5

DEVELOPMENT OF INVENTORY-BALANCE CONTROL CHART

Calculations and data	Product lines								
	101	102	103	104	105	106	107	108	109
a. Start-of-month inventory, (1000 pieces)	6	10	8	5	8	4	3	9	10
b. Outstanding orders to be shipped during month (1000 pieces)	2	2	4	0	0	2	1	4	15
c. Currently planned rate of production (1000 pieces per month)	10	15	20	15	10	10	8	18	22
d. Expected rate of sales (1000 pieces per month)	17.5	22	15	20	16	10	10	15	13
e. Combined effect of start-of-month inventory, outstanding orders and planned production $(a - b + c)$	14	23	24	20	18	12	10	23	17
f. *Balancing Index*[b] $= e/d \times 100$	80	105	160[a]	100	113	120	100	153	131
g. Moving range[c]		25	55	60	13	7	20	53	22

[a]Excessive, based on 95 percent probability level. Since average range $\overline{R} = (25 + 55 + 60 + 13 + 7 + 20 + 53 + 22)/8 = 32$, and factor $0.89 \times 32 = 28.5 =$ standard deviation, and ±2 standard deviations $= \pm57 = 95$ percent confidence band. Therefore, $100 \pm 57 = 43$ and 157, = upper and lower control limits. See also Figure 19-5.

[b]Index of 100 indicates excellent balance. Index above 100 may signal overproduction. Index below 100 may signal tendency to underproduction.

[c]The moving range is the absolute difference between successive product line balancing indexes. For example, $80 - 105 = 25$, $105 - 160 = 55$, $160 - 100 = 60$, etc.

Inventory control led to a substantial improvement in the orderliness of our entire thinking and planning in the areas of manufacturing and merchandising.

Knowledge that our inventories were coming under control gave confidence to our sales organization to display firmness on price, which would not have existed without inventory control.

. . . between direct and indirect, tangible and intangible and all other benefits, inventory control will save us . . . some place between $200,000 and $250,000 for the current fiscal year.

EXHIBIT 19-2   Sources and Data For Market Forecasting

1. *INTERNAL*
    a. Past patterns of sales by various end uses
    b. Current trends developing for various product lines
    c. Salesmen's estimates, customer activities, management meetings, management forecasts
    d. Constant review, surveillance, and revision of forecasts in the light of continuing developments, internal, within the firm, external, within the industry, and external, within the economy.
    e. Analysis of competitive developments affecting the company

2. *EXTERNAL*
    a. General industry forecasts, such as published in trade journals and trade associations
    b. Current government publications:
       (1) United States Department of Commerce
           (a) Business cycle developments
           (b) New plant and equipment outlays
       (2) United States Department of Labor
           (a) Industry hourly wages and wage rates
           (b) Wholesale price index
           (c) Number of workers in the industry
       (3) Federal Reserve Board
           (a) Index of production
    c. Private forecasting services

▶ ▶ ▶ ▶ **20**

Management
of Waiting Lines
(Queues)

All of us are familiar with waiting lines or queues. Many situations give rise to queues, and the most common types are classified relatively simply. These are illustrated in Table 20-1. In the management of sales and production, problems of the number of sales personnel to have in a store, the number of trucks to use, or the number of automated or semiautomated machines to assign to one operator or one repair crew, are all amenable to optimization through analysis of their queuing effects.

Illustrative Example

The type of queuing problems to be discussed in this chapter represents the cases of one waiting line and one servicing station, such as occurs when one operator attends a bank, or other group of similar machines. Usually, even though such machines may be highly automated, occasions for servicing by personnel nevertheless arise, such as when a machine stops because of a choke or a break of the material, because of depletion of stock in the hopper, because of an overfill in the output receptacle, or because of the need to make style changes or other adjustments. In essence, the occurrence of stops for any of the above causes may be largely random, and the operator will usually service stops as they arise, under the first-in first-out servicing principle.

What happens if a machine stops while the operator is busy with another machine that stopped earlier? The machine that just stopped must wait, or "queue-up," until he can get to it. In many modern assignments, such as 100 coil-winding spindles per operator, several spindles may at some time queue up, while at other times all spindles will be running.

Using the definitions in Table 20-2 and the service ratios of Table 20-3, we can readily determine the queuing loss (*Q* percent). This queuing loss directly reduces machine efficiency.

Analysis of Waiting Time

After analyzing machine assignments, it soon becomes apparent that actually there are two types of queues. If an operator has a large number of machines to tend, there may be a considerable queuing-up of machines that are idle and waiting to be repaired and started. On the other hand, if an operator has few machines to take care of, there may be little queuing of stopped machines, but now the operator will often be idle, waiting until a machine stops. How do we find the optimal assignment with this dual problem? We must balance the

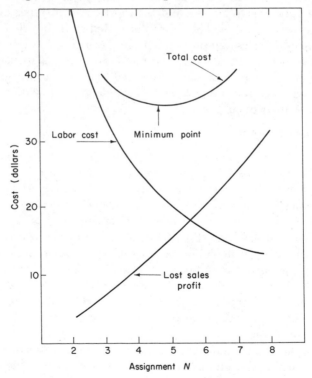

FIGURE 20-1. With increasing assignments, labor costs decrease but the cost of lost profits from sales rises. The lowest total cost occurs at the combined minimum point of the two individual cost curves.

cost of idle machines in terms of lost production or lost profit from sales against the cost of idle manpower in terms of wages and salaries. Table 20-4 gives an illustrative example.

The illustration leads to an optimal assignment of five machines per operator.   With 20 machines in a bank or group, four operators will be needed.   Often, of course, the data will not break up evenly, and the actual assignment cannot fully conform to the theoretical optimum.   Moreover, when a graphic analysis is made, as in Figure 20-1 for the data of Table 20-4, it may be found that the optimal assignment is somewhere between two integers.   In the present example, the optimum assignment, strictly speaking, is about halfway between four and five machines.   Do we assign half a machine to each of two operators? Usually this solution would not be feasible.   Instead, a slightly higher pay rate might be offered for the higher assignment of five machines, and this assignment would then be awarded to the superior operator.   He would handle the extra load and would receive the extra pay.

An optimum solution in terms of a theoretically fractional machine assignment is generally the rule rather than the exception. In practice, variations in incentive rate offered will not only solve the problem, but are a means of rewarding superior operators or special effort.

Optimum Assignment

The optimum machine assignment just illustrated represents an optimum as regards a minimum-cost maximum-profit assignment. Labor cost data came from time-study standards, while the potential cost of lost sales represents a long-term average of variable margin profit.   The latter is also known as "contribution to overhead and profit."   Variable margin profit is larger than "net profit."   Some persons may object that in adverse times there may be little if any profit on sales, and that then the "optimum assignment" is not longer correct.   This is true.   But in practice the purchase of machinery and the setting of incentive standards and machine assignments must be based on a long-term expectation.   Changing of assignments from month to month would involve grave problems of operator morale. It would also incur the extra costs of recalculating incentives and making the necessary floor layout and other changes that will be required.   The optimum assignment is thus a long-term value.

One may ask "Why use a queuing table to determine expected

queuing loss and machine efficiency?" We might, for example, try each of the several assignments (calculated in Table 20-3) in actual production, so as to discover the optimum by trial and error. Such an approach is, however, tedious and time consuming. The analytical method, using the tables presented, accomplishes in minutes what would otherwise take months.

In practice, it is of course always desirable to make a trial run for the calculated best assignment. Only after the trial run has confirmed the validity of the predicted optimum should the assignment set up as standard.

Precautions

In using the table of values of queuing loss (Q percent), it should be remembered that the calculations are based on the following assumptions:

1. Stops occur more or less at random. In precise statistical terms, the arrival rate of stops has a Poisson distribution.
2. Servicing times vary, some taking more time and others less. Statistically speaking, an "exponential distribution" of service times (the most frequently found actual situation) is assumed.
3. One operator is assigned to a group of machines. For two or more operators, representing teamwork, a slightly different treatment is needed. Also, for priority run-time work, special allowances may be needed.

Where doubts about a distribution exist, it is always desirable to make a plot of actual data, to ascertain the distribution of arrivals of stops and the times to service the various types of stops that occur.

Further Illustration

A commercial counterpart to the machine-assignment problem, in terms of single-line, single-operator queuing, would be an analysis of the busiest 60-minute period at the drive-in window of a bank. If it takes an average of 1.17 minutes to serve a customer, then the time span of 60 minutes minus 1.17 minutes, divided into 1.17 minutes, gives a service ratio P of 2 percent. From Table 20-3, we note that the teller can take care of N equals 50 customers, arriving randomly during the hour, with an 8.5 percent wait per customer. This percentage, applied to 60 minutes, represents approximately 5 minutes.

For 60 customers per hour, the queue would be 16.5 percent or 10 minutes per customer, as the table indicates. Actually, however, the table is no longer applicable, because servicing 60 customers at an average 1.17 minutes per customer will exceed the 60 minutes of the hour. The teller's job is thus unmanageable, and if continued, the queuing line would grow and grow. In practice, such an "explosion" of queuing at the drive-in window of a bank would be unlikely because some customers, seeing a long line, would simply drive by without entering. Yet, other situations may represent serious problems from potential queuing explosions, such as aircraft over an airport running out of fuel while waiting to land.

Returning to the teller's window problem, we may examine also the assumption of exponential servicing times, against actual times. Using an average servicing time of 1.20 minutes (a rounding of the more precise 1.17 minutes) per customer, we would expect a service time distribution as shown in Figure 20-2. From time study or

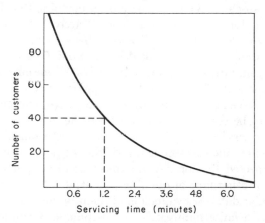

FIGURE 20-2. Exponential servicing time distribution. Average servicing time is 1.2 minutes in this illustration. If 40 customers require 1.2 minutes, then under a negative exponential distribution, 20 customers will require as much as about 2.8 minutes, and 80 customers will require about as little as only 0.4 minutes. Only when actual distributions are found to conform at least roughly to the distribution assumed for the problem will the queuing formulas give valid answers. When no suitable distributions are applicable, simulation procedures must be used.

occasional sampling observations (work sampling), we may now obtain actual distributions, and compare these against the smooth theoretical curve. As long as there are no great deviations, our assumption of a negative distribution of service times will be adequate for use of the tables. When there are large deviations, however, resort must be had to other techniques, such as more refined and complex queuing formulas or else, computer simulation, which will be demonstrated in Chapter 21.

Finite and Infinite Populations

The first example, utilizing the assignment of a definite number of machines to an operator, deals with a finite number of units to be serviced. Therefore, if an operator is assigned some 50 machines, the fact that there is not an infinite number of machines will reduce the arrival of stops. This occurs because a machine that has stopped and is waiting for service cannot again "arrive" for service until after it has completed its "wait" and is back in operation.

On the other hand, the bank drive-in window is an example of a theoretically infinite population. The arrival of one customer is completely independent of the fact that a prior customer, then being serviced, may have been waiting for some time. Anyone, theoretically, can come in to be serviced. Once serviced, he is not again likely to come back for service for quite some time; but a machine that has been serviced may indeed stop again within the hour or day, and is in fact often expected to stop several times within a particular cycle, time period, or other unit of queuing potential.

The tabular data for evaluation of queuing loss are based on the assumption of a finite number N, of customers, machines, or other units to be serviced by one operator. As such, they are exact for the machine assignment example (provided the assumptions of negative exponential servicing times are fulfilled). For the bank teller example, however, the tabular loss values are somewhat understated, to the extent that the difference in finite versus infinite population of units is important.

Queuing and the optimal management of waiting lines represents a large and growing area of operations research, so that it is beyond the scope of any individual chapter to deal with any but the most important aspects and applications of the subject.

Background of Queuing Statistics

Queuing tables are derived from mathematical probability calculations, such as illustrated in Table 20-5 for a coin-tossing experiment. The principles shown can be readily adapted to machine stoppages, as in Table 20-6. Queuing tables were developed from this type of reasoning, but with one modification: provision was made for the fact, previously emphasized, that service times are usually not the same at each occurrence. Instead, they will be most likely to vary in accordance with a negative exponential distribution.

The actual calculation of Table 20-2 was based on Ashcroft's formulation,[1] which states that the average number of machines running A_n, in a group of N similar machines, tended by one operator is:

$$A_n = NY_n/(1 + PNY_n)$$

P retains its old meaning, while Y_n represents the average number of stops that must be serviced in the average interval between two consecutive spells during which all machines are running. It is apparent that, when N is 1, Y_n must also be 1. In the case of exponential service time distributions, therefore,

$$Y_{n+1} = 1 + PNY_n$$

and

$$A_n = NY_n/Y_{n+1}$$

Values of Y_n and, thus A_n can be built up readily. Since machine efficiency E, is found directly from the ratio of A_n/N, it is apparent that Q is simply $E' - E$.

The material presented is applicable to single-line, single service-station queues only. For other queuing situations, the tables by Peck and Hazelwood[2] should be consulted. A large variety of optimization problems requiring special queuing analysis are also given in another book edited by this author.[3]

---

[1]Ashcroft, H. J., *Royal Statistical Society Bulletin*, vol. 12, no. 1 (1950), pp. 145–151.

[2]Peck, L. G. and R. N. Hazelwood, *Finite Queuing Tables*. New York: John Wiley & Sons, Inc., 1958.

[3]Enrick, N. L., "Machine Interference," *Industrial Engineering Manual*. New York: John Wiley & Sons, Inc., 1962.

Conclusion

A large body of mathematical literature has been developed relating to queuing theory, analysis, and management. But often these highly refined approaches alone are still inadequate in dealing with the complexity of a real-life queue formation. Therefore, it then becomes desirable to prepare computer simulation. That is, the problem data is fed into the memory tape, drum, or disc of a computer, and a small-scale, but very realistic model of the problem and its logical structure is expressed in the form of equations. The computer is then permitted to run for a period of time, simulating in mathematical steps the parallel real-life steps of the actual problems. The outcome of this simulated run, in miniature, then yields the amount of queuing that may be expected in the actual situation. Applications will be discussed in Chapter 21.

TABLE 20-1

MAJOR TYPES OF QUEUING SITUATIONS

Waiting lines (number)	Service stations (number)	Illustrative examples
1	1	Tool crib. Repairmen line up in single queue at checkout window, receive tools and parts from single clerk in attendance.
1	2	Two clerks attend to one check-out window at tool crib.
2	2	Two clerks attend to two check-out windows, and a line forms behind each window.
1	Several	Restaurant. Customers wait in one line. Many tables are available for seating. As tables become free, they are filled from the waiting line.
Several	Several	Toll bridge. Several toll stations collect tolls, and lines form behind each station.

SERVICING OF QUEUES

1. First-in, first-out servicing: A unit goes into service as soon as a prior arrival goes out of service.
2. Random servicing: Operator cannot keep track of sequence of arrivals and attends to units at random.
3. Cyclic servicing: Operator patrols an assigned route (such as a group of automated machines), taking care of servicing (refilling empty

hoppers, relieving chokes, making needed adjustments, and such.) as he comes to a machine needing attention.

4. Selective servicing: Operator will interrupt a major long-time repair job to take care of minor breakdowns. For example, while replacing a bearing on one machine (repair time of 30 to 40 minutes) a belt-slippage on another machine occurs (repair time, 5 minutes). Longer job is interrupted to get quickly-repaired machine back into production.

TABLE 20-2
QUEUING SYMBOLS AND DEFINITIONS

Symbol	Definition, formula, and example
N	Number of machines per operator. Example, an operator is assigned to care for five machines. $N = 5$.
t	Time span during which a stopped machine is serviced. Stops are assumed to occur more or less at random, caused by chokes, breaks, settings out of adjustment, and similar reasons. During a 48-hour week, if a machine is stopped 8 hours for such servicing needs, then $t = 8$.
T	Time span during which a machine is actually producing. For the example just given, $T = 48 - 8 = 40$ hours.
P	Service ratio in percent. $P = 100\ (t/T)$. For the data just given, $P = 100\ (8/40) = 20$ percent.
Q	Queuing loss, in percent, from Table 20-3. Q represents the average time during which a machine, having stopped, must wait until it is serviced, because the operator happens to be busy on a prior machine breakdown. If $N = 5$ and $P = 20$ percent, we find that Q is 11.8 percent.
E'	Machine efficiency percent without the effect of Q. The basic formula, illustrated for the example-data above, is: $$E' = T/(T + t) = 40/(40 + 8) = 83.3 \text{ percent}$$
E	Expected machine efficiency percent after allowing for Q. For the data given $$E = E' - Q = 83.3 \text{ percent} - 11.8 \text{ percent} = 71.5 \text{ percent}$$ Because of queuing loss in multi-machine assignments, E is always lower than E'. E is of course the efficiency to be expected in actual production.

Statistical note: The probability calculations leading to Q, based on the ratio $P = t/T$, use an assumption of Poisson arrival rate of stops ("random-rate") and exponential servicing times (t is the average repair time, but for each individual stop the repair time will vary, in a manner described by the negative exponential distribution.)

TABLE 20-3

QUEUING LOSS (Q PERCENT) FOR VARIOUS ASSIGNMENTS (N) AND SERVICE RATIOS (P PERCENT)

	Service ratio, P percent												
N	0.5	0.6	0.7	0.8	0.9	1.0	1.1	1.2	1.3	1.5	1.6	1.8	2.0
5	0.00	0.02	0.02	0.02	0.02	0.04	0.04	0.04	0.06	0.06	0.08	0.10	0.12
10	0.02	0.03	0.04	0.05	0.07	0.08	0.10	0.12	0.15	0.20	0.22	0.29	0.36
15	0.03	0.05	0.07	0.08	0.11	0.15	0.18	0.21	0.26	0.35	0.40	0.51	0.65
20	0.05	0.07	0.10	0.13	0.17	0.21	0.26	0.33	0.38	0.52	0.61	0.80	1.02
25	0.06	0.10	0.13	0.18	0.23	0.29	0.36	0.44	0.53	0.74	0.86	1.15	1.50
30	0.08	0.12	0.17	0.22	0.29	0.37	0.47	0.58	0.70	1.01	1.18	1.61	2.14
35	0.10	0.15	0.21	0.28	0.37	0.47	0.59	0.75	0.91	1.32	1.58	2.20	3.01
40	0.11	0.17	0.25	0.34	0.45	0.59	0.84	0.93	1.15	1.73	2.09	3.00	4.22
45	0.13	0.20	0.29	0.40	0.54	0.71	1.02	1.16	1.46	2.25	2.77	4.11	5.97
50	0.16	0.24	0.34	0.48	0.65	0.86	1.12	1.45	1.85	2.95	3.69	5.67	8.48
55	0.18	0.27	0.38	0.56	0.77	1.05	1.37	1.83	2.34	3.88	4.95	7.88	11.98
60	0.20	0.31	0.46	0.64	0.91	1.25	1.69	2.25	2.98	5.17	6.72	10.94	16.47
65	0.22	0.35	0.53	0.76	1.08	1.50	2.17	2.82	3.84	6.94	9.16	14.91	
70	0.25	0.40	0.61	0.89	1.28	1.81	2.55	3.58	4.98	9.35	12.38	19.52	
75	0.28	0.45	0.69	1.03	1.51	2.20	3.18	4.58	6.54	12.50	16.32		
80	0.31	0.51	0.79	1.20	1.80	2.69	4.00	5.92	7.62	16.28			
85	0.34	0.57	0.90	1.40	2.16	3.31	5.08	7.80	11.31				
90	0.38	0.64	1.03	1.64	2.60	4.12	6.51	10.02	14.57				
95	0.42	0.72	1.18	1.93	3.16	5.18	8.39	12.89					
100	0.46	0.80	1.35	2.28	3.87	6.57	10.76	16.18					
105	0.51	0.90	1.56	2.72	4.80	8.36	13.59						
110	0.56	1.01	1.81	3.27	5.99	10.59							
115	0.62	1.14	2.11	3.97	7.52	13.22							
120	0.68	1.39	2.47	4.87	9.43								
125	0.75	1.47	2.93	6.00	11.72								
130	0.83	1.67	3.49	7.44	14.31								
135	0.92	1.92	4.19	9.21									
140	1.02	2.21	5.18	11.30									
145	1.13	2.56	6.20										
150	1.26	3.00	7.57										
155	1.41	3.53	9.22										
160	1.58	4.20	11.14										
165	1.78	5.12											
170	2.02	6.02											
175	2.31	7.26											
180	2.65	9.72											
185	3.07	10.39											
190	3.57												
195	4.19												
200	4.93												

N	2.2	2.4	2.6	2.8	3.0	3.2	3.4	3.6	3.8	4.0	4.2	4.4	4.6
2	0.00	0.10	0.10	0.10	0.10	0.10	0.10	0.10	0.10	0.20	0.20	0.20	0.20
4	0.10	0.20	0.22	0.25	0.27	0.30	0.32	0.35	0.37	0.50	0.52	0.57	0.60
6	0.20	0.33	0.38	0.42	0.47	0.52	0.58	0.63	0.70	0.87	0.93	1.02	1.08
8	0.31	0.47	0.54	0.61	0.70	0.79	0.94	0.97	1.05	1.29	1.41	1.54	1.66
10	0.44	0.63	0.73	0.83	0.95	1.08	1.21	1.36	1.52	1.79	1.97	2.16	2.36

TABLE 20-3 (continued)

Queuing Loss (*Q* percent) for Various Assignments (*N*) and Service Ratios (*P* percent)

| Service ratio, *P* percent | | | | | | | | | | | | |
| | | | | | | | | | | | | |

N	2.2	2.4	2.6	2.8	3.0	3.2	3.4	3.6	3.8	4.0	4.2	4.4	4.6
12	0.57	0.79	0.92	1.07	1.24	1.42	1.61	1.82	2.03	2.47	2.63	2.91	3.20
14	0.73	0.99	1.16	1.35	1.56	1.80	2.06	2.34	2.65	3.09	3.44	3.81	4.22
16	0.89	1.19	1.42	1.67	1.94	2.26	2.59	2.97	3.37	3.92	4.40	4.92	5.47
18	1.08	1.43	1.71	2.03	2.38	2.78	3.23	3.72	4.26	4.94	5.58	6.28	7.02
20	1.28	1.69	2.04	2.34	2.89	3.40	3.97	4.70	5.31	6.18	7.03	7.94	8.92
22	1.52	1.99	2.43	2.92	3.50	4.15	4.87	5.69	6.60	7.70	8.79	9.97	11.24
24	1.78	2.34	2.87	3.49	4.20	5.02	5.95	7.00	8.15	9.53	10.92	12.41	14.00
25	1.92	2.52	3.12	3.80	4.60	5.52	6.57	7.74	9.05	10.58	12.14	13.80	15.54
26	2.08	2.73	3.38	4.15	5.04	6.07	7.25	8.56	10.03	11.73	13.45	15.28	17.19
27	2.24	2.95	3.67	4.53	5.51	6.67	7.98	9.46	11.09	12.97	14.87	16.87	18.93
28	2.41	3.18	3.98	4.93	6.04	7.33	8.80	10.44	12.25	14.31	16.38	18.54	20.73
29	2.60	3.43	4.32	5.37	6.61	8.05	9.68	11.56	13.50	15.74	17.98	20.28	22.59
30	2.80	3.71	4.69	5.86	7.23	8.83	10.64	12.65	14.84	17.25	19.65	22.07	24.48
31	3.01	4.00	5.08	6.38	7.91	9.68	11.68	13.89	16.25	18.84	21.37	23.90	26.37
32	3.24	4.32	5.51	6.95	8.65	10.60	12.80	15.20	17.75	20.48	23.13	25.73	28.25
33	3.49	4.66	5.98	7.57	9.45	11.60	14.00	16.59	19.31	22.17	24.91	27.56	
34	3.75	5.03	6.49	8.24	10.31	12.67	15.27	18.05	20.91	23.88	26.68		
35	4.04	5.44	7.04	8.98	11.25	13.81	16.62	19.56	22.55	25.60	28.44		
36	4.34	5.87	7.64	9.77	12.25	15.03	18.02	21.12	24.21	27.31			
37	4.68	6.34	8.29	10.62	13.32	16.31	19.48	22.70	25.87				
38	5.03	6.85	8.98	11.54	14.46	17.65	20.97	24.30	27.51				
39	5.43	7.40	9.74	12.51	15.66	19.04	22.49	25.89					
40	5.83	8.00	10.55	13.56	16.92	20.46	24.03						
41	6.28	8.64	11.42	14.66	18.22	21.91	25.56						
42	6.77	9.34	12.35	15.82	19.57	23.38							
43	7.29	10.08	13.37	17.03	20.94	24.85							
44	7.85	10.88	14.38	18.28	22.34								
45	8.46	11.73	15.47	19.57	23.74								
46	9.11	12.63	16.61	20.88	25.14								
47	9.81	13.58	17.79	22.21									
48	10.55	14.59	19.00	23.54									
49	11.34	15.63	20.24										
50	12.18	16.72	21.50										
51	13.08	17.84											
52	14.00	18.99											
53	14.97	20.46											
54	15.98	21.35											
55	17.03	22.54											

N	5.0	5.5	6.0	6.5	7.0	7.5	8.0	8.5	9.0	9.5	10.0	10.5	11.0
2	0.20	0.25	0.25	0.35	0.45	0.45	0.50	0.60	0.60	0.65	0.75	0.80	0.90
3	0.40	0.57	0.60	0.73	0.87	0.93	1.07	1.23	1.27	1.43	1.60	1.73	1.90
4	0.67	0.85	0.95	1.17	1.37	1.50	1.72	1.95	2.07	2.32	2.57	2.80	3.05
5	0.94	1.20	1.36	1.64	1.92	2.14	2.44	2.76	3.00	3.34	3.70	4.04	4.42

TABLE 20-3 (continued)

QUEUING LOSS (*Q* PERCENT) FOR VARIOUS ASSIGNMENTS (*N*)
AND SERVICE RATIOS (*P* PERCENT)

Service ratio, *P* percent

N	5.0	5.5	6.0	6.5	7.0	7.5	8.0	8.5	9.0	9.5	10.0	10.5	11.0
6	1.25	1.57	1.82	2.17	2.55	2.85	3.27	3.70	4.05	4.52	4.98	5.48	5.98
7	1.59	1.97	2.30	2.76	3.24	3.66	4.20	4.76	5.24	5.86	6.47	7.11	7.79
8	1.95	2.44	2.86	3.42	4.04	4.57	5.26	5.97	6.61	7.39	8.19	9.01	9.85
9	2.34	2.93	3.58	4.18	4.92	5.62	6.47	7.36	8.19	9.16	10.14	11.17	12.12
10	2.79	3.50	4.18	5.02	5.93	6.81	7.84	8.93	9.97	11.15	12.36	13.59	14.85
11	3.28	4.13	4.95	5.97	7.07	8.15	9.40	10.72	11.98	13.39	14.83	16.29	17.75
12	3.83	4.82	5.83	7.04	8.36	9.67	11.16	12.72	14.22	15.87	17.54	19.22	23.12
13	4.44	5.61	6.81	8.25	9.81	11.37	13.11	14.94	16.70	18.58	20.46	22.32	24.15
14	5.11	6.48	7.91	9.60	11.42	13.26	15.29	17.36	19.36	21.46	23.53	25.54	27.48
15	5.87	7.46	9.15	11.11	13.22	15.35	17.64	19.97	22.19	24.47	26.67	28.77	30.77
16	6.71	8.55	10.52	12.78	15.19	17.61	20.16	22.71	25.11	27.51	29.79	31.94	33.97
17	7.63	9.76	12.05	14.62	17.33	20.24	22.81	25.53	28.05	30.52	32.83	34.98	36.96
18	8.67	11.12	13.72	16.61	19.63	22.56	25.52	28.37	30.95	33.44	35.74		
19	9.82	12.60	15.54	18.76	22.03	25.16	28.25	31.16	33.76	36.23			
20	11.09	14.22	17.50	21.01	24.60	27.78	30.94	33.86					
21	12.48	15.97	19.59	23.35	27.01	30.37	33.55						
22	14.00	17.85	21.76	25.74	29.51	32.89							
23	15.63	19.83	24.00	28.12	31.94								
24	17.37	21.90	26.27	30.47									
25	19.22	24.01	28.52	32.76									
26	21.14	26.15	30.74										
27	23.11	28.28											
28	25.11	30.55											
29	27.12												
30	29.10												

N	11.5	12.0	13.0	14.0	15.0	16.0	17.0	18.0	20.0	22.0	24.0	26.0	28.0
2	0.95	1.05	1.15	1.30	1.50	1.60	1.80	1.90	2.20	2.60	2.82	3.30	3.55
3	2.03	2.20	2.50	2.80	3.20	3.50	3.90	4.17	4.90	5.70	6.37	7.17	7.80
4	3.32	3.57	4.06	4.60	5.22	5.75	6.37	6.90	8.10	9.35	10.45	11.67	12.72
5	4.78	5.16	5.92	6.70	7.60	8.38	9.28	10.06	11.78	13.54	15.10	16.72	18.14
6	6.48	7.00	8.07	9.14	10.33	11.43	12.62	13.68	15.95	18.18	20.13	22.10	23.77
7	8.46	9.14	10.53	11.96	13.47	14.89	16.37	17.73	20.46	23.09	25.33	27.49	29.26
8	10.71	11.57	13.37	15.11	16.97	18.69	20.45	22.05	25.17	28.02	30.39	32.56	34.29
9	13.27	14.43	16.47	18.59	20.76	22.74	24.72	26.49	29.22	32.74	35.06	37.13	38.71
10	16.11	17.37	19.88	22.31	24.72	26.90	29.01	30.85	34.22	37.05	39.22	41.10	
11	19.22	20.64	23.47	26.15	28.72	30.98	33.14	34.96	38.22	40.86			
12	22.51	24.11	27.16	29.97	32.61	34.87	36.97	38.72					
13	25.91	27.62	30.80	33.65	36.26	38.45	40.45						
14	29.33	31.09	34.29	37.10	39.62								
15	32.65	34.41	37.57										
16	35.82	37.54											

TABLE 20-3 (continued)

QUEUING LOSS (Q PERCENT) FOR VARIOUS ASSIGNMENTS (N)
AND SERVICE RATIOS (P PERCENT)

	Service ratio, P percent												
N	30.0	34.0	38.0	42.0	46.0	50.0	55.0	60.0	65.0	70.0	75.0	80.0	85.0
2	3.85	4.50	5.15	5.65	6.20	6.70	7.20	7.70	8.15	8.50	8.80	9.20	9.45
3	8.50	9.80	11.07	12.13	13.17	14.07	15.00	15.83	16.50	17.07	17.50	17.97	18.27
4	13.77	15.75	17.55	19.00	20.32	21.45	22.52	23.42	24.10	24.60	24.95	25.27	25.42
5	19.52	21.96	24.06	25.68	27.08	28.16	29.12	29.84	30.30	30.56	30.68	30.78	30.70
6	25.33	27.98	30.12	31.65	32.88	33.77	34.45	34.88	35.07	35.05			
7	30.86	33.43	35.37	36.66	37.60	38.23							
8	35.80	38.10	39.74										
9	40.04												

TABLE 20-4

BALANCING OF LABOR COST AND SALES PROFIT IN
OPTIMIZING AN ASSIGNMENT

Illustrative service ratio of 25 percent, potential weekly profit from sale
of each machine's output (without queuing loss) of $100, and labor cost
of $100 per operator per week

Weekly costs per machine (in dollars)	Machines assigned, N						
	2	3	4	5	6	7	8
a. Labor Cost ($= \$100/N$)	50.00	33.33	25.00	20.00	16.67	14.29	12.50
b. Queuing loss, Q percent (from table 20-3)	3.10	6.80	11.10	15.90	21.10	26.40	31.50
c. Lost sales profit ($\$100 \times Q$ percent)	3.10	6.80	11.10	15.90	21.10	26.40	31.50
d. Total effect of labor cost + sales loss, in dollars ($= a + c$)	53.10	40.13	36.10	35.90[a]	37.77	40.69	44.00

[a]Optimal assignment, which minimizes a plus c.
1. The $100 in line a represents labor cost per week if only one machine is
serviced.
2. The $100 in line c represents profit per machine if only one machine is
serviced (namely, profit from sale of output of that machine without any
queuing).

3. Machine efficiency E is found from E'. For an N of 5

$E' = 100$ percent/(100 percent $+ P$ percent)

$= 100$ percent/(100 percent $+ 25$ percent) $= 80$ percent.

Since $Q = 15.9$ percent, E is 80 percent less 15.9 percent or 64.1 percent. Therefore, if a machine produces 1000 units per hour without stoppage for servicing or queuing, it produces an expected 641 units per hour after allowing for a 64.1 percent machine efficiency.

4. If there are 20 machines in a group, then an assignment of five machines means that there will be 20/5 or four operators needed each tending his five machines.

EXHIBIT 20-1   Simple Coin-Tossing Probabilities Used to Calculate Queuing Effects

PROBABILITIES

Tossing a pair of coins will tend, in the long run, to produce these outcomes:

TABLE 20-5

	Probability of Outcome		Calculation		
(A) Outcomes possible	(B) Fraction	(C) Percent	(D) Number of tails	(E) Formula (in percent)	(F) Result, (in percent)
Head, head	¼	25	0	25	25
Head, tail	¼	25			
Tail, head	¼	25	1	2×25	50
Tail, tail	¼	25	2	25	25
Totals	1.0	100			100

There is thus a 25 percent chance of no tail, a 50 percent chance of one tail, and a 25 percent chance of two tails in any single toss of two coins.

BINOMIAL FORMULATION

The results for the above, using $n = 2$ coins, with each coin having half a chance of coming out as head (probability of head is 1/2 or

50 percent or 0.5) or as a tail (probability of tail is 1/2 or 50 percent or 0.5), could have been found more quickly from the simple binomial formula:

$$(0.5 + 0.5)^n = (0.5)^2 \quad + 2(0.5 \times 0.5) + (0.5)^2$$
$$= 25 \text{ percent} + 50 \text{ percent} \quad + 25 \text{ percent}$$
$$= 0^a \quad\quad\quad + 1^a \quad\quad\quad\quad + 2^a$$

---

[a]Outcomes 0, 1, or 2 tails, corresponding to the percentage values above.

The results correspond to the tabulated F column above. The binomial distribution thus yields the probabilities desired to be evaluated.

QUEUING FORMULATION

Assume that t represents the average time that a machine is down for servicing. Then, instead of a 25 percent chance of two tails, there would be a 25 percent chance that one machine is down simultaneously while another machine is down also. Being down and waiting for service means being in a queue. Waiting time of queuing loss is 25 percent. Coin-tossing and queuing probabilities are thus both calculated from probability formulas.

EXHIBIT 20-2   Queuing Effect on Machine Efficiency

PROBLEM DATA

    A. Machine down time occurs at random and averages 12 minutes per hour, or 20 percent.

    B. One operator services two machines.

    C. Without overlap or "interference" of down time occurrences, machine efficiency would be $100 - 20 = 80$ percent.

    D. Designate theoretical run time of 80 percent as p, and theoretical downtime of 20 percent as q. Then determine the queuing effect from overlapping occurrences of down time.

TABLE 20-6

(A) Number of machines down at any one time	(B) Binomial Expansion		Probability of (A) occurring, (in percent)	Overlap or Interference	
	formula	Result, (in percent)		formula[a]	(in percent)
0	(80 percent)²	64	64		0
1	2 × (80 percent × 20 percent)	32	32		0
2	(20 percent)²	4	4	1 × 4 percent/n	2

[a]Interference occurs only with two or more machines, since a single machine can not wait for itself. When two machines are down, one of them has a 4 percent wait (1 × 4 percent). Therefore, with n = two machines in the operator's assignment, the average loss from interference is (1 × 4 percent)/2 = 2 percent.

SOLUTION

The probability of 0, 1, or 2 machines being down at any one time is found from the binomial expansion of

$$(p + q)^n = (80 \text{ percent} + 20 \text{ percent})^2 = (80 \text{ percent})^2$$
$$+ 2(80 \text{ percent} \times 20 \text{ percent}) + (20 \text{ percent})^2$$

where the figures inserted represent the problem example. Table 20-6 shows this in detail.

RESULT

Machine efficiency E after considering the interference effect, whereby one machine must wait for servicing 2 percent of the time is therefore:

$$E = 100 - 20 - 2 = 78 \text{ percent}$$

The theoretical figure of 80 percent would have been attained if stops could be scheduled instead of occurring at random.

Simulation of
Inventories and Queues
and Other Business Problems

In seeking to optimize inventories and queues, one may on occasions encounter complex factors that can not be solved with simple formulas or tabular data. Even quite advanced mathematical approaches may turn out to be inadequate or too unwieldy. In such situations, the only practical resort available is to use simulation techniques, usually with the aid of a computer.

Simulation, in essence, involves the use of a large number of trial-and-error investigations, seeking to discover the optimal inventory policy, waiting-line servicing system, or other best procedure. These trials are, of course, not performed in actuality. Such would involve extremely lengthy and costly study. Instead, the experimentation occurs relatively inexpensively and quickly on paper, or on computer circuits, utilizing data and relationships among these data that correspond to the "real world" situation under study. The figures simulate the real world, and the resulting outcome of expected costs or profits under various simulated conditions guide management towards formulating an optimal plan, policy, or procedure regarding inventories, queues, or related problems. The following problem will show how simulation works.

Problem Data

The illustrative problem is concerned with cost minimization of inventory of a consumer product. Customer demand throughout a period of 12 to 13 weeks of winter season is relatively stable, calling for 2 or 3 units per week most of the time. During some weeks, however, larger and lesser quantities are called for, as shown by the distribution pattern in Table 21-1. The data are based on records accumulated for the past four winter seasons, and the actual fre-

194

quencies (column B) have been converted to relative frequencies (column C).

The relative frequencies always add up to 100 percent. Assuming that nothing has happened to alter our expectation that demand patterns will be unchanged during the coming season, then we note for example that there is a four percent chance (or that odds are 4 out of 100, or 1 out of 25) that at a given week we might not sell any units, an 8 percent chance of demand for only one unit, a 28 percent chance of demand for 2 units, and so on, with a 2 percent chance that as many as six units may be demanded in that week by customers.

There is also variation in delivery times, and past patterns of this fluctuation are given in Table 21-2. The cumulative column in both tables is provided for future analyses in the simulation procedure.

The following pertinent cost data were also gathered for use in the simulation study:

1. Inventory carrying charge, per unit per week, $5.
2. Cost of placing an order, per occurrence, $10.
3. Lost net revenue (selling price less cost) per unit, if out-of-stock, $50.

It is apparent that the data are not quite complete. In particular' allowance should be made for such factors as (1) loss in customer good will when his demand cannot be met in a particular week, (2) the possibility that a customer's requirements can be met from another, similar unit, or that the customer may be willing to wait, (3) the means of speeding-up delivery when a tight inventory situation seems to be developing, such as by means of special handling of shipments, and (4) possible within-season cycles or patterns of demand. In actual computer simulations, these factors can be allowed for quite readily, but for the purpose of a simplified demonstration we may assume that these factors are negligible and can thus be ignored.

Trial Decisions

We are now ready to begin trials. The first such set will be based on a reorder point of 4 units and a reorder quantity of 8 units. These values were chosen by examination of the cost, demand, and delivery time data, using some purely preliminary calculations. The objective of such determinations is to come as close as possible to an optimal balance of the three cost-factors: inventory carrying, order placing, and shortage or stockout. In this manner, the number of simulations required to find the optimal solution will naturally tend to be minimized.

Utilization of Random Events

While we know from the distribution pattern that there is, for example, a 40 percent probability of a demand for 3 units in a particular week, and a 28 percent probability of a demand for 2 units, we do not know in advance which week will represent a particular demand. If the assumption of relatively random demand fluctuations during the winter season holds, then the behavior of demand during any week might best be approximated from a table of random numbers (Table 21-3). We may enter this table at any randomly selected spot, and then proceed in sequence, horizontally or vertically, from row to row or column to column, selecting random numbers.

Let us assume, as an illustration, that the first random number found is 31, and that it is supposed to represent customer demand for week 1. Entering the cumulative probability column of the distribution pattern of customer demand table (Table 21-1), one finds that 31 is larger than the column value 12, but equal to or smaller than the next column value of 40. Since the value of 40 appears in the table opposite the Quantity Demanded column of 2 units per week, we have therefore determined that for week 1 the randomly found demand is 2.

The next figure in the random numbers table is 07, which is found to correspond to a cumulative probability of customer demand greater than 4, but equal to or smaller than 12. The cumulative probability of 12, in turn, has a quantity demanded of 1 unit per week, which is thus our randomly found demand for week 2.

Delivery times may be found similarly, but with reference to the cumulative probability column of the distribution pattern of delivery times table (Table 21-2). Such times, however, need be found only during those weeks when an order is placed.

Simulation

Utilizing the method of determining random demand and delivery times, based on the demand and delivery patterns given, we may next evaluate the operation of the inventory system by purely arithmetic methods.

The data in Table 21-4, "Simulated Inventory Experience and Costs," should be considered illustrative only, since they involve only

20 weeks. In practice, many more weeks should be studied, especially when a computer is used. A week-by-week review of the weekly events shown by the simulation is provided in Table 21-5.

The simulation has yielded the following average costs per week: (1) inventory carrying of $25, (2) order placing of $2.50 and (3) shortages of $10. It is not likely that with such imbalance of costs the optimum has been reached. Further simulations are required in the direction of lower costs than the present $37.50 per week, ($25 + $2.50 + $10). It seems logical to try smaller reorder quantities but more frequent occurrence of reordering through use of a higher reorder point.

A systematic approach towards search for the optimum is provided by the record of simulation outcomes in Table 21-6. The entry

COMPUTER PROGRAM
(venture simulator)

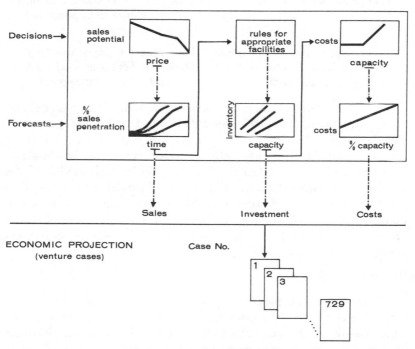

FIGURE 21-1. Schematic of computer program and economic projections in a venture simulation. (Reprinted from Sigurd L. Andersen, "Venture Analysis," *Chemical Engineering Progress*, vol. 57, no. 3, (March 1961) p. 81.

of the first simulation, yielding a cost of $37.50 per week, is placed opposite the reorder point of 4 units and the reorder quantity of 8 units. As subsequent outcomes are recorded and noted, the search towards the optimum — a minimum cost in this illustration — gradually narrows down.

Simulation of Queues

Simulation of a waiting line would have been parallel to the simulation of an inventory. The following would be the pertinent correspondences:

INVENTORY SIMULATION	WAITING-LINE SIMULATION
Distribution of customer demand and delivery times.	Distribution of customer arrival rates and of servicing times.
Cost of carrying inventory, placing orders and lost sales revenue.	Cost of idle servicing personnel (waiting for customers), cost of idle facilities, cost of lost customers from excessive queues.
Trial runs (on paper or electronic circuit) to minimize total cost, or conversely, maximize profit.	Trial runs (on paper or electronic circuit) to minimize total cost, or, conversely, to maximize profit.

In waiting line situations, it is often appropriate to assume that arrival rates are random, which usually means that they are patterned after a Poisson distribution. When such a distribution of arrivals prevails, then the time intervals between arrivals can be shown to follow a negative exponential distribution. Similarly, if servicing rates are Poisson in nature, then the distribution of servicing times follows a negative exponential distribution. When simulating queuing situations involving exponential distributions, the outcome will of course depend on the extent to which actual patterns conform to this exponential assumption.

Venture Simulation

Inventories and queues are only typical of complex problems for which solutions may be sought with the aid of computer simulation. The range of useful applications of simulation in evaluating business problems of various types is increasing constantly. One of the most interesting of these uses is represented by venture analysis, such as occurs in planning the commercialization of a new product. In such a situation, all available facts, forecasts, and related data must be reviewed and considered to the utmost. On the basis of computer-simulated analysis, improved decisions can be made, even though various degrees of risks and a variety of market counteractions may be involved.

For simplified illustrative material of venture simulation as a management planning tool, the writer is indebted to Sigurd L. Andersen, Engineering Services Division, the Du Pont company[1], who employed these techniques in attacking the typical problems in Table 21-7. Venture analysis is thus an aid to management in planning the commercialization of a new product.

Venture Simulation Method

Venture analysis is an evaluation of various possible strategies of commercializing new products or processes. It will permit explicit consideration of the risks involved, as related to forecast uncertainties and the potential counteractions of customers and competitors who must adjust their tactics in the face of the new market factors. The analysis relies heavily on large-scale computer simulation of the entire prospective business enterprise. The purpose is to reduce the normal desire of executives, to delay decisions, by providing quantitative guides in foreseeing, to the extent possible, the economic consequences of alternate routes of commercialization in a variety of circumstances. As Table 21-7 shows, among the decisions that need to be weighed carefully are pricing policies, extent of product differentiation, productive capacity, and number of end-use markets to develop. Uncertainties which must be reckoned with in evaluating risk include the size of market, rate of market penetration, degree of product substitutability, investment and cost estimates, and duration of markets.

The computer simulation program must provide for analyzing and summarizing in a logical manner all of the available information about markets, investments, costs, customers, and competitors. Pertinent equations, developed by the operations research specialist, form the structured logical system within which the proposed new enterprise is described. The mathematical model of the firm should be so formulated that a variety of alternative decisions and forecasts may be studied from case to case. The appropriate logical changes in

---

[1]Data adapted from Andersen, S. L., "Venture Analysis," *Chemical Engineering Progress*, vol. 57, no. 3, March 1961, pp. 80–83.

markets, facilities, and costs should be reflected accordingly. Venture models are thus similar to queuing and inventory situations, except that a higher degree of complexity is generally involved. The graphic sketch of the venture program structure in Figure 21-1 will serve to illustrate the variety of problem factors in their logical relationships. Mathematical synthesis of these factors should then characterize the details of markets, sales, investments, and costs, so that the effects of alternate plant sizes, pricing policies, and related decisions, can be appropriately reflected in the economic projections.

Once the data and logic are summarized in the computer program and the pertinent feasible decisions and uncertainties have been characterized quantitatively, one can explore a wide range of alternatives. For a problem with two decisions and four forecasts, each considered at three levels of activity there are $3^2 \times 3^4$ or 729 separate cases or "ventures," each with its own economic projection as shown in Figure 21-1. When more than 1000 separate cases need review, computer simulation is likely to become uneconomical. Moreover human comprehension of the results becomes increasingly difficult, if not impossible.

Management Evaluation

Once a series of economic projections for a large variety of decisions and possible market conditions have been prepared, a means must be found of reviewing the results in a systematic manner. As an illustration, we may assume an application of a simplified nature in Table 21-8, in which three plant sizes are considered in relation to three possible rates of market penetration. By themselves, these simulation outcomes do not show the best decision to be made. One approach of a venture manager, having this table of numbers available to him, might be to insist upon the selection of the most likely market penetration among the three forecast. The appropriate decision will then become clear. If a high market penetration is the favored forecast, as an example, then the manager would select the large plant. Similarly, he would choose the medium and small plants for the medium and low market penetration forecasts. Such a procedure, resting heavily on the choice of one particular forecast, leaves much to be desired.

An alternate method is that of introducing the notion of regret. For example, a look on that situation in which the high rate of market penetration occurs, shows that the large plant is the best of the three sizes. The medium plant would then result in a 16-million dollar (86 million less 70 million) loss, or regret, relative to what would be achieved with the best decision. Similarly, the small plant would result in a 36 million dollar regret relative to the best possible decision. The calculations are summarized in Table 21-9, in which the zero regret is associated with the best decision, and the 16 and 36 million dollar regrets with the other two decisions under this forecast.

An inspection of the possible economic results of each decision can now be undertaken. The small plant, for example, results in regrets of 36, 16, or zero million dollars, depending upon which forecast holds. In the right-hand column of the table, the maximum of these, 36 million dollars, is written. Proceeding in a similar manner for each decision, the maximum regrets can be obtained. Minimizing of the maximum regret would result in the choice of the large-scale plant.

This minimization of the maximum, also called "minimax," need not be the unique best solution. However, it is one logical way of taking into account the risk nature of decisions. The ability to simulate and generate a large number of economic projections for a variety of venture cases, does however permit management to make decisions on the basis of more logical analyses and comparisons than could otherwise be achieved.

Anticipation of Counteractions

A firm's mode of commercializing a new product changes the power relationships existing in the market. Customers and competitors must take note and develop their own responses. Therefore, in selecting one's own best decisions, one must evaluate and anticipate the likely actions of other companies. For example, we may consider a manufacturer of a new product, which is the raw material for another industry. That industry, in turn, converts the material to another form prior to reaching the market. Moreover, this industry is the sole outlet for the firm's product. Many such situations exist, such as when a basic plastics producer supplies a new type of plastic to extruders. Two further major factors complete the structural data for the illustrative example: (1) the raw material involved is one of the customer industry's major items of cost, and (2) the customer industry's pricing policy affects the number of end uses for which the new product will be an economic substitute, thereby displacing existing products. Pricing policies will thus determine the size of the market and the rate of sales penetration.

Table 21-10 represents a series of cases obtained from the venture simulator to clarify this pricing problem. It is based on five customer pricing policies and three pricing policies for the supplier firm. For each of the 15 simulation results a number has been computed, which is a measure of the firm's profitability. Next to this number, there is a further entry showing profitability for the customer industry. These profit determinations were made from simulated accounting records maintained and kept up-to-date automatically within the computer.

Management must now use the results of the simulations to arrive at a rational decision for the firm. A first glance at the table suggests that the case in the lower right-hand corner, in which the new product is supplied at $1 and the customer industry sells it at $1.25 is optimal, since the 178 units of profit shown represent a maximum for the firm. However, at this point, the customer is losing money and we quite rightly conclude that this will not be acceptable to him.

For a more complete analysis, let us begin with a possible firm's price of 50¢ per pound, which is also the raw material cost to the customer. From the left-hand column of the table, note that five prices for the converted product are open to the customer industry. The most logical assumption is that this industry will seek maximum profit of 119 units by choosing a price of $1.50 per pound. Further analysis shows optimal customer profits to move diagonally upward with price, as the raw material cost increases, first to 75¢ and then to $1.

The firm's problem is to select that one of the three prices, 50¢, 75¢, and $1, that would appear most profitable. Inspecting the aforementioned diagonal of cases, the maximum value obtainable is found at a raw material price of 75¢, corresponding to a firm's profit of 76 units. In the language of the operations research worker, we have thus found the correct "gaming" solution to the pricing problem. The word "gaming" refers to the simulated game of rational actions and counteractions of firm and customer respectively, regarding prices of raw material and the corresponding response in pricing the converted goods.

The completion of one gaming analysis will usually be merely the beginning of management decision making. In the present example, many more questions may now be raised, leading to further simulations and evaluations. For example, it may be pointed out that the customer response will change in the course of time. Competition within the customer industry may develop to an extent where supply of product exceeds demand, thus creating strong downward pressures on prices. One question asked by management may then be along this line: "What would be the best pricing policy if we adopt forward integration?" In this context, forward integration involves the production by the firm of both the new raw material and the converted product derived therefrom. Again, simulation will aid in resolving this question.

Principles of Venture Simulation

The case-histories presented are very much simplified for illustrative purposes. But the real world problems, on which computer simulation is brought to bear in a quantitative manner, run parallel. The principles of venture simulation technique will now be clear. They involve these steps:

1. Organize the relevant data, facts, and relationships in mathematical form. From this material, computer programs serving as venture simulators are readily derived. The program thus reflects the expected logical developments that should be the outcome of the interplay of the data and relationships specified.
2. Review the material prepared. Are there any gaps between facts and relationships of significance? If key data should be missing, further work in obtaining such material — including additional market and consumer research where required — will be called for.
3. Structure the pattern of venture simulations to take account of both the risk-uncertainty as well as the action-counteraction aspects involved.
4. Exploit the computer's ability to calculate rapidly and inexpensively, thus permitting the evaluation of a large number of risk and game situations.

Venture simulation thus aids management in its judgement by presenting analyzed information within a logically structured framework, considering both risk and gaming factors, and indicating the expected economic impact of various possible decision routes. In this manner, management's "batting average" regarding decisions under economic conditions of risk and uncertainties can be improved. Moreover, the understandable but often costly tendency on the part of executives to delay decisions and commitment will be softened to the extent that simulation-gained information replaces what would otherwise have to be pure conjecture.

TABLE 21-1

DISTRIBUTION PATTERN OF CUSTOMER DEMAND

Illustration for a Typical Product

(A) Quantity demanded (units per week)	(B) Frequency of demand (number of weeks)[a]	(C) Relative frequency (in percent)[b]	(D) Cumulative probability, (in percent)[c]
0	2	4	4
1	4	8	12
2	14	28	40
3	20	40	80
4	8	16	96
5	1	2	98
6	1	2	100
Total	50	100	

[a]For example, from accumulated data for several weeks of past seasons for this product, it was found that in two instances (weeks) no product was demanded by customers, in four instances 1 unit was demanded, and in fourteen instances 2 units were demanded in one week. A total of 50 weeks, representing four midwinter seasons, were so analyzed.

[b]The actual frequencies from column B are expressed as a percent of their total (50). For example, $2/50 = 4$ percent. If past frequency distribution patterns of demand continue in the coming season, then the probability that in any week no product will be demanded by customers is 4 percent. Similarly, the probability that one unit will be demanded is 8 percent; and there is a 28 percent probability that two units will be demanded.

[c]Obtained by cumulating the relative frequencies from column C. Thus, $4 + 8$ is 12, and $12 + 28$ is 40, in percentage terms.

Conclusion

Simulation is a general tool of analysis capable of being used with a large variety of problems, of which queuing, inventories, and ventures are typical topic areas. No generalized system of procedures for simulation has been developed. In each individual instance, the management group using simulation must develop the best approach. When the results of simulation have been tabulated, whether in terms of comparative costs, risks, profits, or other returns, or action-counteraction effects, additional quantitative and managerial analyses and judgement should be applied. These procedures, in turn, lead to further simulations, analyses, and judgements, until management is satisfied that sound decisions, based on the utmost in economical and efficient use of available information, can be made.

TABLE 21-2

DISTRIBUTION PATTERN OF DELIVERY TIMES

Time lapse from point of ordering until receipt in stock
for an illustrative item of product[a]

Delivery time required, (in weeks)[b]	Relative frequency (in percent)	Cumulative probability (in percent)
1	60	60
2	30	90
3	9	99
4	1	100
Total	100	

[a]Data shown are illustrative, and are normally derived from past experience and records for several prior years, using steps previously shown for customer demand distribution patterns (Table 21-1).

[b]The utilization of a time unit of one week is for purposes of simplified demonstration. In practice, it is usually advisable to obtain a more precise evaluation by working with days (instead of weeks) as units for establishing patterns of demand, delivery, and similar data.

TABLE 21-3

An Illustrative Page of Random Numbers

Line	(1)	(2)	(3)	(4)	(5)	(6)	(7)	(8)
1	78994	36244	02673	25475	84953	61793	50243	63423
2	04909	58485	70686	93930	34880	73059	06823	80257
3	46582	73570	33004	51795	86477	46736	60460	70345
4	29242	89792	88634	60285	07190	07795	27011	85941
5	68104	81339	97090	20601	78940	20228	22802	96070
6	17156	02182	82504	19880	93747	80910	78260	25136
7	50711	94789	07171	02103	99057	98775	37997	18325
8	39449	52409	75095	77720	39729	03205	09313	43545
9	75629	82729	76916	72657	58992	32756	01154	84890
10	01020	55151	36132	51971	32155	60735	64867	35424
11	08337	89989	24260	08618	66798	25889	52860	57375
12	76829	47229	19706	30094	68430	92399	98749	22081
13	39708	30641	21267	56501	95182	72442	21445	17276
14	89836	55817	56747	75195	06818	83043	47403	58266
15	25903	61370	66081	54076	67442	52964	23823	02718
16	71345	03422	01015	68025	19703	77313	04555	83425
17	61454	92263	14647	08473	34124	10740	40839	05620
18	80376	08909	30470	40200	46558	61742	11643	92121
19	45144	54373	05505	90074	24783	86299	20900	15144
20	12191	88527	58852	51175	11534	87218	04876	85584
21	62936	59120	73957	35969	21598	47287	39394	08778
22	31588	96798	43668	12611	01714	77266	55079	24690
23	20787	96048	84726	17512	39450	43618	30629	24356
24	45603	00745	84635	43079	52724	14262	05750	89373
25	31606	64782	34027	56734	09365	20008	93559	78384
26	10452	33074	76718	99556	16026	00013	78411	95107
27	37016	64633	67301	50949	91298	74968	73631	57397
28	66725	97865	25409	37498	00816	99262	14471	10232
29	07380	74438	82120	17890	40963	55757	13492	68294
30	71621	57688	58256	47702	74724	89419	08025	68519
31	03466	13263	23917	20417	11315	52805	33072	07723
32	12692	32931	97387	34822	53775	91674	76549	37635
33	52192	30941	44998	17833	94563	23062	95725	38463
34	56691	72529	66063	73570	86860	68125	40436	31303
35	74952	43041	58869	15677	78598	43520	97521	83428
36	18752	43693	32867	53017	22661	39610	03796	02622
37	61691	04944	43111	28325	82319	65589	66048	98498
38	49197	63948	38947	60207	70667	39843	60607	15328
39	19436	87291	71684	74859	76501	93456	95714	92518
40	39143	64893	14606	13543	09621	68301	69817	52140
41	82244	67549	76491	09761	74494	91307	64222	66592
42	55847	56155	42878	23708	97999	40131	52360	90390
43	94095	95970	07826	25991	37584	56966	68623	83454
44	11751	69469	25521	44097	07511	88976	30122	67542
45	69902	08995	27821	11758	64989	61902	32121	28165
46	21850	25352	25556	92161	23592	43294	10479	37879
47	75850	46992	25165	55906	62339	88958	91717	15756
48	29648	22086	42581	85677	20251	39641	65786	80689
49	82740	28443	42734	25518	82827	35825	90288	32911
50	36842	42092	52075	83926	42875	71500	69216	01350

These random digits are from page 5 of a statement issued by the Interstate Commerce Commission in 1949, entitled: *Table of 105,000 Random Decimal Digits.*

TABLE 21-4
Simulated Inventory Experience and Costs

Illustrative evaluation of 20 weeks' experience, based on a reorder point of 4 units and reorder quantity of 8 units

Simu-lated week number	Random numbers		Simulated weekly activity			Simulated Costs[a]		
	For customer demand	For delivery time	Demand units	Receipt units	Balance units	Inventory (in dollars)	Ordering (in dollars)	Shortage (in dollars)
0					8c			
1	31		2		6	30		
2	07		1		5	25		
3	36	83b	2		3	15	10	
4	17		2		1	5		
5	32		2	8	7	35		
6	13		2		5	25		
7	74	17	3		2	10	10	
8	59		3	8	7	35		
9	53	19	3		4	20	10	
10	01		0	8	12	60		
11	04		0		12	60		
12	85		4		8	40		
13	57		3		5	25		
14	85	92	4		1	5	10	
15	41		3		(−2)			100
16	36		2		(−2)			100
17	07		1	8	7	35		
18	29		2		5	25		
19	52	51	3		2	10	10	
20	15		2	8	8	40		
Totals			44	40	100	500	50	200
Averages, (total/20),			2.2	2	5	25	2.50	10

[a]Inventory carrying costs of $5 per week, order-placing cost of $10 per occurrence, and loss in net revenue from shortage of $50 per unit.

[b]Random number "83" means that it will require 2 weeks, until week 5, for the normal order quantity of 8 units to be received.

[c]An assumed starting quantity.

TABLE 21-5
Weekly Occurrences Under Inventory Simulation Procedure

Successive week numbers	Occurrence of events and their effects
1	Random Number "31" indicates, by reference to table of demand patterns (Table 21-1), that customers wanted 2 units, leaving an inventory balance of 8 minus 2 or 6 units, at a carrying cost of $5 per unit or 6 times $5 equaling $30.
2	Random number "07", indicating demand for 1 unit and leaving an inventory balance of 5 units.
3	Inventory balance dropped to 3 units, while reorder point has been set at 4 units. It costs $10 to reorder. Random number "83" indicates that it will take 2 weeks to receive the new units ordered.

TABLE 21-5 (continued)

WEEKLY OCCURRENCES UNDER INVENTORY SIMULATION PROCEDURE

Successive week numbers	Occurrence of events and their effects
4	Further sales, but fortunately no shortage yet.
5	The quantity of 8 units ordered in week 3 has arrived; 1 unit was in stock from prior week and 2 units were sold, leaving a balance of 7 units.
7 to 14	No special events.
15	There was customer demand for 3 units, but only 1 unit was sold because of inventory exhaustion. Under the assumption that customers went elsewhere, the 2 units not sold represent a loss in net revenue (selling price minus cost) of 2 times $50 or $100.
16	New stock still has not arrived, and a further loss of potential sales of 2 units at a cost of $100 occurred.
17 to 20	No special events.

Under the assumptions of the simulation procedure, it is noted that weekly costs averaged $25 to carry inventory, $2.50 to order, and $10 from shortages. A new simulation analysis, using smaller but possibly more frequently occurring order quantities should be tried next.

TABLE 21-6

SUMMARY OF SIMULATION OUTCOMES

Successive entry of outcomes will aid in the search for an optimal policy[a]

Reorder point (in units)	Reorder quantity (in units)								
	4	5	6	7	8	9	10	11	12
2									
3									
4					37.50				
5									
6									
7									
8									
9									
10									

[a]Entries show total cost of inventory policy. For example, for Reorder point of 4 and Reorder quantity of 8, the total cost was $25 for inventory carrying, $2.50 for order placing and $10 for shortages, which equals $37.50 as entered above.

TABLE 21-7

Problem factor	Problem characteristics
Complexity of market	Effect of market structure on degree of product differentiation required, plant capacity investment, and end-use markets to be developed. The attendant investment and cost factors will directly influence the over-all profitability of the new venture.
Alternatives	A large variety of alternative courses of action are usually open to management. These alternatives and their interaction with production and marketing requirements must be stated clearly. Thereafter, a thorough investigation, analysis and evaluation of alternatives will lead to an eventual selection of the actual course to be taken.
Risks	In evaluating the risks in a new venture, a large number of uncertainties must be taken into account. Among these factors are the size of the market or markets, expected rate of market penetration under various promotional and pricing policies, degree of product substitutability, investment and cost assumptions, and expected duration of consumer or military markets.
Counteractions	The new market factors brought about through the introduction of a new product or process will, in turn, evoke counteractions by both customers and competitors. All firms affected must adjust their own tactics, strategies, and policies to cope with the new situations that will have been brought about.
Complex interrelations	In reviewing the factors just enumerated, it must be kept in mind that there is usually a high degree of interaction and interrelation among all problem characteristics. For example, the expected size of the market and the degree of end-use differentiation will affect the detailed planning of the plant and its capacity. Next, product costs will hinge on plant size and detail, which in turn, dictates certain minimum prices, if a profit is to be made. Pricing policy, in turn, must take cognizance of expected demand and market penetration. Market complexities, alternatives of action, risks, and probable counteractions must thus be viewed in relation to the interacting forces that operate in production and marketing.

TABLE 21-8

EXPECTED CASH POSITION IN TENTH YEAR OF OPERATION

Data obtained from computer simulation for three alternative
plant sizes and three feasible forecasts of market penetration

Plant size	Rate of market penetration and resultant tenth-year net cash position, in $1,000,000[a]		
	High	Medium	Low
Small	50	32	17
Medium	70	48	12
Large	86	41	9

[a]Net cash is defined as cumulative net earnings plus reserve for depreciation
minus permanent investment and working capital.

TABLE 21-9

EXPECTED NET CASH REGRETS IN TENTH YEAR OF OPERATION

Data show loss in tenth-year net cash position, resulting from use of
other than optimal plant size in relation to market penetration

Plant size	Rate of market penetration and resultant tenth-year net cash regret, in $1,000,000[a]			Maximum regret[b] $1,000,000
	High	Medium	Low	
Small	36	16	0	36
Medium	16	0	5	16
Large	0	7	8	8

[a]Net cash regret is obtained from data on net cash position of Table 21-8.
For example, if a high rate of market penetration is achieved, then that table
shows the highest attainable net cash position of 86 million dollars, based on a
large plant. Had a small plant been built, then the new cash position would be
only 50. The difference between 86 and 50 equals 36, which is the amount of
net cash regret shown above for high market penetration but small plant size.
As a further illustration, under low market penetration a small plant is optimal,
with a net cash position of 17. A medium or large plant would result in a poorer
net cash position. The small plant thus becomes best, with zero regrets.

[b]Maximum regret is merely the highest row entry. The column shows that
from an overall viewpoint maximum regret is minimized when a large plant is
built.

TABLE 21-10

Pricing Profitability Comparisons

Data from computer simulation, showing units of profit for
producer firm, followed by units of profit for customer industry.

Industry price for converted product, (dollars per pound)	Firm's price for its product, (dollars per pound)[a]		
	0.50	0.75	1.00
2.25	14, 62	26, 50	38, 38
2.00	28, 96	50, 74	72, 52
1.75	43, 113	76, 80[b]	109, 47
1.50	58, 119	101, 71	143, 29
1.25	73, 100	126, 47	178, −5

[a]For example, when firm's price is 0.50 and the industry price is 2.25, then the firm will make 14 units of profit and the industry will make 62 units. The industry will, however, make a better profit if it charges 1.50. In fact, this price represents the highest profit (119 units) for the industry at the 0.50 cost and also a relatively good profit (58 units) for the firm. At costs of 0.75 and 1.00, the corresponding maximum-profit pricing of the industry would be at 1.75 and 2.00 respectively.

[b]At 0.75 per pound, the firm is likely to attain maximal profit (76 units), provided the industry adopts a price of 1.75, which will yield it maximum profit of 80 units.

PART FOUR

Sampling and
Statistical Analysis

▶ ▶ ▶ ▶ **22**

Statistical Surveys
Using
Probability Samples

The operations research worker's raw materials are the data and information used by him. Often such information can be obtained only through a relatively large-scale survey, which in turn requires a complex combination of various types of knowledge and skill. All participants in the survey: management, statistician, and management scientist or OR specialist, should be aware of the need for applying survey methods and probability sampling properly, so as to avoid faulty logic, inadequate organization, and misleading results.

For the essential principles of proper survey management, followed by several illustrative examples, presented in this chapter the author is indebted to W. Edwards Deming.[1] We begin with several principal operational definitions.

Operational Definition

It has been emphasized by Walter A. Shewhart, a leading authority in statistical sampling methodology, that a concept of definition has communicative meaning only when it is operational:

> Every sentence, in order to have definite scientific meaning, must be practically or at least theoretically verifiable as either true or false upon the basis of experimental measurements either practically or theoretically obtainable by carrying out a definite and previously specified operation. The meaning of such a sentence is the method of its verification.

---

[1]Deming, W. Edwards, "Uncertainties in statistical data, and their relation to the design and management of statistical surveys and experiments," *Bulletin of the International Statistical Institute*, vol. 38, part iv, Tokyo, 1961.

The Universe

The universe is all the people, firms material, conditions, concentrations, units, models, levels, that one wishes to study. The universe, for any study, becomes clear from a careful statement of the problem, and of the uses intended for the data. An example is all the firms that make a certain product, or that may buy it. Other examples are all housewives, all school children, all the pigs in a country, both in rural areas and in towns, or all the material or piece-parts covered by a certain contract or specification. The universe may be all the records of transactions dated within a specified period of time, where the aim of the study is to estimate the company's revenue from certain types of business. A further example is all people, or old people, or young people, when we wish to compare two medical treatments.

The Frame

The frame is a means of access to the universe[2] or to enough of the universe to be worth studying. What census data, lists, maps, will form a suitable frame? In the case of accounts, the question is very often at what point may we study the records that show the transactions of interest? A frame is composed of sampling units, which enable us to take hold of portions of the universe, piece by piece. Every piece of material that the frame covers will belong to one definite sampling unit. Without a frame there can be neither a complete coverage nor a probability sample, because there would be no way to lay out the work nor to know the probability of selection of any sampling unit.

Every sampling unit in a frame should bear a serial number. A random number will thus select a definite sampling unit, and will lead to the investigation of all or the designated random sample of what ever material in the sampling unit belongs to the universe.

A question of vital importance in the early stages of a survey is how much of the universe does a proposed frame cover (90, 96, 100 percent)? What groups, classes, areas, or conditions does it omit, wholly or partially? Figure 22-1 is a schematic diagram that portrays

---

[2]The concept of the frame was first stated by Frederick F. Stephan in "Practical problems of sampling procedure," *American Sociological Review*, vol. 1, 1936, pp. 569–580.

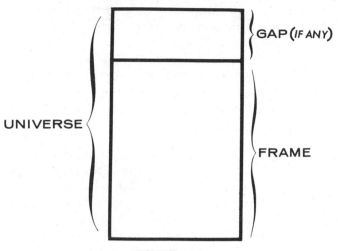

FIGURE 22-1.

the material in the universe, part or all of which lies in the frame. The portion of the universe that the frame fails to include, if any, is the gap between the frame and the universe.

A frame may be useless or nearly so for the purpose intended if it omits too much of certain important classes of the universe. It is substantive judgment and not knowledge of statistical theory that must decide whether a proposed frame is satisfactory. Thus, if we carry out a study of the uses and purchases of typewriters for example, in business establishments with a frame that omits small establishments and nonprofit institutions, substantive judgment must decide whether the results will nevertheless be useful.

Equal Complete Coverage

Equal complete coverage[3] is the result that would be obtained from investigation of all the sampling units in the frame (segments of area, business establishments, accounts, manufactured articles) by the same field workers or inspectors, using the same definitions and

---

[3]The concept of the equal complete coverage originated with Morris H. Hansen and W. Edwards Deming, "On an important limitation to the use of data from samples", Bern: *Bulletin de l'Institute International de Statistique*, vol. xxxii, part 2, 1950: pp. 214–219.

procedures, and exercising the same care as they exercised on the sample, and at about the same period of time. The concept of the equal complete coverage is fundamental to the use of samples. The term "equal" signifies that the same methods must be used for the equal complete coverage as for the sample. Every sample is a selected portion of the sampling units in the frame; hence a sample is a selected portion of results of the equal complete coverage.

Division of Responsibility

For an example of samples drawn from complete coverages we may refer to the census of population. For every person enumerated in the census there is a punched card, but many of the volumes of tables published by the census are made, not from tabulations of all these cards, but from a sample thereof. Sampling thus greatly enlarges the scope of publication in the census. Many special studies, such as studies of fertility, are made by the examination of a sample of families drawn by a prescribed rule from the original census records. The census is in such examples the equal complete coverage for the sample. Complete census and sample both contain the same proportion of careful and careless responses, of nonresponses, of careful coverage and of careless coverage.

The concept of equal complete coverage provides a logical basis for effective division of responsibility between (1) the subject matter (chemistry, demography, sociology, medicine, psychology, engineering, agricultural science), (2) application of statistical theory of sample design, controls of the operations, interpretation of the sampling and nonsampling errors, and (3) the carrying out of the survey.

The expert in subject matter has the responsibility at the outset when the question of a possible survey first occurs, to state how he expects to use the results. This statement automatically defines the universe. The statistician, as a logician, has a duty to explain to the expert in the subject matter that the latter must decide whether a complete coverage of the proposed frame, by the proposed methods of questioning or testing, would provide useful information. Any inference that is to come from the study can only cover the frame and the materials, methods, levels, types, and conditions presented for study in the frame. Generalizations to other materials, levels, types, and conditions outside the frame can come only through knowledge of the subject matter. The results may be a disappointment if the frame and experimental conditions proposed for the study fail to include all the materials, methods, levels, types, and conditions on which the expert in the subject matter desires information.

The next step is to design a suitable sampling plan or statistical experiment and to estimate the cost for a few selected levels of precision. The design of a sample or experiment is definitely a statistical problem. But the decision on whether the survey will be worth its cost belongs to the man who will pay for the study or who will be responsible for using the results.

Error of Sampling

Suppose that the sampling units of a frame bear the serial numbers 1, 2, 3, and on to N. A complete coverage of this frame involving investigation of 100 percent of the sampling units therein is to be made.

The investigators have had a certain course of training, or maybe none at all. Some of them may be careful and others careless. They may fail to find all the dwelling units, all the people, or all the material, or report on nonexistent sampling units. They may make mistakes. Some respondents may misunderstand some questions; others may not be at home when the interviewer calls, or refuse to be interviewed. There may be errors in the original records that constitute the frame. The complete count, of whatever quality, is the equal complete coverage for all the samples that may be drawn and processed in the manner prescribed.

However carried out, and whatever be the rules for coding and for adjustment for nonresponse, the complete coverage of the N sampling units will yield the N numerical values:

$$a_1, a_2\ a_3, \cdot \ \cdot \ \cdot \ , a_N$$

for the x-characteristic under study, and

$$b_1, b_2, b_3, \cdot \ \cdot \ \cdot \ , b_N$$

for the y-characteristics

Denote the sum of these N individual populations by:

$$A = a_1 + a_2 + a_3 + \cdot \cdot \cdot + a_n = N\bar{a} \quad \text{Equation (1)}$$

$$B = b_1 + b_2 + b_3 + \cdot \cdot \cdot + b_n = N\bar{b} \quad \text{Equation (2)}$$

We may have interest in A and B. We should like to estimate these values by use of a sample.

The numbers a_1, a_2, and such, are not "true" values of the populations in the N sampling units. They are instead only the results of the complete coverage. They contain all the errors mentioned above.

An operational definition of the error of sampling is contained in the following experiment.

1. Write each of the N observed values a_i on a card, and number the cards serially 1, 2, 3, to N.

2. Draw in the manner specified in the sampling plan a sample of n cards. Let

   x_1 be the observed value on the sampling unit drawn by the first random number

   x_2 be the observed value on the sampling unit drawn by the second random number

   .

   .

   .

   x_n be the observed value on the sampling unit drawn by the nth random number and likewise for y_1, y_2, $\cdots$, y_n.

3. Form estimators by the formula specified in the sampling plan. To be specific, we may focus attention on possible functions like

$$\bar{x} = (x_1 + x_2 + x_3 + \cdots + x_n)/n \qquad \text{Equation (3)}$$

$$\bar{y} = (y_1 + y_2 + y_3 + \cdots + y_n)/n \qquad \text{Equation (4)}$$

and,

$$X = N\bar{x} \qquad \text{Equation (5)}$$

$$Y = N\bar{y} \qquad \text{Equation (6)}$$

If we use these functions as estimators of a, b, A, B, respectively, we could compute the errors of sampling.

In practice, we do not usually have the complete coverage and cannot compute the sampling errors for our sample. However, a single sample, provided it is big enough and laid out properly, will provide an estimate of the margin of sampling variation of all the estimates that one can form by repeatedly drawing samples from a given complete coverage. The same theory enables the statistician to design in advance a sample that will deliver the approximate precision required. This is the contribution of modern statistical theory.

Expected Value, Standard Error, and Sampling Bias[4]

We continue our experiment.

4. Return the sample of n cards to the frame, and repeat steps 2 and 3 to form a new estimate by the same sampling procedure. Repeat these steps again and again, 10,000 or more times.

5. Plot the distribution of $\bar{x}$, using any suitable class-interval. Compute the mean and the standard deviation of this distribution. Any one of the above samples is a random selection from all the $N!/(N-n)!n!$ possible samples of size n, all of which samples have the same probability. $\bar{x}, \bar{y}, X, Y,$ are therefore random variables, whereas A, B, and other results of the complete coverage are constants in this experiment. The $N!/(N-n)!n!$ possible values of any estimator x form the theoretical sampling distribution of x. The mean, $E(x)$, and the standard deviation, σ_x, of this theoretical distribution are of special interest. $E(x)$ is by definition the "expected" values of x. Let X' be the characteristic of the complete coverage that x estimates. Then, if

$$E(x) = X' \qquad \text{Equation (7)}$$

the sampling procedure is said to be unbiased. But if

$$E(x) = X' + C \qquad \text{Equation (8)}$$

the sampling procedure has the mathematical bias C. In any case, the variance of the distribution of x is

$$\sigma_x^2 = E(x - Ex)^2 \qquad \text{Equation (9)}$$

By definition, this is the variance of the sampling procedure for the estimator x, and its square root (σ_x) is the standard error of the sampling procedure for the estimator x. Thus, a sampling procedure has, for any estimator, an expected value, a standard error, and possibly a mathematical bias C. The bias C, if it exists at all, dis-

---

[4]Further discussion of these concepts occurs in Chapter 24.

appears rapidly as the number of sampling units in the sample increases. It is not related to the bias of poor performance, nor to bias built into the questionnaire, as will be discussed.

The standard error thus includes not only the variability of sampling, but also the variability from fluctuations in the investigators' judgment and performance, which may be different before and after lunch, also the variable effect of the order of interviewing, the weather and other conditions that change over the period of the survey. It includes the variance between interviewers.

Sampling Variation

The results (X) of repeated samples from the same complete coverage will distribute themselves as a random variable about $E(X)$. The maximum variation between the results of repeated samples all drawn from the same complete coverage, and following a prescribed sampling procedure, is usefully placed at 3 standard deviations $(3\sigma_x)$ in either direction from $E(X)$. This rule is a statistical standard long used to give the user of an estimate what he needs to know about the sampling variation. However, when large operational nonsampling errors are obvious, the standard error, under such circumstances, is sure to mislead the user of the data.

The correction of the operational nonsampling errors is the responsibility of the supervisor of operations (interviewing, testing, pricing, computing). It is not the responsibility of the statistician, although statistical methods may be very helpful in detecting the existence of blemishes in procedure. Once these mistakes are apprehended and corrected, then one may usefully discuss the standard error.

Nonsampling Sources of Uncertainty

To the user of the data of a survey, it is only the total error that counts; he does not care whether it is a standard error or some other kind of error. The more we know about the limitations of a figure, or of a procedure, the more useful it becomes. Once we learn something about the nature and cause of any uncertainty, we may find some way to reduce it. We accordingly turn our attention now to the various nonsampling errors.

When the nonsampling errors are large, it is uneconomical and ineffective to waste funds on a big sample. The latter, though it decreases the sampling error, will reduce the total error only very little. In the management of statistical surveys one may enhance the over-all usefulness and reliability of a survey by cutting down on the size of the sample and using the money saved to reduce the non-sampling errors. In the sampling of records, this might mean tracing and correcting wrong and missing information. In a survey of human populations, this might mean more time and money on the preparation of the questionnaire, hiring fewer and better interviewers, providing better training and better supervision in the field, and making second calls on people not at home on a previous call.

Classification of Uncertainties and Deficiencies

The classification that follows in this section has been helpful in statistical practice, since it shows where to lay responsibility and emphasis in the planning of surveys. Responsibility for decreasing uncertainties of Type 1 rests definitely with the expert in the subject matter, and with experts in questioning, interviewing, or testing. The uncertainties of Type 2 are completely different in nature. They arise from operational blemishes. Responsibility for holding them to a minimum rests with the supervision of the job.

Type 1 Built-in deficiencies, missing the point, measuring properties of the material not well suited to the problem. The distinguishing characteristic of this type of uncertainty is that it is built into the questionnaire, or into the method of tests, or into the rules for coding. It does not arise from flaws in carrying out the specified survey procedure: a recanvass (audit or control) will not discover it. Examples of Type 1 are:

1. Failure to perceive what information would be useful or eliciting information that is of little help on the problem. In the sampling of accounts, errors in source-documents will carry through into the final estimates. Failure to know or correct these errors, best done in the sample, is an error of Type 1.
2. Too big a gap between the frame and the universe.
3. Ineffective rules for coding, or ineffective tabulations.
4. Failure to recognize changes that take place in the universe before the results are written up and recommendations made.
5. Bias arising from bad curve fitting, wrong weighting, incorrect adjustment.
6. Unwarranted deductions from the results. Reports that may

lead to misunderstanding and to misuse of the survey. The report should take into account the fact that the users of the figures may lack experience with surveys, and be unable to comprehend uncertainty in a figure. The report should evaluate and interpret the margin of sampling error and the possible effect of blemishes. It should call attention especially to the possible misinterpretation that could arise from nonresponse, or from any gap between the frame and the universe. Although a recanvass will not discover the existence of an uncertainty of Type 1, an outside comparison may do so.

Type 2   Blemishes and blunders made in carrying out the field work, the testing, the interviewing, the coding, the computations, and other work. These errors have their origin in imperfect workmanship. They are discoverable and measurable by repetition or recanvass (called the audit or control) of a sample of the main sample. Examples of Type 2 are:

1. Failure to find or to visit all the sampling units called for.
2. Lack of definite boundaries or clear definition of a sampling unit. As a result, or possibly through carelessness, or by accident, the investigators may fail to test or to interview some part of a sampling unit, or may go out of bounds and test or interview units not intended for the sample.
3. Failure to cover a sampling unit completely, such as failure to find all the dwelling units or all the people therein.
4. Covering some material twice.
5. Failure to ask some of the questions, or to make all the tests prescribed. Eliciting wrong answers. Asking questions not on the questionnaire.
6. Using the wrong test instrument. Errors in counting and in weighting. Looking up the wrong price, or computing it incorrectly.
7. Nonresponse and refusal.
8. Mistakes in calculation and in transcription.

Persistent omission or inclusion of material above or below average value, or persistent mistakes in one direction will cause biases. The only way to evaluate them is by the audit or statistical control, or with the help of outside sources of information.

Preferred Techniques

We may speak of the methods used for the testing, interviewing, supervision, and for the treatment of nonresponse as the survey technique. Whatever the survey technique, a complete coverage of all the sampling units in the frame will produce some result, like the numbers a_1, a_2, and a_3 in Equation (1). Another complete coverage carried out with the same survey technique, before changes have taken place, would give results slightly different from the results of the first coverage. There is a random element in a complete coverage, even when the questionnaire and procedure of interviewing are fixed. This is because people do not always give the same answer when you ask them a second time, or, because some other member of the household may answer on the second coverage.

Any result, whatever it be, is the result of applying some set of operations. Although there is no true value, we do have the liberty to define and to accept a specified set of operations as preferred. Thus, there may be, by agreement of the experts in the subject matter, a preferred survey technique.

Working Techniques

Unfortunately, it often happens that the preferred technique, usable on a laboratory scale, is too expensive to apply in a full-scale survey. Experts in the subject matter must then supply also a working technique. For example, the preferred technique of defining a person's age might be to compute the difference in time between today and the date shown on his birth certificate. But some people do not have birth certificates at all, and few people have them on hand. Moreover, some people would be embarrassed by an interviewer who asked for birth certificates. Interviewers can only ask the person how old he is and record the result. This would be the working technique by which to measure age.

The preferred technique and the working technique will give different results. A working technique is acceptable to the experts if it gives results not too far, in their judgment, from the results of the preferred technique. The difference in the two techniques is the bias of the working technique. A working technique is "accurate" if its bias is small.

It is important to remember that the bias of a working technique is not an error of sampling. The sampling error will disappear as the size of the sample increases, but the bias of the working technique will remain fixed, independent of the size of the sample. The sampling error is calculable from the results of the sample. The bias of a working technique is measurable only by a properly designed experiment, which will compare by the use of interpenetrating samples, with proper randomization of the interviewers, the results from the two techniques, the preferred technique, and the working technique.

▶ ▶ ▶ ▶ **23**

Statistical Reports
Based on
Probability Samples

From the examples of statistical reports given in this chapter, it will be noted that (1) the reports stay within the bounds of statistical inference, (2) the defense of the frame, the questions, methods of investigation, the field work, and the processing, were entirely the responsibility of the designated experts in the subject matter, (3) that the statistician, as the logician, prescribed the responsibilities for each phase of preparation and execution, and (4) that the statistical report gives no advice on what action to take as a result of the information derived from the study. Such advice, however important and necessary for the user of the data, is not properly part of statistical practice.

In fact, these reports do not even say that the results are precise or accurate enough for the purpose. Instead, they stamp the results with a label of the precision and accuracy actually found. The user has the privilege of accepting the results, or of discarding them.

Survey of Buying Power

The first example of a statistical report is a brief one because there was no formal statistical control of the field work. It refers to a survey conducted in two counties by the firm O'Brien Sherwood Associates, Inc., to estimate certain financial, economic, and social characteristics of the readers of a certain newspaper. The statistician's statement was included in a bulletin that the newspaper published to describe the purpose of the survey and to exhibit the results, along with the standard errors of the most important results. The purpose was to show that advertisements in this newspaper reach purchasing power considerably above the average.

227

Statistician's Statement in Regard to Survey

The specifications of the sample for this survey followed generally accepted theory and practice of probability sampling. The specifications if followed would yield results for the responses whose standard errors have the usual interpretation.

The standard error of a result does not measure the effect of nonresponse nor of persistent omissions, inclusions, or departures from procedure. It does include, however, in this survey, the effects of variable performance of an interviewer, also the differences between interviewers.

I had no responsibility for the questionnaire. The sampling plan in this survey did not call for any formal statistical audit of the field work, nor of the tabulations or of the computations, nor do I take any responsibility therefor. I did satisfy myself that the firm O'Brien Sherwood Associates, Inc. understood the sampling procedure, including the formation of the estimates and of the standard errors. I was on hand at strategic times (my substantive judgment) to ask and to answer questions, and could always be reached by telephone.

I may say, however, in respect to coverage, that the sample gave an estimate of 470,000 dwelling units in the two counties combined, with a standard error of about 1.5 percent. The census count, taken about a year previously, was 454,400. The difference is two standard errors, which could arise from sampling error, or from growth, or from some of both. The direction and magnitude of the difference appear to indicate successful coverage of the selected segments by the field workers. Incomplete coverage would have produced a deficit. The figures on which I base this estimate, the total number of dwelling units in the whole area, and the standard error thereof, came from O'Brien Sherwood Associates, Inc. at my request for the results of the sample.

The firm also informed me that the interviewers obtained responses in 87.3 percent of the households visited, and that the nonresponses were distributed among all interviewers, and in all areas, not being confined nor concentrated in any one class. My instructions asked the firm to make no adjustment for nonresponse, but to show in the tables the figures that came from the households that actually responded show the proportion of nonresponses. I offer no adjustment for the 12.7 percent of nonresponses.

Survey of Telephone Plant

The second example is an excerpt from legal testimony, in which a telephone company had carried out an inspection of the various classes of telephone plant through the aid of sampling, to arrive at a figure for the overall percent physical condition of the entire plant that was subject to sampling. Phrases in parentheses are explanatory, and were not part of the testimony.

Direct Examination

Q. Would you please explain the nature of your engagement with the Illinois Bell Telephone Company?

A. Mr. B., general staff engineer of the company, informed me that he wished to make a survey to determine the over-all physical condition of the company's plant, and he asked me to draw up the proper sampling procedures.

Q. What was the scope of your engagement?

A. To furnish sampling plans for the plant that Mr. B asked me to sample. These plans included instructions on how to serialize the sampling units, exactly how to construct, by use of a table of random numbers, the sampling tables for the selection of the sample. I also developed procedures for forming the estimate desired and for estimating its standard error. My engagement also covered the statistical interpretation of the results by which I would explain to Mr. B., on the basis of figures that he would furnish to me, as the result of appling the sampling procedures that I would supply, and as the result of an audit (statistical control) that I would prescribe to examine the inspectors' performance, the reliability of the over-all percent condition derived from the sample. I used as a norm a 100 percent inspection (equal complete coverage) of every one of the millions of items on the lists that he presented to me for sampling, carried out by the same definitions and methods of inspection as were used on the samples, and calculated in the same way. I satisfied myself that he (and the men directly responsible to him) understood the sampling procedure. I was on hand at strategic times to ask and to answer questions, and could always be reached by telephone.

Q. Were there any special terms about your engagement?

A. No, there was nothing unusual about it. I accepted the engagement subject to my code of professional conduct,[1] which binds me to complete technical responsibility with respect to the sampling procedures, and which binds the company to follow them in every detail, and to make no departures without authorization from me.

Q. Did you explain to Mr. B. what his responsibilities would be?

A. I explained to him that he must take full responsibility for the completeness and the accuracy of the engineering records and other lists (the frame) that he would present to me for sampling, that he would be

---

[1]See Chapter 1 of W. Edwards Deming: *Sample Design in Business Research*, New York: John Wiley & Sons, Inc., 1960.

responsible for the methods of inspection, the supervision of the inspectors, the weights of the various classes of property, and the accuracy of the computations that I would prescribe. I told him that I would assist him to introduce statistical controls on the supervision and on the summaries and on the computations, but that he alone would be responsible for the final product.

Survey of Parts Inventory

This example is the report on the results of a sample whose purpose was to estimate certain components of the inventory of parts on hand of a large manufacturing concern, and the LIFO adjustment (change in value over the year) on the inventory. This statement is a legal document because it forms the basis for the corporation's income tax, as well as for information for the management.

Statement to the Comptroller of the Corporation   The following is a statement about the reliability of estimates of the dollar-value of year-end corporate material, of prior-plant conversion-costs, and of unrealized earnings, for the portion of plant in the paint-and-glass-products pool subject to sampling.

This statement refers to the reliability of the results that you derived from a sample that I prescribed. I understood from you that the lists that you presented to me for sampling were prepared from records maintained by the corporation for purposes of production programing and inventory control. They showed serial numbers and descriptions of items, and they met a fundamental requirement, namely, your assurance that processing all these part-numbers would constitute a 100 percent evaluation of the problem.

My responsibility is limited to statistical methodology: the procedure of selection, the procedure for forming the estimates that you required along with the standard errors thereof and their interpretation, statistical tests of compliance with the sampling procedure specified, an audit to test the performance of your people, and finally, the statistical evaluation of the reliability of the results. Your responsibility covers those aspects of the study that would be the same whether you used sampling or not.

I designed a sampling plan to apply to the lists (the frame) that you provided. I worked from time to time with your people on the selection of the sample and on the sample for the audit. I worked with them on the forms, controls, and verifications to apply to the selection of the sample and to the arithmetic processing. I have confidence in their ability and desire to follow accurately the whole procedure. I have reason to believe, by my own subjective judgment based on experience, that the numerical results of the sample are an accurate summary of the figures fed into the routine of processing.

According to figures that you furnished to me at my request, the results of the sampling are in the table herewith. The book inventory came from the financial statement, the other figures came from ratios estimated from the sample.

TABLE 23-1

Book inventory, 1957 year end (from financial statement)	$202,850,010
Corporate material	170,243,916
Prior-plant conversion costs, active	19,995,647
Prior-plant conversion costs, inactive	1,210,756
Unrealized earnings	11,399,691

The design of the sample made it possible to calculate objectively by standard methods, from the results of the sample itself, the tolerance to allow for the outside margin of difference between any of these results and the result that would have come from a complete processing of all the items on the lists that you provided. The outside margin of difference (3-sigma limits) for material falls within one half of 1 percent of the figures in the table. The outside margin of difference for the corporate conversion-costs, active, falls within 3 percent of the figure in the table. The outside margin of difference for the unrealized earnings falls within 5 percent of the figure in the table. Theory and experience show that limits so calculated include the results that you would have gotten from a complete processing of all the items on the lists that you provided, were you to carry out the complete processing under the same rules and with the same care that you exercised on the samples.

The above tolerances include the possible effects of any accidental errors of a canceling nature that might have occurred in the pricing and in the processing, as well as the uncertainty that arises from sampling, but they do not detect nor evaluate the effect of any possible persistent error that there might have been in the pricing or in the processing. The sampling plan therefore called for an audit by which to detect persistence, if any, and to evaluate what effect it could have on the results of a complete pricing and processing of all the items on the lists that you presented to me for sampling, were you to carry out the complete pricing and processing with the same care that you exercised on the sample.

The audit consisted of a probe of a subsample of items drawn from the main sample. It called for repetition of the entire procedure for the items in the audit, by use of the original instructions, including recalculation, with other investigations that seemed warranted. Analysis of the differences found in the audit indicates the possibility of a small amount of persistence and that it could act in either direction to affect any of the figures in Table 23-1. If there should be any persistence, it would affect the complete pricing in exactly the same way that it would affect the sample. With respect to the total inventory, the maximum overestimate that could arise from persistence, if there be an overestimate from this source, does not exceed 5 parts in 10,000. The maximum underestimate, if there be an underestimate, does not exceed 13 parts in 10,000. With respect to the material in the inventory, the maximum overestimate that could arise from persistence, if there be an overestimate from this source, does not exceed 2.4 percent. The maximum underestimate of the material, if there be an underestimate, does not exceed 9 parts in 1000. With respect to the conversion costs, active plus inactive, the maximum overestimate that could arise from persistence, if there be an overestimate from this source, does not exceed 2.6 percent. The maximum underestimate of the conversion costs, active plus inactive, if there be an underestimate, does not exceed 15 percent. With respect to the unrealized earnings, the maximum overestimate that could arise from persistence, if there be an overestimate from this source, does not exceed 11.7 percent. The maximum underestimate of the unrealized earnings, if there be an underestimate, does not exceed 6.6 percent.

I recommend that you accept the results of the sample as figures whose reliability is objectively evaluated in the statements contained above.

Survey of In-process Inventory

This example is a report on the results of a sample whose purpose was to estimate the dollar value of the inventory of material-in-process of a large manufacturing company. This statement is a legal document because it will go into the company's financial statement and is subject to review by the auditors and by any stockholder.

Statement from the Consulting Statistician to the Comptroller of the Company

This statement is predicated on figures and other information furnished to me by your company, on the assumption that your people followed correctly my sampling procedures. I may point out that the method of counting, the pricing, the extensions, and the verification of the existence of the inventory, including the existence of the materials in process, are outside my province, and I undertake no responsibility on these aspects of the inventory nor for anything other than for the statistical methodology and for the interpretation of the results that you have furnished to me.

The sampling plan that I designed for your inventory provided procedures for (1) the selection of lots for the sample, (2) the formation of an estimate of the aggregate inventory of the materials in process, (3) the calculation of the margin of sampling error in this estimate, and (4) a probe of a subsample of the main sample to evaluate some of the non-sampling errors.

I shall deal first with the margin of error of the sampling itself. In my opinion, the results that your company obtained for the inventory of the materials in process in June 1957 falls within a maximum sampling tolerance of $224,000 in either direction from what your company would have obtained had you counted and physically processed every lot of the designated inventory of the materials in process with the same care and with the same degree of skill that you exercised in applying the sampling procedures. The maximum sampling tolerance, $224,000, is 1.9 percent of $12,098,069, this being the figure that your company furnished to me for the estimated total regular inventory, including the materials in process and other and additional items.

I turn my attention now to the nonsampling errors, which are dependent on human observation and have not the objectivity of the calculation of a sampling tolerance. The sampling plan contained within itself a systematic probe for the evaluation of certain nonsampling errors, namely: lots missed, wrong count of parts, wrong part number, wrong name for the part, wrong operation-number, missing operation number, and mixed parts on one ticket.

The error of sampling, mentioned above, includes the effect of the variable part of the nonsampling errors, such as wrong counts, wrong part number, wrong operation number, and mixed parts. It does not include the constant or systematic part of the nonsampling errors, such as a persistent tendency to overcount or to undercount.

A complete check for any lots missed or counted twice detected no lot counted twice, and only 2 lots missed, out of the 47,370 or so lots in the regular inventory. This flaw was corrected, so it should lead to no error whatever, and I shall make this assumption.

I have evaluated the other nonsampling errors with the aid of a probability model, with figures furnished by you. The results indicate a possible overestimate. The maximum overestimate, if there be an overestimate, can hardly exceed $58,000. It is possible that there is no overestimate at all, because the probability model gives $1650 as the limit of any underestimate attributable to the nonsampling errors.

The limits of error from the combination of the sampling and the nonsampling errors are in my opinion a maximum overestimate of $255,300, and a maximum underestimate of $199,000, those figures being respectively 2.1 percent and 1.7 percent of $12,098,069. The actual magnitude of the overestimate or of the possible underestimate lies, in my opinion, well inside these two extremes.

Conclusion

The reports given in this chapter will serve to demonstrate the wide range of useful applications of sampling, provided that the procedures have been planned well, and the resulting precision and accuracy are evaluated and understood. Facts and figures continue to be the OR worker's most crucial raw materials. OR analyses, using ingeniously constructed models and procedures, can be no better than the raw materials used. For this reason, maximum effort in proper sampling and getting all pertinent data, although tedious and time consuming, is nevertheless crucial to the success of all management-science work.

► ► ► ► **24**

Statistical Analysis Techniques
Pertinent to Samples

It is difficult, if not impossible, to think of any set of data that does not exhibit variation. No two grass blades in a meadow, or leaves on a tree are identical, and in mass production, no two pieces from a production process are identical either. Ball bearings, for example, will vary within a few ten-millionth of an inch in a lot, no matter how carefully they were made. Plastic parts coming off the same mold, will yet vary slightly in dimensions, color, and other characteristics. Relays coming off the most careful assembly line will exhibit differences in response rate and reliability. If any two items occurring in nature or produced by man seem identical in all respects, it is merely an illusion; if we had sensitive enough measuring instruments we would see the difference.

When sampling is done, we may expect to find in the sample a reflection of the variability in the group or "universe." But, because of chance fluctuations or "errors," often referred to colloquially as "the luck of the draw," both the average and the variability observed in the sampled measurements will not be an exact replica of the group or "universe" sampled. Sampling error will occur.

In the following chapter, some basic aspects of variability and its measurement will be discussed. As a starting point, however, the arithmetic mean or average will be considered.

Measurement of Variability

Sample Average The arithmetic mean or average is determined in practically all cases when a series of tests or other observations and measurements have been performed. For example, the six randomly spaced observations of time required to fill orders in a wholesale warehouse, in Table 24-1, totaled 36. Therefore, the arithmetic average or mean is found to be 36/6 or 6 minutes per order.

Let us assume, now, that various decisions were to be based on this sampling result, such as how many order filling clerks to employ for various seasonal requirements, or the possible advantage (or disadvantage) of carrying more (or fewer) lines of merchandise in stock. Not only would we consider the amount of sampling inadequate for any far-reaching decision, but we also would need to know the amount of variability present. As a matter of fact, a determination as to whether or not a certain amount of sampling is adequate can only be made after some information about variability of the data is acquired.

Range as a Measure of Variability The simple range R is probably the quickest means of indicating the amount of variability in a set of data, whether a sample or a universe. The range is the difference between the highest and lowest value of the set. For the example just discussed, we find that the first observation yielded the highest time-value of 9 minutes, while the fifth observation was giving the lowest of 3 minutes. Therefore, the range R is 9 minus 3, or 6. Expressed as a percent of the arithmetic mean, the range becomes:

$$R \text{ percent} = 100R/\bar{X} = 100 \times 6/6 = 100 \text{ percent}$$

For this example we happen to be dealing with a relatively large range. If the time values had been differently distributed, a different range would have been obtained.

While the range is simple, it is also deficient in that it utilizes only two values in a set of measurements, no matter how many measurements were obtained. Moreover, the two extremes of highest and lowest observed reading are often suspect as possibly representing some mistake, and are again not the two values on which we would wish to make an evaluation of the true variation in the lot, group, or other form of universe from which the sample came.

Standard Deviation A criterion that is based on all the data in a set of measurements is vastly preferable to the range that utilizes only the two extremes. Such a criterion is provided by the standard deviation σ. The calculation procedure is shown in Table 24-2.

The column headed "Deviation, $d = (X - \bar{X})$" shows how each individual processing time differed from the average time of 6 minutes per order. For example, in the first line, 9 minutes is greater by 3 minutes than the average of 6. When these calculations are completed, the greater (+) values and lower (−) values will always balance out to zero. This result follows naturally from the fact that the arithmetic average represents the center of a group of measurements.

Since the individual deviations must balance out to zero, if calculations have been performed correctly, we can not use these values directly to evaluate variability. One way to overcome this problem, which has found the predominant acceptance, is to square each of the deviations. Thus, the deviation of +3, squared, yields 9. The deviation of −1, for the second observation, becomes (−1) × (−1) = +1. The total of the squared deviations is 20 pounds, which divided by the degrees of freedom shown of 5 (see note 2, Table 24-2), yields 4. This value, 4, is known as the variance. It is the average of the squared deviations. In order to compensate for the fact that the individual deviations were squared, we now take the square root. In particular, $\sqrt{4} = 2$, which is the standard deviation in terms of minutes to process an order. The standard deviation serves as an index of variability. The lower its magnitude, the less is the variability present in the data from which it was calculated.

Expressed as a percentage of the arithmetic mean, the standard deviation σ, is referred to as the coefficient of variation v. For the data at hand, with $\sigma = 2$ and mean of 6, both in minutes, we have:

$$v = 100\sigma/\bar{X} = 100 \times 2/6 = 33.3 \text{ percent}$$

If we wish to compare relatively variability, regardless of whether the original data were in pounds, yards, degrees centigrade, or any other absolute unit, then the variation coefficient will permit such comparisons in terms of the common denominator of percent.

The Concept of Degrees of Freedom   In the calculation of σ, we have used a relatively small sample of only six tests (or observations). It is apparent that such a small sample cannot fully reflect the variability existing in the universe of order processing times itself. A downward bias is likely to exist.

From statistical-mathematical considerations it has been found that this bias can be compensated for in the calculation of the standard deviation if, when finding the variance, one uses the form:

$$\frac{\text{Deviations squared}}{\text{One less than the sample size}}$$

Or, for the example used:

$$\frac{20^2}{6-1}$$

In other words, when the average of the squared deviations is found, instead of dividing by the true sample size, $N = 6$ for our illustration, we divide by the degrees of freedom, $N - 1 = 5$ in our example. The effect of this subtraction prior to the division is to increase the resultant variance obtained. This increase is a full compensation for the downward bias that would otherwise occur.

For an intuitive understanding of the concept of degrees of freedom, let us assume, as an extreme case, that the sample had consisted of only one observation, such as the first one of 9 minutes. If we had used N in place of $N - 1$, we would have found that, since 9 is its own average, the standard deviation is the square root of the variance $(9 - 9)^2/1$, or zero. Therefore, no matter how wide the spread of the true lot or universe, our estimate of its variability, based on a sample of one unit, measurement, or observation only, is "zero." Had we substituted degrees of freedom in the denominator, we would have had $DF = N - 1 = 1 - 1 = 0$, and division of zero by zero is indefinite. It tells us that one can never evaluate variability of a lot from a sample of one unit only. The least that is needed is a sample of 2 units. Now, a sample of 2 units is only 1 unit larger than a situation where no evaluation of variability can be made — no matter what method is chosen. Similarly, a sample of 6 units is only $6 - 1 = 5$ units larger than "impossibility." It will be noted that, as N becomes larger, the relative effect of $N - 1$ decreases. For a sample size of 2 units, $N - 1$ increases the aforementioned ratio for the variance by 100 percent because the division is now by $2 - 1 = 1$ instead of 2. On the other hand, for $N = 20$, the effect of the DF of 19 is only approximately a 4 percent increase. For this reason, the use of $N - 1$ is often neglected when sample sizes exceed an N of 20 to 25.

Sum-of-Squares Method   In practice, it is often desirable to use another formulation to calculate the standard deviation. The advantage of this method, known as "sum-of-squares formula," is that one need not find individual deviations from the average. The formula, which gives results identical to the prior method, is shown in Table 24-3. The steps in this table are self-explanatory, and are designated by the most commonly used terminology and symbols. One fine point, however, has not been brought out. In statistical terminology, care is generally taken to distinguish between a σ from a sample and the universe or true parameter value. This distinction is accomplished in various ways by various authors, one being the use of the symbol σ for the parameter or true universe standard deviation,[1] and indicating by means of a caret that the standard deviation has been estimated and thus represents an estimating statistic, — therefore $\hat{\sigma}$. In our illustration, because the nature of the estimate is apparent from the context, the use of carets has been omitted.

Frequency Distributions When a relatively large number of units is to be analyzed, it is convenient to group them, such as in Figure 24-1, for the profit, in dollars per unit sold, of certain items in a highly fluctuating market. It is noted that 2 units sold at $4, 3 units at $3, and such, and one unit at $1 loss. The calculation of the standard deviation, as shown, is self-explanatory.

The shape of this distribution is such that it could have been obtained by sampling data from a normal distribution. This distribution has ideally a bell-shaped symmetrical form, as in Figure 24-2, and occurs widely in approximate manner in many business, industrial, and other series. It can be shown from mathematical-statistical calculations that in a normal bell-shaped distribution the following will hold:

1. Approximately 68 percent of the units will fall within $\pm 1\sigma$ around the distribution mean.
2. Approximately 95 percent will fall within $\pm 2\sigma$.
3. Approximately 99.7 or practically all will fall within $\pm 3\sigma$ to both sides of the distribution mean.

---

[1]It may also be noted that the variance of the (indefinitely large) universe is determined by use of N (and not N-1) in the denominator. It is the unbiased estimate of that universe variance, from a sample, which requires the use of Degrees of Freedom (N-1) in the denominator of the formula for the variance. In practice, of course, we do not have the data from which to calculate the universe variance; or else the need for sampling would not exist.

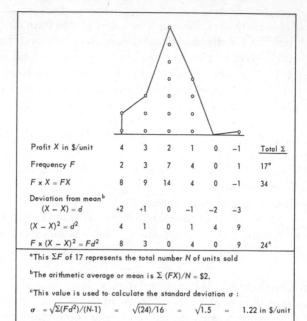

Profit X in \$/unit	4	3	2	1	0	–1	Total Σ
Frequency F	2	3	7	4	0	1	17[a]
$F \times X = FX$	8	9	14	4	0	–1	34
Deviation from mean[b] $(X - \overline{X}) = d$	+2	+1	0	–1	–2	–3	
$(X - \overline{X})^2 = d^2$	4	1	0	1	4	9	
$F \times (X - \overline{X})^2 = Fd^2$	8	3	0	4	0	9	24[c]

[a] This ΣF of 17 represents the total number N of units sold

[b] The arithmetic average or mean is $\Sigma (FX)/N = \$2$.

[c] This value is used to calculate the standard deviation σ :

$$\sigma = \sqrt{\Sigma(Fd^2)/(N-1)} = \sqrt{(24)/16} = \sqrt{1.5} = 1.22 \text{ in \$/unit}$$

FIGURE 24-1.   Illustrative calculation of mean and standard deviation for a frequency distribution.

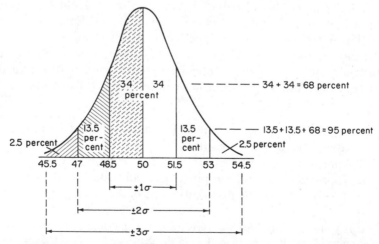

FIGURE 24-2.   Normal curve. The data represent an average product dimension of 50 mm per unit, with a standard deviation σ of 1.5 mm. (Reprinted from N. L. Enrick, *Quality Control*, New York: The Industrial Press, 1962.)

An illustration of the normal curve was previously given for the evaluation of Pert time values, in Chapter 13. For values intermediate between 1, 2 and 3 σ, the mathematically computed Table 24-4 derived from the statistical laws of the normal distribution, may be consulted. Therefore, by knowing just the mean and standard deviation of a set of data, the approximate distribution curve is readily constructed. Also, since the mean and standard deviation are subject to estimation through sampling, the probable entire distribution (from which the sample was drawn) can thus be constructed. Some assurance should be had, however, that an approximately normal distribution is being dealt with.

An example of a non-normal distribution is represented by the distribution of the probable outcome from throwing a six-sided pair of dice 36 times. For each result of "two" or "twelve," colloquially termed "snake eyes" and "box cars" respectively, there may be expected six "sevens." This distribution pattern is of interest as a forerunner of the normal curve. By increasing the number of dice per throw and the number of throws, we come closer and closer to a bell-normal shape. When rates are dealt with, such as accidents per month in a plant, arrivals of customers per hour in a store, or defects-per-unit in production, a Poisson rate is often found, such as in Figure 24-4. Analysis of proportions often involves a binomial distribution, while servicing times generally follow an exponential curve in many instances.

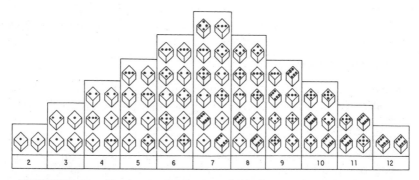

FIGURE 24-3. Expected distribution of 36 throws of a pair of six-sided dice. A 2 ("snake eyes") and a 12 ("box cars") are least likely, and a 7 is most likely. This is a triangular-shaped distribution. If the number of dice per throw and the number of throws are increased, then the distribution will shape itself towards the bell-formed normal pattern. (Reprinted from N. L. Enrick, *Quality Control*, New York: The Industrial Press, 1962.)

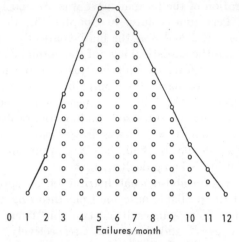

0 1 2 3 4 5 6 7 8 9 10 11 12
Failures/month

FIGURE 24-4. Poisson distribution. Average failure rate per month on a certain type computer is 6 stops. The resultant distribution, assuming a Poisson pattern of failure rates, happens to be close to normal. A tailing-out towards the right-hand side and a steeper ascent at the left-hand side are characteristic for Poisson distributions.

Short-cut Method For many routine purposes of analysis, when distribution patterns are approximately normal, a short-cut method of calculating estimated standard deviations may be employed. This method utilizes a series of ranges, and was shown in connection with inventory control in Chapter 19.

Confidence Intervals

General From properly obtained sampling data, we can make an estimate of the standard deviation of the material, whether it is a lot, population, or "universe." Next, this estimate of the standard deviation will help us establish confidence intervals for the purpose of evaluating future samples. An illustration will serve to clarify this point.

Illustrative Example From past experience, a company had noted that during the summer months, weekly sales averaged $20,000 per each of its medium-sized stores in a large city. The estimated standard deviation was $2000. Since from the table of areas under the normal curve, we know that 95 percent of the individual units will fall within plus and minus 2 standard deviations around the average, we may state, using the term "control limits" for confidence interval:

$$\text{Control Limits} = \$20,000 \pm 2 \times \$2000$$

$$= \$16,000 \text{ to } \$24,000$$

Any excess of actual sales over this amount or any deficiency below this amount represents a significant deviation at the 95 percent confidence level, or 5 percent risk of error.

Had management desired a 90 percent confidence level with a 10 percent risk, then reference to the normal curve table would have given a factor of 1.6 for such a level. The limits would have become:

$$\text{Control Limit} = \$20,000 \pm 1.6 \times \$2000$$

$$= \$20,000 \pm \$3200.$$

Management action in case of off-standard occurrences, such as checking causes of below-expectation sales or providing for beyond-expectation business can be taken accordingly.

Effect of Sample Size   When a sample average is used to evaluate a universe, such as the quality of a lot, a further factor must be considered. In particular, the distribution of sample averages is smaller than that of the lot itself. The standard deviation of sample averages, $\sigma_{\bar{x}}$, is found from the standard deviation of individuals, by means of the general relationship:

$$\sigma_{\bar{x}} = \sigma / \sqrt{n}$$

For example, if average Rockwell hardness, C-scale, has been 50, with a standard deviation of 10, and a sample of four pieces of product is tested from each product, then 95 percent confidence limits (normal curve factor is 2), are:

$$\text{Control Limits} = 50 \pm 2 \times (10/\sqrt{4}) = 50 \pm 10$$

The practical validity of these confidence limits is enhanced by an interesting statistical relationship, known as the "central limit

TABLE 24-1

Calculation of Arithmetical Average

The illustrative data represent random observations
of the time required to process an order in a
wholesale warehouse

Observation number	Processing time per order, (in minutes)
1	9
2	5
3	7
4	6
5	3
6	6
Total, ΣX	36
Arithmetic Average $\overline{X} = \Sigma X/N = 36/6$	6

There are $N = 6$ observations, with an average servicing time of $\overline{X} = 6$ minutes per order. The Greek symbol shown is a capital sigma, denoting "sum of."

TABLE 24-2

Calculation of Standard Deviation

Data represent six random observations of the time
required to process an order in a wholesale warehouse

Observation number	Time (in minutes) X	Average $\overline{X}$	Deviation $d = (X - \overline{X})$	Squared deviation d^2
1	9	6	$+3$	9
2	5	6	-1	1
3	7	6	$+1$	1
4	6	6	0	0
5	3	6	-3	9
6	6	6	0	0
Totals	36		0	20

1. Standard deviation σ of processing an order is:

$$\sigma = \sqrt{\Sigma d^2/(N-1)} = \sqrt{20/(6-1)} = \sqrt{4} = 2 \text{ minutes}$$

   The Greek symbol used is a small "sigma."

2. Note that the number of tests N is 6. When calculating σ, the divisor $N-1$ is used under the square root. The expression $N-1$ is known as "degrees of freedom" (DF). In the present instance $N = 6$, therefore

$$DF = N - 1 = 6 - 1 = 5$$

3. The standard deviation, when expressed as a percent of the average, is known as the "coefficient of variation," (v). In particular:

$$v \text{ percent} = 100\sigma/\bar{X} = 100 \times 2/6 = 33.3 \text{ percent.}$$

TABLE 24-3

STANDARD DEVIATION BY SUM-OF-SQUARES FORMULA

Processing Times, minutes, per order

	Time X	X^2	Result
	9	81	
	5	25	
	7	49	
	6	36	
	3	9	
	6	36	
1. Total of X, ΣX	36		
2. Total of $X^2 = \Sigma X^2$		236	
3. Crude sum of squares (CSS) $CSS = (\Sigma X^2)/N = 236/6$			39.33
4. Correction factor, (C) $= (\Sigma X/N)^2 = (36/6)^2$			36.00
5. Corrected sum of squares (SS) $SS = CSS - C = 39.33 - 36$			3.33
6. $N/(N-1) = 6/5$			1.20
7. Variance, $\sigma^2 = SS \times N/(N-1) = 3.33 \times 1.2$			4.00
8. Standard Deviation (σ) $= \sqrt{\text{variance}} = \sqrt{4}$			2.00[a]

[a]This result checks with the standard deviation found before. The sum-of-squares method shown above may be condensed to:

$$\sigma^2 = [(\Sigma X^2/N) - (\Sigma X/N)^2] \times [N/(N-1)]$$
$$= [N \Sigma X^2 - (\Sigma X)^2]/[N(N-1)]$$

theorem." In particular, the distribution of sample averages tends to be normal even when the universe, from which the samples were randomly selected, is markedly non-normal.

Assume now that a control limit of ±5 or, in other words 10 percent of the average of 50, is desired. To obtain the control limit, what sample size do we need? From transposition of the prior equation

$$\pm 5 = 2 \times (10/\sqrt{n})$$

$$n = (2 \times 10)^2/\pm 5^2$$

$$= 16$$

Therefore, for a 95 percent confidence level and a control limit of ± 10 percent or ± 5 Rockwell hardness scale units, we would need to test 16 in place of the present 4 sample pieces from each lot. Testing costs money but so does the cost of lost customers from shipment of poor quality.

Elaborate cost analyses are possible, within statistical and operations research procedures and techniques, to form decisions as to the best sample size, the best confidence level, and the best control limit or tolerance based on available information. Usually, however, it is difficult to evaluate and quantify the risks of customer losses involved in shipment of lower quality, since these losses depend upon individual customer reactions and the frequency and extent of off-standard product. Therefore, when detailed and reliable data are unavailable, or costly and lengthy to obtain, a rough guide followed in many instances is to decide on a confidence level between 90 and 99 percent, to use a tolerance from established or specific contractual agreement, and to adjust confidence levels when testing is expensive.

Conclusion

In this chapter it has been shown how variability may best be measured, the relationship that exists between sample and universe variability, and how to use these relationships in evaluating sampling data. Of necessity, this relatively vast subject has been treated very briefly.

TABLE 24-4

AREAS UNDER THE NORMAL DISTRIBUTION CURVE

If: the standard deviation is multiplied by the factor t shown below:	Then: the resultant product will include the following percentage of individual items around the grand average[a]
0.1	8
0.2	16
0.3	24
0.4	31
0.5	38
0.6	45
0.7	52
0.8	58
0.9	63
1.0	68[b]
1.1	73
1.2	77
1.3	81
1.4	84
1.5	87
1.6	89
1.7	91
1.8	93
1.9	94
2.0	95[b]
2.1	96
2.2	97
2.3	98
2.6	99
3.0	100[b]

[a]Percentages rounded to nearest integer.
[b]These are the values entered in the graph of the normal distribution curve.

▶ ▶ ▶ ▶ **25**

Work Sampling
as an OR Tool

When probability sampling is applied to the study of activities in a business operation (production or sales) to estimate the amount of time spent on each activity, the study is called "work sampling." The data obtained can be used by management as a basis for determining standards of performance, costs by type of activity or operating function, and benchmarks for managerial and economic analysis and control. The illustrative data used in this chapter were obtained from Leland E. Ott of the Market Development Branch, Marketing Economics Division, Economic Research Service, of the United States Department of Agriculture.[1] They apply to work sampling studies of grocery store operations.

To facilitate the presentation, three arbitrary areas of labor ultilization are set forth that require different uses of work sampling data. These areas also represent three natural steps or stages of a good company research program for lowering costs. They are:

1. Methods improvement
2. Scheduling and supervision
3. Work measurement and budgetary control

Certainly every labor utilization study provides useful results in each of these areas, yet most research places stronger emphasis on only one or two of these categories.

---

[1]Ott, Leland E., *The Application and Use of Work Sampling*, a paper presented at Training Clinic in Retail and Warehouse Operations Research, U. S. D. A., Washington, D. C., February 5, 1962; and, *Using Work Sampling Data to Control Labor Costs in Retail Food Stores*, a paper presented at Third Annual Food Distribution Research Conference, Topeka, Kansas, June 4, 1962.

248

Methods Improvement

Methods improvement research emphasizes the reduction of labor cost through improved layouts of physical facilities, equipment, and work methods. Work sampling can be best used in the preliminary phase of such research for the following purposes:

1. To make management aware of the potentials for reducing labor costs
2. To give the researcher a picture of over-all labor use and the relative amount of time spent performing activities
3. To evaluate the results of installed work improvements

Often the most difficult task in initiating a methods improvement program is to convince management of the need to spend money for equipment or alterations and make available enough time for proper employee training. Work sampling often shows the need for methods improvement, scheduling, supervision, work measurement, and budgetary control.

Time-use data similar to those presented in Table 25-1 can be used for this purpose. For example, these data indicated that efforts to reduce labor cost in dairy and frozen foods should receive less attention since extremely large savings in these departments would be necessary to have the same impact as small savings in some other departments. Likewise, detailed studies should be undertaken to reduce the amount of general activities in dry groceries, since they comprise a large amount of time. Labor scheduling and supervision also appeared to be a much greater problem in the checkout and dry grocery departments than elsewhere.

Through a follow-up study, after work improvements have been made, we can evaluate the cumulative effects of installed methods. Such a follow-up study also provides a natural bridge to the next phase of research on scheduling and supervision.

Scheduling and Supervision

Scheduling and supervision research emphasizes the leveling or evening-out of work loads through better timing of activities and assignment of the most suited employee to each activity. Work sampling will:

1. Measure the variability of total work loads throughout the week.
2. Estimate total weekly labor requirements by each wage-rate classification.
3. Determine the best times to perform individual activities and the amount and type of labor required.

By subsorting the sampled data by days of week and periods of the day, times of high delay are found. When compared with periodic sales readings from cash registers and delivery schedules, we will soon note the times when labor is and is not available. We can then shift activities and readjust employee man-hours accordingly. We can also determine the actual time required and spent by various workers such as full-time versus part-time, checkers, stock clerks, meat cutters and wrappers. Shifting tasks to lower-paid employees where feasible will then reduce labor costs.

For specific departments or operations, work sampling provides valuable data for scheduling purposes. In a study of four check-out departments, work sampling data were used to determine the effect of order size upon labor productivity (Table 25-2).

As expected, time requirements per $1000 sales for all activities except carry out decreased as order size increased. By separating the various parts of the operation to represent different operating conditions, the sales which various types of crew compositions can be expected to handle are developed, as presented in Table 25-3. These results clearly indicate how optimum crew composition varies for different operating conditions. By comparing the results in Tables 25-2 and 25-3 with sales and order size patterns, store managers, and supervisors have concrete guides for improving scheduling and supervision.

Work Measurement and Budgetary Control

This final stage of development in improving labor utilization through work sampling data should provide:

1. Detailed time requirements for operating standards by store size, sales volume, and product mix.
2. Labor-input coefficients for sound judgement and the use of mathematical analysis on the profitability of alternative pricing, merchandising, promotion and other economic decisions.

Work sampling study will aid in developing realistic operating standards and in controlling such operating factors as store layout, equipment, work methods, scheduling, and supervision. Employee performance can be evaluated by means of a special type of work sampling: performance sampling. In this study, the observer who takes random checks of operations and activities, not only records the time involved in a particular activity, but also notes the relative speed and efficiency with which a task is accomplished by an operator clerk.

As a result, the various operating factors given above should be relatively similar in those stores of a retail chain of similar stores where the first two phases of a labor utilization program have been completed. Differences in store size, sales volume, and product mix will, of course, affect the operating standards. Differences in time requirements caused by each of such variables as store size, volume, product mix, and other factors, can be evaluated in comprehensive terms by means of a statistical method known as multiple correlation analysis. Management is now in a position to conduct successive correlation studies, using different pricing, merchandising and promotional practices in different stores, and evaluating their effect on both labor utilization and sales volume. Conversely, management may use differences in labor requirements as criteria for varying man-hour budgets under different types of pricing, merchandising, and promotional efforts.

This use of work sampling data is illustrated by the design of a study to determine labor requirements in a retail meat department. The problem of setting budgetary controls and labor standards is extremely difficult for such an operation, which is characterized by drastic weekly fluctuations in the sales of its various products.

Since variations in man-hours are dependent upon both the amount of total product and the product-mix processed, we must determine time requirements for each major product group. The problem is further complicated if time requirements per unit of individual product groups change with the number of units processed. Such data must then be obtained by selecting four or five departments similar in all respects except size of department as measured in sales volume. Differences in layout, equipment, work methods, scheduling, and supervision that are attributable to size of department should be included in the sample, but these differences should represent good operating practices for departments in their respective size category. Through successive week-long studies that include each of the major types of feature promotions, time requirements by product groupings for different product group and total sales levels can be analyzed statistically to determine departmental requirements. For example, the time requirements for a beef feature as contrasted to a pork, chicken, or combination feature can be used to set different man-hour budgets for each size of department by type of feature promotion. Or alternative feature promotions can be evaluated in terms of their net contribution (gross profit less labor cost) to departmental overhead or profit. In many cases, management may find it desirable to alter feature promotions or pricing policies to even out weekly fluctuations in labor requirements.

Under conditions of extremely fixed labor conditions, common in many meat departments, it is feasible to program mathematically the optimum crew size over time. For example, movement by product category projected weekly for a thirteen-week or other designated period may be used to determine the optimum fixed crew that will minimize total labor costs during the period. This mathematical solution would also determine crew composition, such as the number of cutters and wrappers, and the number of full-time or part-time workers required. Such a model will automatically show when to add or subtract labor and the proper amount of overtime to authorize under specified conditions. The results serve as useful guides at store level when phrased in terms of simplified charts, tables, and rules.

The detailed data available through work sampling studies also provide part of the basic ingredients needed for successful application of mathematical models to other types of decisions. The allocation of capital among such alternative uses as new store expansion, renovation of old stores, or installation of labor saving equipment, is an example of one type of problem requiring detailed labor data for a decision model. Alternative market areas for expansion of store facilities is another example. If such merchandising management decisions as the number of different items to carry, pricing policies, optimum inventory levels, and space allocation are to be phrased in mathematical models, more detailed labor data by commodity under varying conditions are needed than are presently available.

Conclusion

Work sampling is a versatile statistical method for collecting detailed labor data. Its use depends largely upon the firm's stage of development in formulating a program to improve its labor utilization.

TABLE 25-1

WORK SAMPLING DATA ON TIME-USE IN A GROCERY STORE

Department	Activity	Activity time as a percent	
		Departmental total	Store total
Checkout	Checking	34.8	10.3
	Bagging	23.6	7.0
	Carrying-out	6.8	2.0
	General	12.5	3.7
	Delay	22.3	6.6
	Total	100.0	29.6
Dry grocery	Receiving	4.1	1.3
	Price-marking and stocking	42.3	13.3
	General	27.9	8.8
	Delay	25.7	8.1
	Total	100.0	31.5
Dairy and frozen food			3.0
Meat	Receiving	0.9	0.2
	Cutting	25.5	5.6
	Packaging	29.8	6.5
	Displaying	10.5	2.3
	General	20.1	4.4
	Delay	13.2	2.9
	Total	100.0	21.9
Produce	Receiving	3.6	0.5
	Trimming	10.0	1.4
	Packaging	40.8	5.7
	Displaying	15.7	2.2
	General	16.4	2.3
	Delay	13.5	1.9
	Total	100.0	14.0
Store Total			100.0

TABLE 25-2

WORK SAMPLING DATA ON CHECKOUT ACTIVITY BY ORDER SIZE GROUP

Figures shown are in man-hours per $1000 sales

| | Order size (in dollars) | | | | | |
| | 2.00 to 3.99 | | 4.00 to 7.99 | | 8.00 and over | |
Work activity	Individual	Total	Individual	Total	Individual	Total
1. Checking						
a. Ringing up	2.05		1.79		1.76	
b. Handling cash	1.19		0.79		0.51	
c. Trading stamps	0.55		0.38		0.33	
d. Total		3.79		2.96		2.60
2. Moving out						
a. Sacking	2.41		2.12		2.13	
b. Carrying out	0.39		0.73		0.92	
c. General	1.68		1.07		0.74	
d. Total		4.48		3.92		3.79
3. Servicing						
a. Discount certificates	0.05		0.10		0.09	
b. Check cashing	0.05		0.02		0.01	
c. Handling master container	0.16		0.38		0.42	
d. Bottle returns	0.12		0.04		0.02	
e. Total		0.38		0.54		0.54
4. Column Total		8.65		7.42		6.93

The use of work sampling was described for the following three stages: (1) methods improvement, (2) scheduling and supervision, (3) work measurement and budgetary control. A firm will find it more effective to move through each stage in sequence rather than placing primary emphasis on either stage two or three before stage one.

In methods improvement, work sampling can be used very effectively to describe labor use for purposes of creating management's awareness of problems and for orientation of research. It can also serve as a means of evaluating the results of a completed methods-

TABLE 25-3

WORK SAMPLING ANALYSIS: SALES EXPECTATIONS DURING PEAK
PERIOD FOR FOUR TYPES OF CHECK-OUT CONDITIONS

Figures shown are in dollars sold per check-out hour

| | Operating conditions | | | |
| | With trading stamps | | Without trading stamps | |
Crew size	With conveyor	Without conveyor	With conveyor	Without conveyor
	$2.00 to 3.99 order size			
1 checker	157	161	172	177
1 checker and 1 sacker	264	264	309	309
1 ringer, 1 change maker, and 1 sacker	463	482	488	488
	$4.00 to 7.99 order size			
1 checker	183	197	197	213
1 checker and 1 sacker	338	338	388	388
1 ringer, 1 change maker, and 1 sacker	545	559	559	559
	$8.00-and-over order size			
1 checker	194	211	208	227
1 checker and 1 sacker	385	385	414	441
1 ringer, 1 change maker, and 1 sacker	568	568	568	568

improvement program. It provides a transition into the next stage.

In scheduling and supervision, work sampling provides data for leveling the work load during the week. It can reduce payroll costs by providing data on the amount of labor needed by wage rate classifications. A checkout study was used to illustrate how to determine productivity and optimum composition of crew sizes under various types of operating conditions.

In the third stage, the applications of work sampling data appear to be limitless not only from the standpoint of optimizing and controlling labor costs but from the standpoint of applying mathematical models to the total firm's decision making processes.

Further Applications   Retail store management was the vehicle used for illustration of the value of work sampling as an aid in operations research applications. Had we used a production plant, then the various processing departments would have replaced the merchandising departments of a store. Similarly, for the study of a banking house, the various financial, operating and service centers would have been studied in relation to account sizes, customer flow, portfolio distributions, and other banking activities.

From an OR viewpoint, interest is not focused upon the particular activity studied as such, but rather on how to obtain concise and adequate data on each activity, which will allow us to make further economic analyses, leading to worthwhile, and, as a goal, the best recommendations and decisions that can be achieved.

When using sampling data, the desirability of knowing their statistical reliability in terms of confidence limits has been emphasized. In fact, such limits were obtained for the tabulated case history material presented. These limits were relatively narrow around the average values for all of the important activity times. It was therefore not considered essential to include them in the tabulations. When limits are relatively wide, indicative of relatively large sampling error, then prominent attention should be called to this fact, since it is risky and unsound to base decisions on inadequate data.

▶▶▶▶ 26

Principles
of Efficient
Experimentation

Improvements in production and marketing methods involve changes in product design, processing techniques, and sales and promotional approaches. Yet, we dare not make changes on the basis of logic or common sense alone. Facts and data must support and justify any change made, whether it be in the direction of productivity, cost, or sales volume or other areas. Experimental investigations and sample surveys are often the primary source of such facts and data.

There are many reasons for running experiments or making surveys, and Exhibit 26-1 shows some major types. The over-all objectives are usually the same: to obtain information that will aid in achieving lower costs, greater productivity, higher volume, or other benefits leading to more efficient and profitable operations.

Running an Efficient Study

Experimentation should not be left to haphazard arrangements. Sound planning and carefully laid-out procedures are an essential. A typical program set-up is given in Exhibit 26-2. Where proper planning is neglected and reliance is placed on hasty and inadequate trials, rule-of-thumb judgments and "guestimates," it will often mean that a heavy price is paid for poor information. Purchase of other than optimal material for a particular product, reliance on less than optimum marketing methods, and other similar losses, may be the price paid for such neglect.

Precautions in Running Experimental Studies

In order to avoid, as much as possible, faulty or biased information from experiments, it will be well for the experimentor to observe three all-important precautionary conditions in trials and tests:

257

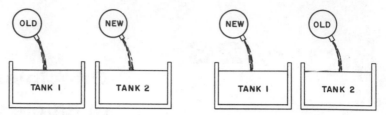

FIGURE 26-1.   Balanced experiment.   When investigating the effect of a "new" versus the "old" degreasing solution, both solutions must be used in each of the two tanks (1 and 2) in the plant.   Otherwise, an effect due to type and design of tank might be mistaken as the effect of one of the solutions.

balance, randomization, and replication.   The meaning and importance of these three concepts is shown in Exhibit 26-3: "How to Balance, Randomize and Replicate an Experiment."

Graphic Illustrations

The several further examples given here will serve to emphasize the importance of using balance, randomization, and replication when running experiments to improve quality, reduce costs, and enhance productivity.

Balance   The manufacturer of communications equipment, in Figure 26-1, wished to compare a new with the old degreasing solution.   He had two degreasing tanks.   A simple experiment, running Tank 1 with the old solution and Tank 2 with the new solution might have sufficed.   However, a wise experimentor knows that there may also be differences among the two tanks that affect the degreasing efficiency.   As a result, one can not say with certainty whether it is the tank or the degreasing solution that produces the effect.   A balanced experiment gives each solution an equal chance in each of the two tanks, as shown by the diagram.   Failure to balance will involve the possibility that the combination of one tank with one solution may be misinterpreted by "confounding" the results.

Randomization   Suppose we wish to know how six different types of heat treatment will affect machineability of a casting.   Six tote boxes, each containing 30 castings, are to be processed on a six-spindle automatic machine.   For convenience of data keeping, it would be expedient to run each heat treatment on one spindle.   However, if there

PAPER SLIPS NUMBERED AI TO A6 AND BI TO B6

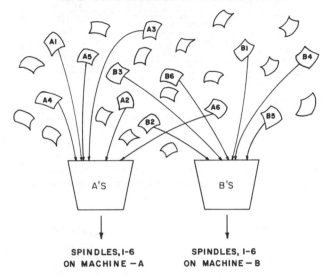

SPINDLES, I-6   SPINDLES, I-6
ON MACHINE —A   ON MACHINE—B

FIGURE 26-2. Random drawings of paper slips, numbered A1 to A6 and B1 to B6, determines the assignment of experimental materials (such as castings from different processing methods) to further stages (such as machining on two 6-spindle automatics). Randomization helps avoid unknown biasing factors in materials, machines, men or methods.

is an unknown deficiency in one of the spindles, such as a misaligned bearing, worn or dull tool, or other factor, then the spindle factor would be erroneously ascribed to the heat treatment. Random assignment of castings, using a table of random numbers, or simply numbered slips of paper, would overcome this problem. In the actual problem, two machines, A and B, were used, so that sets of paper slips numbered A1 to A6 and B1 to B6 were used, with the drawings repeated for each of the 30 castings per tote box (Figure 26-2).

Possible sources of bias that may affect an experiment, are further demonstrated for an automatic polishing machine processing metal blanks (Figure 26-3). Testing instruments, too, may develop bias, such as from gradual wear of tubes, loosening of connections, and other factors associated with usage (Figure 26-4). It does at times happen that bias is discovered during the test runs and that adjustments in the data can be made accordingly. Usually, however, bias goes undetected or else, if discovered, no ready means of correction of

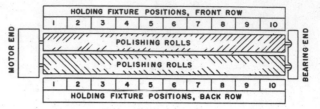

FIGURE 26-3.   Possible sources of bias in a machine. In this illustration, different pretreatments of metal blanks and their effect on polishing quality are under investigation. Random assignment of blanks to fixture positions will avoid possible machine bias, such as (1) distortion of shaft from motor to bearing end, (2) differences in bearing wear, and (3) differences in polishing roll texture, evenness or other factors.

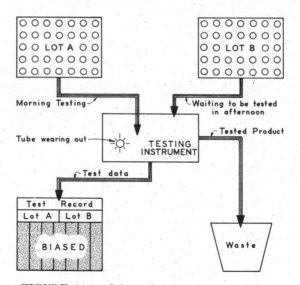

FIGURE 26-4.   Schematic of testing setup, illustrating bias from lack of randomization. Lot A is being tested in the morning and represents experimental condition A, to be compared with condition B. Because product from A is tested first (instead of randomly testing product parts from A and B throughout the day), any time factors (such as tube wear, fatigue, etc.) may introduce a biasing difference in the test results. Pieces from lots A and B should be tested in random sequence.

the data is available. Randomization gives long-term assurance that any bias, whether in machines, instruments, operators, or experimenters, will be minimized.

Replication Any really worthwhile investigation involves sensitive tests and measurements. When such determinations are repeated, such as from two experiments on the same material, involving the

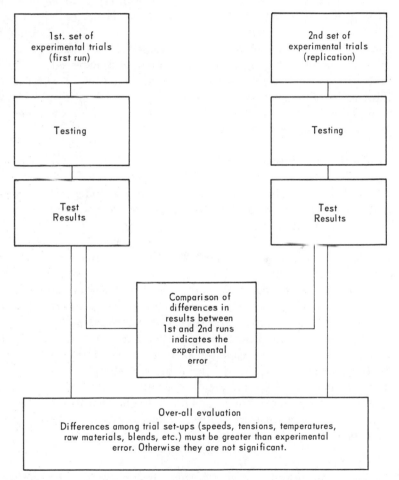

FIGURE 26-5. Replication means that at least two full sets of experimental runs (speeds, tensions, temperatures, materials, blends or admixtures) are made.

same procedures and tests, a difference in results will be observed. A certain amount of this difference is ascribable to normal fluctuations affecting materials, methods, and performances, no matter how much care is taken. We refer to this fluctuation, which can not be traced to any specific effect, as "chance" or "experimental error." Replication requires at least two sets of experimental runs. From the difference in results, inferences regarding the amount of experimental error present can be made. In practice, the experimental-error effect must be significantly exceeded by the main effects if the latter are to have meaning. The main effects may represent the result of different speeds, tensions, temperatures, raw materials, blends, operators, methods, or other experimental conditions, as illustrated in Figure 26-5. The use of repeat samples in surveys (Chapter 22) is a further illustration of replication. These recanvass results, within a framework of balanced and randomized design, served to show certain aspects of the survey errors involved.

Statistical Evaluation

The data, obtained from the tests and measurements performed during the experiment, contain the vital information needed by management for decision making. The decision may be to buy or not to buy a new equipment, to use or not to use a particular marketing approach, or, more often, to run further experiments to obtain still further information until a sound final decision can be reached. It is essential, therefore, that valid statistical procedures are used, with a view towards obtaining the maximum amount of information that can be squeezed out of the test results. Such elements as "experimental error," various main effects, and certain other factors, such as interaction effects, must be evaluated in quantitative terms, and chance fluctuations must be distinguished from real effects.

Examination of the practical application of a balanced, randomized, and replicated experiment, as presented in Chapter 27, will serve as a vehicle for demonstrating how an efficient experiment is designed, executed, and analyzed for its information content.[1]

----

[1] A large number of experimental designs from a variety of business, engineering and research applications, will also be found in a prior book by this author, *Cases in Management Statistics*, New York: Holt, Rinehart and Winston, Inc., 1962.

EXHIBIT 26-1   Typical Reasons for Experiments and Surveys

1. *PRODUCT, PROCESSING AND EQUIPMENT EVALUATION*

    A. Several proportions of alloy constituents for a casting are being considered. Which blend mix is best regarding surface, characteristics, required compressive strength, and machinability?

    B. A new procedure for making a certain type of transistors is being tried. How does reliability of the new product compare with older methods?

    C. How is a new type of torque wrench performing regarding leak proofness of assembled pumps?

2. *INVESTIGATING RELATIONSHIPS*

    A. A new direct-mail promotion brochure has been used on limited experimental mail-sampling basis. How do the results obtained correlate with the older brochure? What revisions, if any, may be needed in the new brochure?

    B. A new automated and high-speed testing machine has been developed. Do the test results from this machine correlate with the older manual standard technique? What is the relative accuracy and precision of the new versus the older method?

3. *MISCELLANEOUS INVESTIGATIONS*

    A. What are the best times of the year for introducing new styles or models, or to run special promotions?

    B. To what relative extent are the factors of (1) store location, (2) salesman's effectiveness, and (3) type of display important regarding sales volume?

EXHIBIT 26-2   Steps in Making an Efficient Experimental Study or Survey

1. Recognition of an area where further knowledge of materials, procedures methods, and other aspects of a business operation may benefit in terms of improvement in costs, safety, volume, or other areas of more effective and better performance.

2. Statement of information to be obtained through the study, and the experimental procedure to be followed. This should include:
    a. Type of data sought
    b. Benefits expected from having the data
    c. Procedures to be followed
    d. Possible outcome of the experiment or survey
    e. Time, manpower, and other cost items to be budgeted for the study
    f. Analysis of total cost of experiment versus expected returns from the investigation (using approximate data and estimates where necessary)
3. Actual running of the experiment, or survey, including checks and controls to assure that all procedures, sampling and testing conform to the design laid out in Step 2.
4. Analysis and evaluation of the data obtained, from a statistical, technological and economic viewpoints.
5. Over-all evaluation of the conclusions derived from Step 4.
6. Development of recommendations, based on Steps 1–5, for consideration by all management personnel concerned with further planning and decision making.
7. Filing of all data from Steps 1–6 in readily accessible form so as to be serviceable and useful in guiding future studies, when needed.
8. Preparation of final report.

EXHIBIT 26-3   How to Balance, Randomize, and Replicate an Experiment

BALANCE

Let us suppose an experiment is being run on four types of extrusion dies A, B, C, and D, using one blend of plastic pellets. We wish to make ten tests per die using extrusion machines 1 and 2. It would be foolish to use machine 1 on dies A and B and machine 2 on dies C and D, because two machines may not yield identical results. There are likely to be differences between them. If, instead of different machines, different blends had been used, then the comments made would have applied to the different blends. Therefore, a better arrangement is the following table.

TABLE 26-1

| Machine | Number of tests per die | | | |
	A	B	C	D
1	5	5	5	5
2	5	5	5	5

With this arrangement, regardless of any differences that may exist between the machines, these differences will be balanced out in the total for each die.

RANDOMIZE

Just as there are known differences in machines, blends, operators, and testing equipment, there are other differences that are not realized but that may in some way influence results. To minimize the possibility that such factors may bias the experimental findings, we randomize. For example, in assigning die A, 5 tests, to machine 1 we should not just run the 5 tests successively on one day. Instead, we should have some random scheme, whereby we use one die first (A, B, C, or D), then another die, and so on, until all four dies each have been tested five times in random sequence. It is realized that in actual practice, problems of feasibility may arise that interfere with the degree of randomization attained. However, to the extent possible, random selection of tests and test conditions is desirable.

REPLICATE

No one observation, individual test result, or occurrence means much. At least one "repeat" or replication is necessary, or else we may be badly fooled by an erratic or otherwise freak result. In Table 26-3 there were five "repeats" or replications within each block or "cell" of die-machine combination. In a sense, of course, the use of two machines also means that there was some replication.

Experimental
Design Application

The principles of randomization, replication, and balance in experimental design, as brought out in Chapter 26 will now be demonstrated with the aid of the following illustrative example. The data, while adapted from an actual case history,[1] have been altered for purposes of simplified presentation. They refer to an experiment made for the purpose of discovering the effect of three variables on the usable core output in millivolts (*mv*) of finished cores: pressed density of magnetic cores, sintering time in processing, and calcine temperature. From such analysis, a means of accomplishing the relatively highest and thus best output, may often be uncovered.

Layout of Experiment

The layout of the experiment is revealed by Table 27-5. In particular, two levels of each of the three factors were run as follows:

TABLE 27-1

Factor	Unit of measurement	High level	Low level
Density	gm/cm	3.06	3.02
Time	minutes	10	5
Temperature	°C	800	700

[1]Jacobsen, A. C. *Process control concepts for manufacturing*, 16th Annual Convention Transactions, American Society for Quality Control, May 23–25, 1962, Cincinnati, Ohio, pp. 459–469.

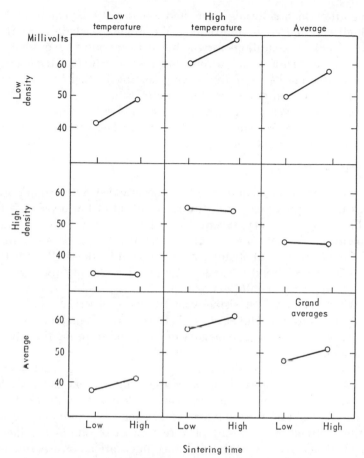

FIGURE 27-1. Experiment result, magnetic core outputs.

Combining the three factors at two levels each requires $2 \times 2 \times 2$, or 2^3, which is eight experimental conditions. Completing two full sets of runs, in order to achieve a replicated experiment, involves 2×2^3 or 16 test conditions, as revealed by the individual data in the table. Totals and averages obtained from the test results are inserted next as shown.

Graphing the Results

The graphic presentation of the results in Figure 27-1, affords a better visualization of the magnetic core output of the cores produced by the various experimental conditions. It is seen at once that high temperature, high sintering time, and low density appear to be best for high core output in millivolts. We might conclude from these findings that the conditions for the highest core output represent not only excellent factor combinations, but also that further trials might be considered in seeking to investigate possible further benefits from, say, even higher sintering times and temperatures.

Often, however, the experimental results are not quite as clear cut. We then need to evaluate, statistically, all experimental findings of a less than clear-cut nature.

Interaction Effects

An inconsistency is observed in the graphed data. While high sintering time produces higher millivolt output at low density, it has no effect at high density, except for a slight downward effect at high temperature. This downward effect is only a difference of one millivolt, from 56 to 55, and obviously insignificant by itself. But the lack of consistency of trend between high and low density for high and low sintering time is quite marked.

When such an inconsistency of trends is observed, the experimenter refers to it as "interaction." In the present instance, there is interaction between pressed density of cores and sintering time during processing.

Supposing the inconsistency of trends had been less glaring and the differences in observed effect of the three factors had been less clear cut. Then, in such a case, we cannot assume that all trends and points observed lead toward a firm conclusion. We would not be sure whether a trend is the result of a real effect of one of the factors studied, or merely the result of chance fluctuations of experimentation, the so-called experimental error. We need a statistical method to separate real effects from chance fluctuations.

Experimental Error

Experimental error does not refer to errors in the sense of "mistakes." Instead, it refers to the fact that in any test, some — hopefully small — fluctuations or variations occur that cannot be traced to a specific cause. While special tests and experiments may be designed seeking to pinpoint most types of causes of variation, in a particular experiment it is impractical to investigate more than a few factors. We can only expect that the factors not specifically investigated will balance themselves out in a more or less random manner. A small amount of untraceable variability, "noise" or fluctuations will remain, which may be said to represent chance variation or experimental error.

In the magnetic core experiment, we are investigating three factors and their interactions, and we have run two tests, Tests 1 and 2, for each condition. Each time, there was a slight difference between the two tests. For example, at 3.02 density, 5 minutes and 700°C temperature, Test 1 gave a core output of 43 and Test 2 yielded 39. The difference between these two readings, which is the range R equals 4. We may consider this range as representative of chance fluctuations or "error" in the experiment.

Proceeding similarly for all cells, that is, for each range of the eight factor-level combinations, we obtain the following:

TABLE 27-2

Test 1	Test 2	Range
43	39	4
50	48	2
58	64	6
70	68	2
38	32	6
37	33	4
54	58	4
57	53	4

The total of these ranges, 32, divided by the number of ranges, 8, yields 4.0. The number of tests comprising each range, or the sample size per range, is two. For ranges based on sample sizes of 2 each, the factor for converting to standard deviation (Table 19-3) is 0.89. Therefore, the standard deviation of the experimental error is:

$$\sigma_{error} = \overline{R}_{within\ cells} \times F_d$$

$$= 4.0 \times 0.89$$

$$= 3.56\ (in\ millivolts)$$

We know, of course, that this calculation is only an approximate procedure. The more appropriate method is to calculate the error term by means of sums of squares, as shown in Table 27-6, with explanations in Exhibit 27-1. The standard deviation of the error so found is slightly smaller, namely 3.0.

Variance Analysis Calculations

The determination of sums of squares, a method discussed in Chapter 24, leads to the variances and standard deviations for all of the following:

1. The total variation present, with a variance of 270 millivolts.
2. The error term, as just noted, with variance of 9 and standard deviation of 3.
3. The factor variances:
   a. Density, 39 mv.
   b. Temperature, 206 mv.
   c. Time, which is found to be not important for the range of the levels (5 to 10 minutes) studied.
4. The interaction variances, of which only the density-and-time combination is important, with variance of 16 and standard deviation of 4.

We call the variances from 2 to 4 components of variance, since they together add up to the total. In order to realize the relative contribution of each component, within the range of factors and levels studied by the experiment, we may express them in percentages of the total.

TABLE 27-3

	Variance component	Ratio to over-all variance	Result = component (in percent)
Density	39	39/270	14
Temperature	206	206/270	76
Interaction	16	16/270	6
Error	9	9/270	3
Rounding effect			1
Total	270	270/270	100

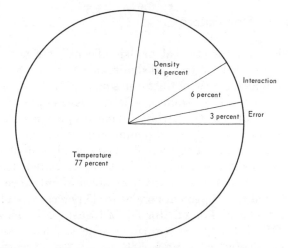

FIGURE 27-2.   Experimental design application.   Variance components expressed as slices of a pie chart.   (Temperature component increased by 0.7 percent to achieve correction for rounding of all decimals).

Rounding effect refers to the fact that by using integers in place of decimals, a slight shortage of one percent has happened to occur in the variance components expressed as a proportion of total variance. It is often of value to show these data in the form of a pie chart. Noting that a circle has 360°, the pie-chart in Figure 27-2 is obtained by means of the following calculations:

TABLE 27-4

	Component percent	Component percent × 360°
Density	14	50
Temperature	76	277[a]
Interaction	6	22
Error	3	11

[a]Increased by 3° in order to obtain 360 degrees.

Evaluation of Significance

In order to segregate real or "significant" effects from chance fluctuations, we need a statistical significance test. Such a test is provided by forming the ratio of the mean square of each factor and interaction to the error mean square. These values appear in row H of Table 27-6. Recall that the within-cell mean square is pertinent as an estimate of sampling and experimental error.

Each factor and interaction has associated with it degrees of freedom (DF), as shown in line G. In Table 27-2 are listed the minimum values of the F ratio needed to establish significance of a factor or interaction at the 95 percent confidence (5 percent risk of erroneous "significance") level. For a factor DF of 1, such as the density factor, and error DF of 8, we need a ratio of at least 5.3 to establish this significance. The actual ratio is $380/9 = 42.222$. Clearly, we have shown that density has a significant effect on core output in millivolts for the levels studied; chance fluctuations have been ruled out for all practical purposes.

For the sintering time effect, on the other hand, the F ratio is 6.222, which is only very slightly above the minimum of 5.3 required for the one, and 8 DF of numerator and denominator respectively. We may consider this is to be significant by strict application of the tabular requirements, but we also note that the variance component is really nil. (Actually, calculations would have led to a theoretically small negative value, but in practice a factor can never be less than of no effect whatsoever, which is zero.) The explanation of this inconsistency is that probably the interaction of sintering time with pressed density is overestimated slightly at a mean square of 8.111. Then, when this mean square is subtracted from the main-effect mean square of sintering time (row K, column 3), it results in a negative value. In any event, the result is not misleading. It merely indicates that it is somewhat difficult to distinguish precisely between the effect of time itself and the effect of interaction of this time with density. For practical purposes, time must be considered in planning improved processing, based on the results of the experiment. The example illustrates that results of experiments simply cannot be interpreted mechanically by means of mathematics and mathematical tables alone. Judgement must enter in all stages, from initial planning and design stages to evaluation and decision making based on the evaluations.

Evolutionary Operation

The use of relatively widely spaced levels is generally desirable in laboratory experiments. When translating these results into the production floor, usually more conservative spacings are desirable. Conditions under actual production are often quite different from the laboratory or pilot plant. Larger batches mean greater difficulty of controlling uniformity of products and production settings, greater chances for impurities and similar factors to interfere with optimal results and, sometimes, hazards of off-standard quality or even explosion from exceeding safe levels.

A special philosophy of production, which has been gaining increasing acceptance, and which was originated by G. E. P. Box at Imperial Chemical Industries[2] is called "evolutionary operation" or "evop." Using the existing settings of a production process, evop will

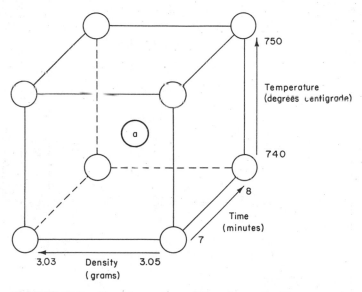

FIGURE 27-3. Experimental conditions for evolutionary operation. Present process settings (a) are 7.5 minutes sintering time, 3.04 grams pressed density, and 745 degrees centigrade temperature. Circles represent slight deviations from present settings (a). Later on, test results from each such deviation can be inserted in the circle.

[2]First published in *Applied Statistics*, entitled "Evolutionary Operation: A Method for Increasing Industrial Productivity", vol. 6, no. 6, 1957.

TABLE 27-5. RESULTS OF EXPERIMENT INVOLVING THREE FACTORS

Usable core output in millivolts (mv), of magnetic cores processed at different densities, temperatures, and sintering times[a]

Pressed density gm/cm	Sinter time (in minutes)	Calcine temperature (degrees centigrade)								Row total
		700				800				
		Test 1	Test 2	Total	Average	Test 1	Test 2	Total	Average	
3.02	5	43	39	82	41	58	64	122	61	204
	10	50	48	98	49	70	68	138	69	236
Total				180				260		440
Average		46.5	43.5			64	66			
3.06	5	38	32	70	35	54	58	112	56	182
	10	37	33	70	35	57	53	110	55	180
Total				140				222		362
Average		37.5	32.5			55.5	55.5			
3.02 and 3.06	5[b]	81	71	152		112	122	234		386
	10	87	81	168		127	121	248		416
Total		168	152	320		239	243	482		802[c]

[a]Three factors (density, temperature, time) at two levels (high, low) each, with replication (two tests per factor-level combination).

[b]Effect of sinter time for densities 3.02 and 3.06 combined. For example, for 700° C, Test 1, at 5 minutes sinter time, core outputs 43 plus 38 add up to 81.   [c]Grand total of all 16 entries.

TABLE 27-6. VARIANCE ANALYSIS FOR CORE OUTPUTS

Computation Steps	(1) Density (D)	(2) Temperature (Te)	(3) Time (Ti)	Interactions (4) $D \times Te$	(5) $D \times Ti$	(6) $Te \times Ti$	(7) Within cells	(8) Overall variation
A. Enter and square totals from prior table	440^2 $+362^2$	320^2 $+482^2$	586^2 $+416^2$	180^2 $+260^2$ $+140^2$ $+222^2$	204^2 $+236^2$ $+182^2$ $+180^2$	152^2 $+168^2$ $+234^2$ $+248^2$	82^2 $+70^2$ $+122^2$ etc.[a]	43^2 $+39^2$ $+38^2$ etc.[b]
B. Sum of A	324,644	334,724	322,052	168,884	162,836	167,588	84,700	42,422
C. Number of tests for each square in A	8	8	8	4	4	4	2	1
D. Crude sum of squares, B/C	40,580	41,840	40,256	42,221	40,709	41,897	42,350	42,422
E. Correction factor[c]	40,200	40,200	40,200	40,200	40,200	40,200		40,200
F. Corrected sum of squares	$D_1 - E$ $= 380$	$D_2 - E$ $= 1,640$	$D_3 - E$ $= 56$	$D_4 - E - F_{1,2}$ $= 1$	$D_5 - E - F_{1,3}$ $= 73$	$D_6 - E - F_{2,3}$ $= 1$	$D_8 - D_7$ $= 72$	$D_8 - E$ $= 2,222$
G. Degrees freedom (number of levels of the factor) − 1	$2 - 1 = 1$	$2 - 1 = 1$	$2 - 1 = 1$	$1 \times 1 = 1$	$1 \times 1 = 1$	$1 \times 1 = 1$	$8 \times (2-1) = 8$	$16 - 1 = 15$[e]
H. Mean square, F/G	380	1,640	56	1	73	1	9	
I. F-ratio, H/H_7	42.222	182.222	6.222	0.111	8.111	0.111		
J. Significant at 95 percent (from F-table)	Yes	Yes	Yes	No	Yes	No		
K. Component of variance[d]	$H_{1+7} - H_{4+5}$ $= 39.375$	$H_{2+7} - H_{4+6}$ $= 205.875$	$H_{3+7} - H_{4+6}$ $= \text{Nil}$	$H_4 - H_7$ $= \text{Nil}$	$H_5 - H_7$ $= 16.000$	$H_6 - H_7$ $= \text{Nil}$	H_7 $= 9.000$	Row total $= 270.250$
L. Standard deviation, $\sqrt{K}$	6.275	14.348	Nil	Nil	4.000	Nil	3.000	16.439

[a]For all 8 test totals. [b]For all 16 individual tests.

[c]E = (Grand total)²/Total number of tests = (802)²/16 = 40,200.

[d]The denominators in the formulas are the entries from row C.

[e]Usually the individual DF add up to the over-all DF; but in the present example they add up to 14, not 15, because the analysis, for reasons of simplification, ignored a small three-way interaction ($D + Te + Ti$) with 1 DF. As a result, the three-way effect is contained in the within-cells or error variance.

TABLE 27-7

MINIMUM VALUES OF THE VARIANCE RATIO F NEEDED TO ESTABLISH
SIGNIFICANCE AT THE 95 PERCENT CONFIDENCE LEVEL[a][b]

Degrees freedom for denominator	Degrees freedom for numerator									
	1	2	3	4	5	6	8	10	15	30
Values of F-ratio										
2	18.5	19.0	19.2	19.2	19.3	19.3	19.4	19.4	19.4	19.5
3	10.1	9.6	9.3	9.1	9.0	8.9	8.8	8.8	8.7	8.6
4	7.7	6.9	6.6	6.4	6.3	6.2	6.0	6.0	5.9	5.7
5	6.6	5.8	5.4	5.2	5.1	5.0	4.8	4.7	4.6	4.5
6	6.0	5.1	4.8	4.5	4.4	4.3	4.1	4.1	4.0	3.8
8	5.3	4.5	4.1	3.8	3.7	3.6	3.4	3.3	3.2	3.1
10	5.0	4.1	3.7	3.5	3.3	3.2	3.1	3.0	2.8	2.7
12	4.7	3.9	3.5	3.3	3.1	3.0	2.8	2.8	2.6	2.5
15	4.5	3.7	3.3	3.1	3.0	2.8	2.6	2.5	2.4	2.2
20	4.4	3.5	3.1	2.9	2.7	2.6	2.4	2.3	2.2	2.0
25	4.2	3.4	3.0	2.8	2.6	2.5	2.3	2.2	2.1	1.9
30	4.2	3.3	2.9	2.7	2.5	2.4	2.3	2.2	2.0	1.8
40	4.1	3.2	2.8	2.6	2.5	2.3	2.2	2.1	1.9	1.7
60	4.0	3.2	2.8	2.5	2.4	2.3	2.0	1.9	1.8	1.6
120	3.9	3.1	2.7	2.4	2.3	2.2	2.0	1.8	1.7	1.5

[a]If the actual F-ratio observed equals or exceeds the tabulated value, then it indicates statistical significance at the 95 percent confidence level.

Example: Degrees Freedom (DF) associated with a main effect are 2, DF associated with the error term are 6. The ratio of main effect mean square to the error term mean square is 8.0. The DF associated with numerator and denominator are therefore 2 and 6 respectively. From column DF of 2 and row DF of 6 in the table, we find the critical value for the F-ratio of 5.1. Since the actual F-ratio is 8.0, we conclude that the main effect tested is significant at the 95 percent level or better.

[b]Abbreviated and rounded, based on the comprehensive tables computed by M. Merrington and C. M. Thompson, Biometrika, (1941) — 33: 80–81.

call for slight deviations to the high and low sides of three of the settings, such as density, time, temperature, and then evaluate the resultant quality, efficiency, and other effects. Successive evop phases, of these and subsequently of further variables, will gradually serve to "nudge" the production process towards an optimum.

Figure 27-3 shows how the present example might have looked in evop form, with the center circle representing "current settings" and the boxed circles around it representing slight experimental deviations from it.

Experiments in whose evaluation line supervisors participate are often best analyzed by range methods, as shown in Table 27-2. Their loss in accuracy is compensated by a more direct understanding of the procedures.[3]

Conclusion

There was a time when experimentation was exclusively in the domain of theoretical and applied research workers. These people, often extremely competent in their field, lacked the aid that they could have received from use of modern principles of effective experimentation. The examples given in this chapter illustrate how the research worker can multiply his efficiency by using effective and well-planned experimental setups.

Moreover, research is no longer confined to the researcher. With the development of the concept of evolutionary operation, research is applied consciously as a daily working tool in actual production operations. Its purpose is that a manufacturing process should not only produce a product, but should also produce continuing information on how to improve its quality, yield, and efficiency.

EXHIBIT 27-1 Variance Analysis Calculation Procedures[a]

Step 1. Enter, and then square the totals for each factor level. For density, the two totals are 440 and 362.

Step 2. Add the squared totals. Thus, $440^2 + 362^2 = 324,644$.

Step 3. Note the number of tests comprising each total in A. For density, each total was based on 8 individual tests.

Step 4. Divide B/C to find the crude sum of squares.

Step 5. The correction factor 40,200, is obtained as shown.

---

[3]For further examples and extended applications, see N.L. Enrick, *Quality Control*. New York: The Industrial Press, 1962.

[a]Steps 1–12 refer to rows A–L of Table 27-6.

Step 6. Find the (corrected) sums of square, (SS) as shown. For density and temperature interaction, (column 4), the formula states:

Interaction SS = 42,221 − 40,200 − (380 + 1640) = 1

Step 7. Degrees of freedom DF is obtained as shown for all columns but 7. The latter is found by multiplying the DF of each cell of two tests (2 − 1) by the number of cells, 8.

Step 8. Meansquare MS is simply SS/DF. The MS for column 7 represents an estimate of experimental error.

Step 9. The F-ratio is MS for each factor and interaction divided by the error MS (column 7) of 9. Thus 380/9 = 42.222.

Step 10. Significance is evaluated from Table 27-7, a table of F-ratios.

Step 11. Obtain the variance components from the formulas given, as estimates of the relative variability contributed by each of the factors and interactions studied.

Step 12. The estimated standard deviation is the square root of the variance. Note that standard deviations cannot be added directly. Column 8 row L is the square root of 270.250, not the row total.

▶▶▶▶ EPILOGUE:
Management
in the Seventies

The impact of an increasing rate of technological change is perhaps the most critical and pervasive problem facing management today. In the years to come it is likely to have far more effect on business management and create more problems than any of the other trends in our economy and society. In part, these are problems concerning the processes by which management puts technology to work. And in part they concern the way in which the technological innovations themselves affect the nature of management and the process of managing. These problems, which are fundamentally managerial in nature, are as yet largely unrecognized and unexplored.

Recognizing that these problems cannot long remain ignored, staff members of the Association of Consulting Management Engineers have prepared a paper considering the expected effects of the technological changes that are just beginning to be felt.[1]

The following questions should be considered:

1. Will traditional organizational structures and management techniques be outdated by technological advance?
2. Can business and industrial processes, designed for a different world, with a different technology, continue to be adequate tomorrow?
3. Will these new technological innovations encourage or even necessitate radical changes in organization and in the process of managing?
4. If radical changes in the process of managing are to be expected, can we anticipate their nature or direction?

---

[1] Material in this chapter taken from Association of Consulting Management Engineers, Inc., *Management Consultant*, issue no. 1 of the 1963 series.

Impact on Top Management

Top management, to keep pace with this burgeoning technology must strive increasingly to become professional, to acquire through training and experience skills that enable it to look at the business enterprise as a whole, as an integrated system. Freed from routine work by information-handling machines, management must learn to focus on broad, long-range business policies rather than on narrow, short-term operating or functional problems. Its primary concern must be the establishment of a proper policy and framework for the guidance of the organization in relation to its changing environment.

But once routine business decisions have been assigned to the computers where they can be done faster and more accurately, top executives will face the unenviable job of having to grapple regularly with a growing number of problems that are too complex for the computers. And they will also have to accept the fact that such business decisions will become even more complex because of lengthened time span (occasioned by forward planning). There will be changes in the scope of decisions (no longer local, regional, or even national, but international), in imposed limits (the increasing role of government), and in resource commitment (needed for larger capital resources).

Management therefore must become steadily more analytical and scientific, with the role of "hunch" and even "informed judgment" becoming steadily smaller. At the most this will mean increasing use of sophisticated analytical approaches to management decision processes such as mathematical programing and the extensive use of computers. At the very least, the manager will have to be able to isolate and clarify the variables that need to be considered in making decisions, to consider carefully the soundness of the quantitative information gathered about these variables, and be able to assign intelligent but frankly subjective weights to variables on the basis of his experience. This is a process of clarifying and bringing to the surface the variables and implicit logical models now being used by managers, and one of improving the logic of the models.

New Tools of Management

In dealing with their new tasks, top managers of the late 1960s and of the 1970s, to a large extent, will not only have to employ the same tools they are employing today, but they will find that they are increasingly expected to know, understand, and handle the new concepts and tools of analysis, programing, and decision making, of communication, computation, and presentation, including:

1. Mathematical and statistical tools that assist in the collection and analysis of data, and computers that process and retrieve this information at incredibly high speeds.
2. Operations research methods, utilizing quantitative analysis and statistical theory, which help to develop and evaluate alternative solutions to problems faster and more comprehensively than once was ever dreamed of.
3. Techniques, such as Linear Programming that help to determine the best solution among available alternatives.
4. Integrated data processing that makes it possible to routinize many decisions at lower levels while permitting a more intensive and comprehensive analysis of data.

Such new concepts and techniques, as awesome as they seem, are going to be welcomed by tomorrow's managers, for their job is going to be so complex, so big, and so demanding as to require all the methods of simplification and systematization that are available.

Because of the intellectual and technical demands that such sophisticated measures will place on top-line managers, another important change will be the employment of numerous staff specialists to advise them on special aspects of their work. The president may have attached to his office a planning staff, a personnel adviser, a scientific adviser, an economist, a legal counsel, an expert on foreign business, and the like. Similarly, the major production, marketing, finance, and engineering executives will be served by operations analysts, marketing research specialists, statisticians, physicists, chemists, and other staff specialists, in order that increasingly complex knowledge from many disciplines can be brought to bear upon strategic decsions of the company.

Middle Management Minimized

Other levels of the organization structure can not escape being affected by these changes in the management process. Many of the present decision-making activities of middle managers are capable of being programed, in the sense that specific procedures can be written in language understandable by electronic computers, which can then perform the necessary operations electronically and tell the manager what is the optimum course of action. Examples include the control of inventories of raw materials and finished goods, checking of credit, optimum routes of shipment, or appropriate standards of quality control. Once programed for computers, it is no longer necessary for a middle manager to give as much time and thought and to exercise "judgment" in reaching decisions on such questions.

Some business scholars feel that the number and content of intermediate management levels will shrink. Here is how their argument goes:

1. It seems clear that information technology will move the boundary between planning and performance upward. Just as planning was taken from the hourly worker and given to the industrial engineer some years ago, it will now be taken from a growing number of middle managers and given to as yet largely nonexistent specialists: operation researchers, organization analysts, information specialists, or planning executives. Jobs at today's middle-management level will become highly structured, and much more of the work will be programed.

2. Programing of middle-management tasks will result in a gradual reorganization of middle-management levels, with certain classes of middle-management jobs moving downward in status and compensation (because they will require less judgment and skill), and other classes moving upward into the top-management group. Consequently, the line separating the top from the middle management of the organization will be drawn more clearly and impenetrably than ever, much like the line drawn in the last few decades between hourly workers and first-line supervisors.

But this argument is subject to challenge by other business thinkers along these lines:

1. It is erroneous to think that in the foreseeable future computers and analytical techniques will be able to perform even a major share of the complex, nonprogramable decisions made by managers. But since it is true that computers will in time be able to make most of the programable decisions (and since many of the decisions made by middle management are of this routine kind), this argument still does not grant

a reprieve to the middle manager. But the next two arguments do.

2. It is false to think that, just because a machine can do something better than a man can, we will automatically use the machine. To believe that we will is to ignore the economics of the situation. If a computer rents for $12,000 per month, for example, it obviously will have to do more and better work than can 12 middle managers each paid $1000 per month. Experience to date, however, indicates that computers are hard pressed to equal efficient human output in areas other than rote arithmetic computation. Once the problems become more complex, difficulties of programing slow down the process considerably, while costs (thanks to machine "downtime") soar.

3. Paper gains projected by machine devotees often fail to materialize once a partially computerized decision system is introduced into an organization of human managers. One would have difficulty knowing this ahead of time. The pro-computer literature glows, the technicians within companies see the machines as new fiefs in a growing estate, a few sample runs by the salesman "proves" the machine's superiority over the middle manager. But what happens after installation? Idealized situations often become complicated by individual and group reactions against the machines, motivation suffers and pressures arise. There is, say the followers of this line of thinking, sufficient case evidence available to indicate that until a greater understanding of the problems arising from the interactions of humans and machines is obtained, the introduction of information-processing devices in many companies is going to be delayed.

Time will tell the impact of the new information technology on the middle manager. But one thing is certain now, anyone who will desire the title of manager in the future will have to understand the theory, applications, and capabilities of the new information and decision-making technologies. If he does not, he will surrender his role as manager, for he will inevitably become subservient to the superior knowledge of professional experts in the new business science. Obviously, then, the managers of today will have to grow with the challenge, through education — formal or otherwise.

Structural Shifts

Tomorrow's managers also must be able to understand and cope with, not only the questions raised about the roles of top and middle management in the vertical structure of an enterprise, but also the effect of technology on the horizontal structure of the business organization. Reactions to organizational trends such as the following will have to be sound and decisive.

There is a growing rift between production and engineering functions, which causes a problem in transferring research results into operations, and there is also a concomitant problem in handling specialized technicians differently from other personnel.

Finance, control, and accounting are gaining added leverage in the functional hierarchy (because they operate the computer and the related systems). Yet these departments often are dominated by people whose previous experience makes them measures of past and present performance rather than planners of future actions.

Marketing also is changing, as companies are forced to find new and better approaches to improve their marketing effectiveness. It is becoming more and more important for companies to organize, manage, and innovate with the market as the focus. This means that marketing should logically precede design and production. In other words, companies must bring their systematic knowledge of the market, its opportunities, its structure, its needs, and its wants into the design and timing of new and improved products, not as the only factor, but as the major one. It also means that marketing should logically precede finance, in the sense that decisions on marketing strategy are so large and so long-term that they involve the company in major capital commitments.

Necessity of Planning

The rapidity of technological change is forcing companies to pay much more attention to the planning process, especially planning for change, and its counterpart, planning necessitated by change. A few of the reasons this is happening are noted herewith.

Product life is being shortened. The traditional cycle of product innovation is being telescoped, not by planned obsolescence or styling changes, but by genuine technological innovation. The scientific revolution, especially the break-throughs in electronics, physics, chemistry, and mathematics, have made possible a surging flood of new products, new materials, new processes, and new techniques. The potential they create for greater change is enormous.

The reaction time of management must be reduced. The time for hesitation in adapting to scientific change has disappeared. Management must keep track of a number of fundamental areas of scientific work, and must be skilled in identifying and exploiting emerging opportunities ahead of its competition. It must continually interpret the total marketing climate in terms of rapid technological change.

The life of business and industrial processes, as well as products, are being both shortened and changed. Much of the new technology, particularly that part of it dealing with the information processing, is beginning to affect the manner in which business is conducted. For example, American Telephone and Telegraph Company spokesmen have said repeatedly that communication between machines in different cities will exceed voice communication over telephone lines by 1970.

The consequences of such a change will be staggering, not only for the telephone system, but for the procedures by which the remainder of business in the United States is conducted! It is only through careful planning that such a rate of change can be made to benefit a corporation rather than its competitors.

The increased complexity and tightened inter relationships of functions within a single organization, together with the ever more complex relationships with other organizations, means that successful and rapid adjustment to change is impossible without the ability to plan effectively.

For these reasons, and many more, management must sharpen its ability to anticipate the future more precisely in its over-all planning responsibilities.

Banished Business Cliches

In their planning, managers of the future will have to recognize that many accepted business concepts will become outmoded as a result of rapid shifts in technology. For example, even as fundamental a concept as the definition of a business may have to change. Familiar examples are all about us.

Yesterday, if the motion picture industry had defined its business as the supply of entertainment rather than of film, it might now be at the heart of the television industry rather than a contract supplier to it. Today, similarly, manufacturers of photocopy or of calculating machines had better view themselves as being in the information handling business, and remain in the forefront of what a few years ago would have seemed unrelated technology, or they may not continue in business tomorrow. Likewise, the auto industry must think of itself not as being in the business of making and selling cars and trucks but of moving people and goods, and be alert for new and better ways of doing this.

Return on investment must be higher in these new technical fields in order to justify the increased risk. Conversely, business must take bigger risks for sufficient return when technological change is great. A case in point is the computer business itself. The costs of entering this new industry have exceeded everyone's expectation. Those manufacturers who planned for a low rate of return have already been forced out of the business.

Management may have to take a longer-run view of profits. It will probably have to get rid of the present concept of the "annual" profit, and will have to learn to think of return in terms of the normal life cycle of the industry: three years, five years, in some industries, ten years. The need to maintain stable production and stable employment means a need for greater flexibility in profits and dividends on the part of the business enterprise. This will be one of the major impacts of automation.

The concepts of labor cost and of labor productivity must change as the number of direct laborers decreases. Skilled labor will become increasingly a fixed cost and a capital resource of the business.

Traditional office-plant distinctions will require overhaul as production is increasingly controlled by businesswide information systems. Not only will the nature of plant work become more clerical (and less manual), but countless small production decisions will actually be made within the office rather than on the factory floor.

Management will have a capacity never possible before to centralize or decentralize its decision functions. The advances made in communications, among machines as well as people, now allow for direct, cheap, and immediate flow and feedback of information among any geographic points. Whether or not centralization is appropriate will vary with the situation, but the decision need no longer fall automatically to decentralization.

Finally, scientific progress has enlarged the most efficient size of business organizations for a given industry, and paradoxically created at the same time, opportunities for new and small firms. Large scale automation brings large economies of cost, but the standardization it involves leaves increasing gaps in the market in the form of customers who want something different and specialized in the way of product or service. The result may be that technological change has, in fact, tended to enlarge the relative importance of both large and small firms, at the expense of medium-sized firms, in the business population.

Conclusion

In conclusion, then, it is clear that we are witnessing a gradual evolution of business and industrial processes, organization structures, and the process of managing under the impact of technological progress. Moreover, this evolution seems to be gathering speed. Conceivably, it could create grave economic and social problems if the business leaders of our society do not recognize this impact of technology on commercial life and adjust our methods and organizations to accommodate them. More certainly, it threatens the survival of established companies with myopic managers, just as it creates opportunities for those managers who fully grasp the nature of the environmental changes that science is producing.

▶ ▶ ▶ ▶ **Appendix**

Problems

and Cases

Although this book has emphasized operations research in its over-all impact on various phases of management planning, decision making, and control, attention also has been given to essential procedures, techniques, and mathematical analyses.

The cases and problems presented in this Appendix are designed as a "do it yourself" check, primarily with reference to those chapters in the book that are quantitative in nature.

Experience has shown that, without some calculating and pencil-pushing work, it is difficult to fully comprehend the meaning and effect of quantitative methods. The material in this Appendix is designed to fill this need, by providing problems for solution. In order to avoid needless tedium of extensive arithmetic, the author has taken some liberty with the original data and figures, so as to simplify calculations to a minimum.

290

Cases and Problems

A. FELTEEN-VELVET MILLS

Simplex Linear Programming for Optimum Product Mix

Felteen-Velvet manufactures woven felts of high quality, incorporating a soft velvetlike finish. The principal operations in processing are spinning and weaving. Further data, regarding unused capacity, two fabrics, A and B, being considered for addition to the line, expected dollar profit per unit of 1000 yards, and related factors are shown in Table A-1.

TABLE A-1

	Fabric A	Fabric B	Total
a. Profit per unit (in dollars)	20	15	
b. Spindle-hours required per unit	100	50	
c. Loom-hours required per unit	20	25	
d. Spindle-hour capacity			1000
e. Loom-hour capacity			300
f. Spun units per fabric at capacity (d/b)	10	20[a]	
g. Woven units per fabric at capacity (e/c)	15[a]	12	
h. Profit at spun capacity, (a × f) (in dollars)	200		200
i. Profit at woven capacity, (a × g)(in dollars)		180	180
j. Optimum units for both fabrics in combination			
k. Profit, in dollars, at optimum, (a × j)			

[a] = impossible because of bottleneck

Required   Find the optimum in terms of units (line j) and dollars (line k).

B. KIMBERLY-CLARK CORPORATION

Simplex Method of Linear Programming to Maximize Profit[1]

Linear programming is a method for optimizing a linear function, $f(x_1, x_2, \cdots x_n)$, when the variables $x_1, x_2 \cdots x_n$ are subject to a set of linear constraints. For purposes of demonstrating the application of linear programming (LP) a simplified example for only two variables, x and y, may be used, in place of the several dozen variables required in actual practice.

Two grades of paper, X and Y, are produced on a paper machine. Because of raw materials restrictions, not more than 400 tons of grade X and

[1]Case data due to Carl E. Noble, European Marketing Manager, Kimberly-Clark Corporation. It is used with Mr. Noble's permission.

300 tons of grade Y can be produced in a week. There are 160 production hours in a week. It requires 0.2 and 0.4 hours to produce a ton of products X and Y respectively, with corresponding profits of $20 and $50 per ton.

Find the optimum product mix, using (a) graphic, and (b) matrix methods.

C. FINESTOCK RANCH

Simplex Method of Linear Programming to Minimize Costs[2]

The ranch desired to purchase four special feeds in a combination which would provide the proper vitamin content, while at the same time minimizing feed costs. The basic data are given below:

TABLE C-1

Feed number	Amount of vitamins A, B, C in each feed (units per pound)			Feed Cost (cents per pound)
	A	B	C	
1	4	1	0	2
2	6	1	2	5
3	1	7	1	6
4	2	5	3	8
Minimum vitamin content needed per feed mix, in units	12	14	8	

Letting x_1, x_2, x_3 and x_4 denote the numbers of pounds of Feeds 1, 2, 3 and 4, respectively, write the objective equation and the inequalities required in order to show total cost Z, in cents. What pounds of each feed should be used per mix to (a) minimize costs, and (b) what is this minimum cost?

D. WRINKLE-FREE KNITWEAR CORPORATION

Simplex Programming with Many Alternatives

Management is considering the addition of one of two possible new styles of knitwear, A and B, which can be produced on the fast K-1 knitting machines or the slower K-2s. It is considered unwise, in view of limited

---

[2]Fictitious name and data. This problem was first formulated by Carl E. Noble, European Marketing Manager, Kimberly-Clark Corporation. It is used with Mr. Noble's permission.

promotional budgets, to add more than one style. The problem data are shown below:

TABLE D-1

Operation	Machine group	Route 1 A	Route 1 B	Route 2 A	Route 2 B	Route 3 A	Route 3 B	Available hours
1. Winding	W	4	10	4	10	4	10	1000
	K-1 ⎫	6	16					600
2. Knitting	K-1a ⎬			6	16			200
	K-2 ⎭					8	20	800
Profit per 100 Dozen (in dollars)		85	160	60	140	70	130	

Each style requires wound yarn from the winders W. Knitting machine group K-1a represents overtime production on machines K-1. Knitwear styles A and B can be produced over three possible routes, namely, wind and then knit on K-1, or wind and then knit on K-1 at overtime pay rates, and finally, wind and then knit on the slower K-2 machines.

Decide whether style A or B should be produced, in what quantities and on what machines, and the corresponding machine hours utilized on each machine. What is the resultant profit?

E. THE HAPPY TWENTIES CLUB

Linear Programming[3]

Your establishment sells jumbo martinis. You never cheat your customers; you always fill the glasses up to the full 5 ounces. Because of liquor controls, you cannot obtain more than the weekly quantities of liquor shown at the cost given.

TABLE E-1

Product used	Quantity obtainable (ounces per week)	Cost per ounce (in cents)
Premium gin	500	20
Cheap gin	2,600	10
Premium vermouth	1,000	15
Cheap vermouth	400	5

[3]Adapted from material formulated by William R. Vogel, Chief, Research Division Data Systems Office, Headquarters, United States Army Materiel Command, Washington, D.C. It is used with Dr. Vogel's permission.

The following drinks can be purchased in your illustrious establishment:

TABLE E-2

Drink[b]	Ingredients, Ounces				Price per Drink, Cents
	Premium Gin	Cheap Gin	Premium Vermouth	Cheap Vermouth	
d_1		2		3	40
d_2		3	2		70
d_3	3			2	80
d_4	4		1		110

[b]Actual names are of course more descriptive.

You can sell up to 100 drinks containing cheap gin, up to 200 drinks with premium gin and up to 150 drinks with cheap vermouth. You can buy any number of ounces of liquor, not necessarily an even number of fifths.

Required

1. Bring this problem into the simplest matrix form possible.
2. Solve, using either the transportation or simplex algorithm, as may be necessary.
3. What quantities of each drink should you sell, so as to maximize profit? What quantities of liquor should you buy? What is your profit per week?

F. CLEARMOUNT SOUTHERN INCORPORATED

Profit Planning with Simplex Method Linear Programming

A forecast of expected business volume and prices for the coming fall season, and a review of production standards, had produced the information in Table F-1 for the production of fabric.

The profits are based on expected costs and prices. More specifically they represent so-called "operating profit," also known as "variable margin," "contribution to profit and overhead" and "gross profit," and were determined from the difference between expected selling price and expected variable costs.

In order to effectively direct sales efforts, keeping in mind the expected profits per yard, the anticipated sales volume on certain styles for which demand was considered limited, as well as productive requirements and capacity, it was desired to ascertain:

1. Optimal yardage to be sold (as a goal or target) for each style.
2. Resultant profit, per style and overall.
3. Resultant utilization of productive facilities, cards through looms.

TABLE F-1

Clearmount Southern Incorporated

Marketable fabric styles, demand limits on sales, productive requirements, and productive capacity

Marketable styles	Sales limit 1000's of yards per week	Profit[a] per 100,000 yards (in dollars)	Production time needed per 100,000 yards of fabric per production process in 100's of delivery hours[b]						
			Cards	Drawing	Roving	Spinning	Loom 40"	Loom 46"	Loom 60"
A	3.0	9020	3.3	2.0	35.2	1348	28.4		
B	6.0	6420	3.7	2.2	34.5	794	22.6		
C	10.0	5480	3.5	2.1	37.7	1128	31.0		
D		4790	4.4	2.7	47.8	1162	33.4		
E		2690	3.1	1.8	34.3	1050		28.4	
F		5620	3.8	2.3	41.4	1228		28.7	
G	10.0	5130	4.5	2.7	42.3	1071		23.7	
H	30.0	6890	5.1	3.1	55.6	1354		34.7	
I	7.5	9080	3.9	2.4	42.9	1468			34.1
J	5.0	7290	2.9	1.7	31.2	1064			25.6
K	4.0	10530	3.6	2.1	38.9	1334			30.8
L	3.0	12040	3.8	2.3	41.8	1436			30.8
M		6900	3.3	2.0	30.9	794			20.5
Normal capacity per 120-hour week in 1000's of delivery hours			27.0	14.4	257	7204	155	21.7	16.3

[a]Estimated from expected selling price less expected variable costs.

[b]Successive processing through carding, drawing, roving, spinning and the loom group shown (40-inch, 46-inch or 60-inch). Fabric styles can not be switched from wider to narrower looms or vice versa. A "delivery" is an output position. For example, a roving frame has some 100 spindles or "deliveries."

G. UNICOIN VENDING CORPORATION

Optimal Assignments through Transportation Method
Linear Programming

Unicoin had discovered that the wear on their candy vending machines was affected by their location. The exposure to weather in a garage or service station, the effect of vibration in a production plant, or the heavy abuse in certain other places, affected the monthly repair costs. The company used two types of vending machines, machines 1 and 2 which were similar in outward appearance, but differed in internal design and construction. The number of machines on hand as well as the repair costs are shown below:

TABLE G-1

Location	Repair costs, (dollars per machine)		Number of machines needed
	Machine 1	Machine 2	
A. Restaurant	16	13	3
B. Plant	20	29	5
C. Garage	40	38	8
D. Other	37	49	2
Number of machines on hand	10	8	

Determine the assignment of machines to each of the four locations which will fulfill requirements and at the same time minimize repair costs.

H. INTERNAL REVENUE SERVICE

Time Allocation Between Field Checks and Office Audits[4]

Business planning often involves questions of best allocation of work time. The specific problem presented here concerns the distribution of work hours between field and office examinations of tax returns. The following are assumed relationships and data for illustrative purposes only:

---

[4]Adapted from a tax problem described by A. C. Rosander, "The Use of Linear Programming to Improve the Quality of Decisions," *Industrial Quality Control*, vol. 12, no. 9. (March 1956) pp. 11–16.

TABLE H-1

Type of tax return examined	Amount of tax error discovered (dollars per hour of audit)		Minimum amount of tax error to be found (in dollars)
	Field check	Office check	
A	100	125	750
B	330	100	1,500
C	100	60	600

It costs three times as much per hour to make field audits as to make office audits. The last column in Table H-1 above represents an assumed goal standard. We wish to minimize total audit cost without violating any of the relations and conditions shown in the tabulation. In order to obtain this objective, how many hours of an eight-hour day should be spent on field checks and how many on office checks?

I. PARAMOUNT PAPERBACKS INCORPORATED

Investment Analysis

Management is considering the publication of a new novel by an author who has never before written a book. The cost of editing, typesetting, and preparing cuts is estimated at $50,000. After considering royalty agreement, printing and binding costs, and promotional expenditures, the following estimates were compiled:

TABLE I-1

End of year	Books sold	Receipts (in dollars)	Cost of sales (in dollars)	Promotion (in dollars)
1	400,000	200,000	150,000	30,000
2	1,000,000	500,000	375,000	25,000
3	200,000	100,000	75,000	20,000

Forecasts are made for only three years, since a book is rarely successful for a longer period. The company considers money to be worth 20 percent per year. Because of the high risks involved in publishing the work of a new author, management usually does not undertake such a venture unless anticipated present value of the cash flowback exceeds by 50 percent the cost of editing, typesetting, and preparing cuts.

You are asked to make recommendations based on the data shown.

J. HAWLEY CITY NATIONAL BANK

Lease-or-Buy Analysis

Management of Hawley City National Bank realized that, in order to service its customers efficiently and economically, it would have to install electronic data processing (EDP) equipment. After extensive studies a decision had been reached regarding the equipment to be used. Two alternatives of acquisition were open:

1. Outright purchase for $80,000.
2. Annual lease, for $20,000, payable at the end of each year.

The lease agreement contained a clause that, once signed, a relatively high discontinuance penalty would be applied, for discontinuance prior to the end of a five-year period. The rapid pace of developments in the EDP field make it likely that, for all practical purposes, equipment becomes obsolete after five years.

The bank considers its money to be worth seven percent per annum. Should the equipment be bought or leased?

K. INVESTMENT CALCULATIONS

Present Value, Annuities, Amortization

1. Eastern Shores Savings Bank The Bank pays 4 percent interest per annum on savings accounts, compounded quarterly. A principal of $1000 is deposited. What is the compound amount after $2\frac{1}{2}$ years?

2. Ingenious Research Corporation The company is engaged in research, developing new fibers, dyes, and finishes, selling successful patents to large manufacturing firms. It has been estimated from past success rates, that on the average a dollar invested at any one time has yielded a return of $1.50 5 years later. You presently have your money invested at the Eastern Shores Savings Bank. Assuming that, 5 years ago, when you put your money in Eastern Shores, you could have invested it in Ingenious Research Corporation Would this have been a better deal? In particular:

1. What would be the compound amount after 5 years?
2. What is the present value, at time of investment, of $1.50 received five years later for each $1 invested?

3. Discounts Mr. Jones expects to inherit $2000 from his uncle's estate, five years from now, when Jones reaches the age of 25. Assuming money to be worth 5 percent per annum, determine:

1. The present value of the $2000.
2. The amount of discount represented.

4. Annuity   Ingenious Research Corporation has developed a new fiber and has been made these offers:

1. $600,000 outright.
2. $100,000 annually, at the end of each year, for 10 years.

You are considering these two offers; and you have been advised that the company can readily borrow money at a 4 percent interest rate, compounded annually, for use in a budgeted expansion program.

a. Which of the two offers, 1 or 2 is preferable?
b. What is the compound amount of offer 2 if left to accumulate at 4 percent interest in a bank?

5. Amortization   You have borrowed $30,000 to build a restaurant, at an interest rate of 6 percent. The debt is to be paid in equal annual instalments at the end of each year, so that by the end of the third year it is fully paid off.

Determine the following amounts, payable at the end of the first year, the second year, and the third year:

1. Interest.
2. Repayment of principal.

L. KEARFOTT DIVISION OF GENERAL PRECISION INC., I

Program Evaluation and Review Technique[5]

In discussing the characteristics of product development, M. Silverman, the program manager of Kearfott, Little Falls, New Jersey, lists these four essentials:

1. Although product development is initially a research and development operation, it must possess the flexibility to grow into a large production organization.
2. Allowances must be made for changes in product requirements.
3. Decisions of front-line supervisors must be evaluated without interfering with the necessary authority and responsibility.
4. Product development must operate profitably within rigid specification limits and must deliver an optimum product on time.

For the purpose of illustrating Program Evaluation and Review Techniques (Pert) as an aid in fulfilling time schedules, Mr. Silverman used a simplified example (Figure L-1).

---

[5]Case data due to Melvin Silverman, Program Manager, Kearfott Division, General Precision, Inc., Little Falls, N. J. Diagrams reprinted from *Product Engineering* for October 15, 1962, pp. 76–78. Copyright © 1962 by McGraw-Hill Publishing Co., Inc.

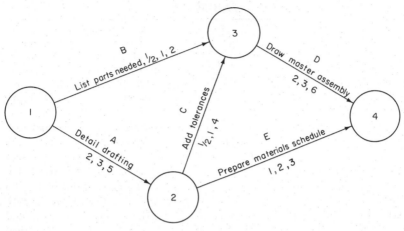

FIGURE L-1. Arrow diagram of events (circled) joined by the activity (arrows) network. Each arrow shows three completion time estimates in days: optimistic, most likely, and pessimistic, as evaluated by managers and supervisors concerned.

In this network diagram, event 1 represents the release by the engineering department to the drafting department of a design layout of a simple device, plus a packet of sketches of the component parts. The three time estimates, in days, given for each activity arrow represent the following:

1. The optimistic estimate, assuming that the work will proceed better than normally expected.
2. The most likely estimate, indicating the time each job is expected to require.
3. The pessimistic estimate, assuming a good many things will go wrong with a job.

These estimates are provided by the supervisors and managers concerned with each job.

Calculations A frequently used formula to show the earliest expected time to accomplish an activity t_e states:

$$t_e = [\text{Optimistic} + (4 \times \text{Most Likely}) + \text{Pessimistic}]/6$$

with variance, σ^2 of t_e given by:

$$\sigma^2 = [(\text{Pessimistic} - \text{Optimistic})/6]^2$$

Applying these formulas to the data in Figure L-1 yields the figures below

TABLE L-1

	Activity				
	A	B	C	D	E
Earliest Expected time, t_e	3.2	1.1	1.4	3.3	2.0
Variance, σ^2	0.250	0.063	0.341	0.445	0.111

On the basis of the expected times t_e, tracing through the network from left to right, we may determine the earliest expected time at which each activity can be completed, T_e. For A through E respectively, T_e values found, in days, are: 3.2, 1.1, 4.6, 7.9 (path A–C–D), and 5.2 (path A–E). Similarly, the longest or latest expected times, T_L are obtained: 3.2, 4.6 (path A–C), 4.6 (again, path A–C), 7.9 (path A–C–D), and 7.9 (again path A–C–D). The differences of T_L minus T_e are, for the various activities, found to be: A = 0, B = 3.5, C = 0, D = 0, and E = 2.7, so that the critical path is A–C–D with corresponding variances 0.250, 0.341, and 0.445, adding to a total variance of 1.036. The corresponding standard deviation σ is found from the square root of 1.036, yielding 1.017, in terms of days.

Required

1. Assuming that the scheduled date of completion is $T_s = 10$ days from event 1. Utilizing a table of areas under the normal curve, evaluate the probability P in percent of meeting the schedule.
2. What is the probability that the schedule will be exceeded?
3. Noting that Mr. Silverman used a somewhat more complex (but more refined and widely advocated) formula than the simplified formula given in the text, rework the problem with the simpler formula and observe the difference. Do you think this difference is worth the extra effort and conceptual difficulties for nonstatistical personnel who would have to work with it?

M. KEARFOTT DIVISION, II

Line of Balance Technique[6]

The program manager of Kearfott, a Division of General Precision Inc., Mr. M. Silverman, points out that for effective control of small projects, a simple plotting of cumulative expenditures of dollars, man-hours and percent completion versus time can be used. An illustrative example is given in Figure M-1. For the week ending April 20, this graph reveals the following data, in dollars:

[6]Case data due to Melvin Silverman, Program Manager, Kearfott Division, General Precision, Inc., Little Falls, N. J. Diagrams reprinted from *Product Engineering* for October 15, 1962, pp. 76–78. Copyright © 1962 by McGraw-Hill Publishing Co., Inc.

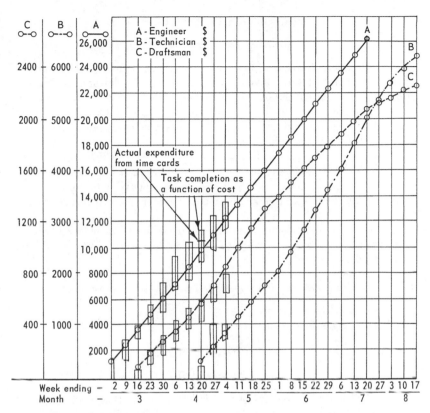

FIGURE M-1. Line of balance chart. Scheduled expenditures (Lines A, B, C, for Engineer, Technician and Draftsman) versus task completion in terms of dollar equivalent (upper limit of truncated bars).

TABLE M-1

	Engineer	Technician	Draftsman
Scheduled Expenditure (from chart) (in dollars)	9,800	260	575
Actual Expenditure (from time cards) (in dollars)	10,500	532	600
Task Completion (from supervisor) (in dollars)	11,200	240	600

Assuming that you are the manager of Kearfott, how would you evaluate and interpret the graphic and tabular data, in relation to line of balance?

N. MERITORIOUS CUTLERY COMPANY

Supplies Inventory Control

Originally formed to produce various items of cutlery, the company had in the course of time developed a well-balanced sales and production program, including silverware and various industrial and military cutlery items. Production equipment included various types of blanking forming and cutting presses, drop hammers, grinding and polishing, degreasing and plating tanks, and assembly fixtures.

The largest item of supplies was polishing wheels, which cost $20 per dozen. About 1000 dozen are used annually. The cost of placing an order is estimated at approximately $4, and there is an approximate 10-day delay from ordering to receipt of goods. Money is considered worth 20 percent per annum.

There are no significant fluctuations in consumption of these wheels since the company has a policy of producing staple items to inventory during slack periods.

Required   Using the cost and consumption data given above, determine:

1. Optimum order quantity
2. Desirable safety-stock

O. UNITINT DYE HOUSE

Optimum Lot Size

Unitint is a subsidiary of an extruder and injection molder of small plastic parts and toys. Dye kettles accommodate the following lot sizes, in dozens: 200, 400, and 500.

A particular item has a yearly sale of 400 dozen and costs $2 per dozen, based on materials and labor expended. There is an extra cost of $20 per dye lot, representing the labor of cleaning the old dye liquor in a kettle, steam consumption, and dye liquor losses. The firm considers money worth 20 percent per annum.

Which kettle should be scheduled for the particular item referred to?

What factors other than those given are likely to have an important bearing in actual practice?

P. UNIBLEND BIOLOGICALS

Finished Product Inventory Control

Sales of injectable "Ivaway," a desensitizing biological, exhibit a strong seasonal pattern, with heavy sales in the summer. A record for the past three years is shown below.

TABLE P-1

Month	3 Years ago	2 Years ago	Last year
		(Vials sold in 1000s)	
January	10	2	12
February	6	9	20
March	8	10	30
April	24	50	100
May	55	149	100
June	140	180	250
July	160	240	370
August	280	300	490
September	110	100	190
October	55	24	13
November	32	10	25
December	5	2	15

Manufacturing facilities are limited, so that production for the peak season must start early, with gradual inventory build-ups. Excess inventories must be avoided, especially because Ivaway cannot be stored for prolonged periods without losing potency. A sales forecast of two million vials has been made for the year just beginning.

Develop a method for control of inventories, based on sales expectations and the actual monthly developing trend of sales volume. The method should permit easy calculations and analyses.

Q. UNICOIL ELECTRIC COMPANY

Queuing Analysis

The coil winding department of Unicoil is equipped with several hundred coil-winding spindles, for making coils that go into small electric motors and relays. Time study analysis has shown that an individual winding spindle requires an average of 4 percent servicing (such as replace spool, remove wound coil, and such) during which the spindle is stopped.

At present, one operator services 12 spindles, and there is very little queuing loss. The time study engineer is thinking about doubling the assignment to 24 spindles per operator. He realizes that the theoretical efficiency of 96 percent per spindle (4 percent down-time and 96 percent run time) would suffer because of this aforementioned queuing.

Required   Assuming a Poisson arrival rate of stops and an equal distribution of servicing times (namely, each servicing requires the same amount of time), calculate the expected queuing and the resultant efficiency per spindle.*
    What is the corresponding efficiency if a negative exponential distribution is assumed?

*Hint: Expansion of $(0.96 + 0.04)^{24}$ gives the successive probabilities of $0, 1, \ldots, 24$ spindles down.   Similar results can be read off (widely tabulated) Poisson distribution values, based on an average expectation of $24 \times 0.4 = 1.0$ (rounded) spindle down at any one time.   We obtain 37, 37, 18, 6, 1.5, and 0.4 in percent for the successive probabilities of 0, 1, 2, 3, 4, and 5 (or more) spindles down at one time.

R. DELTA DISCOUNT STORES

Inventory Simulation Study

Sales data accumulated for the past four winter seasons showed that customer demand for Model K-23 electric hot water heaters exhibited a pattern represented by Table 21-1, of the "Simulation of Inventories and Queues" chapter, while delivery times were represented by Table 21-2 of that chapter.
    Inventory carrying cost is $5 per week, order placing cost is $10 per occurrence, and loss in net revenue (sales price less cost of goods) is $50 per unit, from shortage.
    A prior study has shown that, with a policy of using reorder quantities of 8 and reorder point of 4 units, average weekly costs are $25 to carry inventory, $2.50 to place orders, and $10 for shortages or a total of $37.50.

Question: Investigate the effect of using a smaller reorder quantity of 4 units, but a higher reorder point of 5 units.   Simulate at least 20 weeks.
    Then recommend the next set of reorder quantity and reorder point to simulate, with the objective of minimizing total cost.

S. VIRGINIA ELECTRIC AND POWER COMPANY

Sampling of Watt-hour Meters[7]

The Virginia Electric and Power Company developed a sampling program, for use in determining an effective maintenance program for the

---

[7]Case material from N. L. Enrick: *Cases in Management Statistics.* New York: Holt, Rinehart and Winston, Inc., 1962.

care of the great number of single phase meters in service. As part of the program, a brochure was issued within the company, as an aid in explaining to the personnel concerned the value of the statistically designed sampling program. The essential portions of this brochure are reproduced below:

Purpose The purposes of this outline are to present a proposed plan for improving and assuring sustained accuracy of single phase watt-hour meters in service, and to demonstrate that the customer and the company will benefit by the substitution of a selective test plan for the present system of periodic meter testing.

Regulatory commissions and utilities have long recognized the need for meter testing to maintain over-all meter accuracy as a means of insuring correct customer billing. In former years it was necessary that meters be tested at relatively frequent intervals, therefore, maintenance of meter accuracy was more of a problem than now. The development of overload and temperature compensating devices, new magnetic steels, and other improvements have been reflected in the periodic test system and, as a result, test periods for single phase watt-hour meters have been increased from two or three years to as much as 20 years in some jurisdictions. Under present regulations, the test program of the Virginia Electric and Power Company calls for each meter to be tested once every eight years. The Virginia Commission has established ± 2 percent as the limits of acceptable accuracy.

Advantages of Selective Meter Testing

1. By testing selectively, time spent on meter testing may be utilized more efficiently. A modern sampling procedure will point out the types of meters that may be in need of recalibration and, therefore, time is not wasted in testing meter groups where the need for recalibration is not indicated.
2. Through the use of modern sampling procedures, data of measured reliability about the performance of various meter types and service under varying conditions of use may be obtained. This is not possible under the periodic testing system now in use.
3. Meter types that may not retain accuracy for extended periods of time will be disclosed by the sampling procedure and will be tested more frequently than every eighth year, and will be subject to earlier retirement.
4. Selective testing is compatible with what is believed to be the ultimate solution of the meter accuracy problem: development of a low cost single phase watt-hour meter which will maintain desired accuracy for its life of 15 to 20 years and then be replaced by a new meter.

Present Periodic Test Program   Under the existing periodic test program, the company tests something over 100,000 meters each year and, with the anticipated growth in customers, this number will increase substantially. Experience over a number of years indicates that more than 98 percent of all single phase watt-hour meters in service are recording within the established limits of accuracy. Thus, in order to locate two meters that are in need of recalibration, it is necessary to test 100 meters. This is an inefficient, unwieldy and time consuming operation.

Selective Testing Procedure   The fundamentals of the selective plan are these:

1. Devise a means for determining the meters or groups of meters which require recalibration.
2. Concentrate meter test activity on such meters.
3. Retire as rapidly as possible meters which will not hold calibration.

The basic problem of any test program is to determine which meters are in need of recalibration. In view of major meter design improvements made around 1928, 1934, and 1939, it is logical to expect that meters built prior to 1928 will not maintain their accuracies as well as later models. On this basis, a 10 percent sample of meters tested during 1955 was drawn in three company districts; each of these three samples supports the belief that the older meters would be those most often found outside of the accuracy limits. Under the 8-year test schedule, in the Richmond District, 5.24 percent of the meters manufactured between 1910 and 1928 were found to be more than 2 percent fast, whereas, all of the meters manufactured between 1939 and 1955 were well within the established limits of accuracy. Similar conditions of relative accuracy by age groups were found in the other two districts. These data demonstrate that the age of meters is a definite indication of the proportion of meters which may be expected to require recalibration.

Modern sampling methods currently in use in market research industrial quality control and in the gathering of business statistics, may be applied to the determination of meter types which may need calibration. The manufacturer's type and serial number will indicate which meters contain the modern improvements and may be used as a key for classification purposes.

After selection, testing, and analysis of a proper sample group of meters per year, each district will concentrate test activities on those types of meters which the sample indicates are in need of attention. Little or no testing would be required within the groups which, according to the sample, are within the established limits of accuracy, since data now available indicate that the newer types of meters may be expected to remain within the accepted limits of accuracy until scheduled retirement.

The drawing of a new sample each year will result in an annual appraisal of the relative performance of meters by types in service and of changes in over-all accuracy. Under the present program, no reliable measure of over-all accuracy is possible because of the method used in selecting meters for test. Under periodic testing, activity in one year may be concentrated on new meters, while in other years older types will predominate, thus giving false indications of over-all accuracies from year to year.

For analytical purposes the sample may be broken down into subgroups by areas or by certain characteristics which affect performance. Such analysis will include a study of performance in areas particularly subject to lightning damage or exposure to corrosive atmospheric conditions.

In future years, the types of meters and adverse locations now affecting meters may no longer be important, but new problems may develop. Such changes will be revealed as they occur by analysis of the annual sample, thus directing concentrated test activity to areas of greatest need.

Under the proposed program, at any time, any meter which is suspected of being inaccurate will be tested. Meters which become inoperative either through mechanical or electrical damage will be located, repaired, or replaced under existing procedures.

Required   You are asked to develop recommended sampling procedures for use with the proposed meter sampling program.

T BRISTOL LABORATORIES, INCORPORATED

Frequency-distribution Analysis[8]

In order to establish a manufacturing specification for tablet thickness of a particular product, the individual thicknesses of 200 tablets, taken from the production stream, were tabulated as shown in the table below.

TABLE T-1

THICKNESS OF TABLETS	
Thickness (in inches)	Number of tablets
0.238	1
0.239	13
0.240	32
0.241	29
0.242	18

---

[8]Case material from *Cases in Management Statistics, op. cit.*

TABLE T-1 (continued)

THICKNESS OF TABLETS Thickness (in inches)	Number of tablets
0.243	21
0.244	20
0.245	22
0.246	22
0.247	13
0.248	3
0.249	0
0.250	1
0.251	1
0.252	0
0.253	1
0.254	0
0.255	2

Questions: What conclusions would you draw from a frequency distribution plot analysis, assuming the following:

1. The 200 tablets were taken from two machines.
2. The 200 tablets were taken from one machine.

U. COLGATE JERSEY CITY PLANT

Statistical Analysis[9]

Routine test results, obtained from control of product and processing quality and cost, can often be useful to management. Careful analysis of such data may yield clues leading to improvement of raw stock and additives used, processing settings and adjustments, and product design or formulation of constituents.

The results of the determination of volatile matter in soap are given in Table U-1, and represent 30 successive production lots. A random sample consisting of four cakes of soaps was selected for test from a lot.

Required   As an aid in evaluating processing, prepare the following:

1. Frequency distribution of the individual test results.
2. Frequency distribution of the 30 averages.
3. Other analyses that you may consider useful such as standard deviations of the distributions and control limits.
    Be prepared to discuss the findings from the analyses made.

[9]Case material from *Cases in Management Statistics, op. cit.*

TABLE U-1
COLGATE JERSEY CITY PLANT
Amount Volatile Matter in Soap, (in percent)

Lot number[a]	Sampling specimen number				Sample results		
	1	2	3	4	Total	Average	Range
1	35.37	35.22	34.64	35.29	140.52	35.13	0.73
2	34.99	34.77	34.97	34.96	139.69	34.92	0.22
3	34.29	34.24	34.32	34.27	137.12	34.28	0.08
4	34.20	34.75	34.03	34.59	137.57	34.39	0.72
5	34.36	34.69	34.23	34.40	137.68	34.42	0.46
6	34.50	34.24	34.37	34.25	137.36	34.34	0.26
7	34.53	34.47	34.83	34.43	138.26	34.57	0.40
8	35.88	34.43	34.79	34.58	139.68	34.92	1.45
9	34.81	34.78	34.53	35.13	104.44	34.81	0.60
10	34.71	34.69	34.95	35.58	139.93	34.98	0.89
11	35.31	34.85	34.54	34.32	139.02	34.76	0.99
12	34.24	34.20	34.04	34.14	136.62	34.16	0.20
13	34.32	35.44	34.35	34.50	138.61	34.65	1.12
14	34.46	34.91	34.32	34.31	138.00	34.50	0.60
15	34.30	34.13	34.56	34.51	137.50	34.38	0.43
16	34.24	34.41	34.26	34.16	137.07	34.27	0.25
17	34.85	34.43	34.72	34.93	138.93	34.73	0.50
18	34.53	34.02	34.09	33.50	136.14	34.04	1.03
19	34.41	33.83	34.39	32.86	135.49	33.87	1.55
20	34.08	34.40	34.06	34.68	137.22	34.31	0.62
21	33.72	34.39	33.75	33.39	135.25	33.81	1.00
22	32.85	33.76	33.60	33.32	133.53	33.38	0.91
23	34.39	34.08	34.66	34.18	137.31	34.33	0.58
24	34.20	33.39	33.28	33.99	134.86	33.72	0.92
25	32.90	33.34	33.67	33.27	133.18	33.29	0.77
26	34.20	34.10	33.91	34.15	136.36	34.09	0.29
27	33.31	34.73	34.41	34.70	137.15	34.29	1.42
28	34.97	35.84	35.06	34.95	140.82	35.20	0.89
29	34.02	34.02	35.19	34.59	137.82	34.45	1.17
30	34.41	33.88	34.10	34.69	137.08	34.27	0.81

[a]These are successive production lots tested.

V. UNITED STATES INSTRUMENT CORPORATION

Statistical Analysis of Vendor Quality[10]

As part of an intensive reliability control program, United States Instrument Corporation maintains a thoroughly worked out program of receiving inspection for purchased parts. A check of a shipment of 2000 bushings, Part No. 1382-1, supplied by one vendor, yielded the following results:

TABLE V-1

Sample number	Dimension (in inches) for each of five bushings tested					Sample range
1	0.169	0.158	0.162	0.167	0.161	0.011
2	0.165	0.163	0.164	0.162	0.165	0.003
3	0.165	0.164	0.165	0.165	0.165	0.001
4	0.164	0.164	0.159	0.165	0.163	0.006
5	0.165	0.163	0.164	0.164	0.162	0.003
6	0.165	0.164	0.166	0.164	0.158	0.008
7	0.159	0.162	0.161	0.165	0.165	0.006
8	0.162	0.164	0.163	0.165	0.164	0.003
9	0.167	0.164	0.164	0.164	0.164	0.003
10	0.166	0.165	0.167	0.165	0.168	0.003
Total						0.047

In evaluating these findings against the specified dimension of 0.164 ± 0.004 inch, the following was determined:

1. Percent of bushings in the total sample which (a) failed to meet the upper specification tolerance, and (b) fell below the lower specification tolerance.
2. The percentages of nonconforming parts that would have been expected from a normal curve distribution.
3. A plot of the actual distribution of the sample of 50 bushings.

The sharp disagreement of the results from findings 1 and 2 was noted, and the desirability of further analyses received consideration.

W. BLACKWELL CONSTRUCTION COMPANY

Statistical Analysis[11]

Concrete specimens, collected from construction, have yielded the compressive strengths (in 100 psi) shown below:

---

[10]Case material from *Cases in Management Statistics, op. cit.*
[11]Case material from *Cases in Management Statistics, op. cit.*

TABLE W-1

Date	\\multicolumn{5}{c}{Specimen Number}					Sample average	Sample range
	1	2	3	4	5		
1/2	46.0	43.5	43.1	47.3	45.1	45.00	4.2
1/3	45.0	45.7	40.9	44.0	43.6	43.84	2.1
1/4	42.0	47.3	44.5	45.6	48.0	45.48	6.0
1/5	49.1	45.7	46.4	46.0	47.1	46.86	3.4
1/6	47.1	44.2	49.6	45.1	47.4	46.68	5.4
1/9	43.1	44.4	43.4	45.8	46.4	44.62	3.3
1/10	41.2	45.5	45.9	46.5	43.8	44.58	7.3
1/11	41.0	46.7	43.3	49.4	48.0	45.68	8.4
1/12	45.4	43.7	47.3	44.8	49.2	46.08	5.5
1/13	40.0	43.1	48.3	44.5	46.7	45.72	5.2
1/16	45.2	46.7	47.3	47.1	49.8	47.22	4.6
1/17	44.2	43.5	45.0	44.0	44.7	44.28	1.5
Total						546.24	56.9
Average						45.50	4.7

Required (1) Prepare frequency distribution of the individual specimen strengths. (2) Determine the standard deviation and variation coefficient of (a) the individual strengths and (b) the sample averages.

X. CUTLER-HAMMER INCORPORATED

Statistical Analysis[12]

The mounting complexity of control systems and space-age instrumentation forces statistical techniques into the forefront of vital analytical methods in the aerospace industries. As an illustration of the application of these techniques, the data below, obtained by random sampling of twenty 10K-ohm carbon composition resistors from a vendor's shipment checked on an ohmmeter, are discussed:

---

[12]Case material from *Cases in Management Statistics, op. cit.*

TABLE X-1

Resistance	Number of units	Resistance	Number of units
7.5	0	10.5	2
8.0	2	11.0	3
8.5	1	11.5	1
9.0	2	12.0	0
9.5	4	12.5	1
10.0	4	13.0	0

In order to contribute to this discussion, you are asked to perform the statistical analyses you consider pertinent, such as:

1. Frequency distribution pattern
2. Grand average
3. Standard deviation
4. Variation coefficient

What does this analysis reveal?

Y. UNIPACK CONTROL SYSTEMS

Two Factor Variance Analysis with Replications

The production of highly sensitive control systems of miniaturized components requires assembly in practically dust-free "white rooms." Using an Armour Research Foundation dust particle counter, the following was found by checking the air in such a white room at Unipack:

TABLE Y-1

CONTAMINATION PARTICLE COUNTS PER HOUR BY SAMPLING
STATIONS AND SHIFTS. TWO TESTS PER SHIFT

Item	Shifts	Test num- ber	A	B	C	D	Totals	Aver- ages
	I	1	2	1	3	2		
		2	1	7	1	3		
Totals			3.0	8.0	4.0	5.0	20	
Averages			1.5	4.0	2.0	2.5		2.50
	II	1	3	9	9	3		
		2	1	8	3	0		
Totals			4.0	17.0	12.0	3.0	36	
Averages			2.0	8.5	6.0	1.5		4.50
	III	1	3	7	2	0		
		2	2	8	6	4		
Totals			5.0	15.0	8.0	4.0	32	
Averages			2.5	7.5	4.0	2.0		4.00
Column Totals			12.00	40.00	24.00	12.00	88	
Column Averages			2.00	6.67	4.00	2.00		3.67

Analyze the results and present your findings.

Index

317